To President
Jake Warner

with best regards from

Fred Rossini

# EXPERIMENTAL THERMOCHEMISTRY
## *Measurement of Heats of Reaction*

# EXPERIMENTAL THERMOCHEMISTRY

## Measurement of Heats of Reaction

Prepared under the
INTERNATIONAL UNION OF PURE AND APPLIED CHEMISTRY
by the
SUBCOMMISSION ON EXPERIMENTAL THERMOCHEMISTRY

**Edited by FREDERICK D. ROSSINI**

*Carnegie Institute of Technology, Pittsburgh, Pennsylvania*

**INTERSCIENCE PUBLISHERS, INC., NEW YORK**

**Interscience Publishers Ltd., London**

© 1956, by Interscience Publishers, Inc.

LIBRARY OF CONGRESS CATALOG CARD NUMBER 55-11450

Interscience Publishers, Inc.
250 Fifth Avenue, New York 1, N. Y.
*For Great Britain and Northern Ireland:*
Interscience Publishers Ltd.
88/90 Chancery Lane, London W.C. 2, England

PRINTED IN THE UNITED STATES OF AMERICA BY
MACK PRINTING COMPANY, EASTON, PENNSYLVANIA

# Foreword

The former Commission on Thermochemistry of the International Union of Pure and Applied Chemistry (IUPAC) issued three reports as follows:

1. "Premier Rapport de la Commission Permanente de Thermochimie." Text by W. Swietoslawski and L. J. P. Keffler. Approved by the members of the Commission: W. Swietoslawski, President, Warsaw; L. J. P. Keffler, Secretary, Liverpool; C. Matignon, Paris; W. A. Roth, Braunschweig; F. Swarts, Ghent; P. E. Verkade, Rotterdam; E. W. Washburn, Washington. Issued from the office of the Secretary General, IUPAC, at Paris, in 1934. This report, consisting of ten pages of text, discussed the "basis for thermochemical calculations" and the "determination of the heat of combustion of solid and liquid substances containing the elements carbon, hydrogen, oxygen, and nitrogen" and made recommendations regarding two primary standards for combustion calorimetry, benzoic acid for combustions in a bomb at constant volume and the reaction of hydrogen and oxygen for combustions in a flame at constant pressure.

2. "Revue Analytique et Critique de Thermochimie Organique. Appendices au Premier Rapport de la Commission Permanente de Thermochimie." Text (in German) by W. A. Roth, with translations into English and French by L. J. P. Keffler. Members of the Commission: W. A. Roth, President, Braunschweig; L. J. P. Keffler, Secretary, Liverpool; M. Delepine, Paris; F. D. Rossini, Washington; F. Swarts, Ghent; W. Swietoslawski, Poland; P. E. Verkade, Rotterdam. Issued from the office of the Secretary General, IUPAC, at Paris, in 1936. This report, of thirteen pages, gave an "analytical review of the methods relative to the determination of the heat of combustion of organic substances containing sulfur or halogens" and included appendices concerning benzoic acid as the primary standard for combustion in a bomb at constant volume, the combustion of hydrogen to form water as the primary standard for combustion in a flame at constant pressure, the heat of formation of

v

nitric acid in dilute aqueous solution, and succinic acid as a secondary standard for combustion in a bomb at constant volume.

3. "Deuxième Appendice au Premier Rapport de la Commission Permanente de Thermochimie." Text (in German) by W. A. Roth, with translations into English and French by L. J. P. Keffler. Members of the Commission: W. A. Roth, President, Freiburg im Breisgau; L. J. P. Keffler, Liverpool; M. Delepine, Paris; F. D. Rossini, Washington; F. Swarts, Ghent; W. Swietoslawski, Warsaw; P. E. Verkade, Rotterdam. Issued from the office of the Secretary General, IUPAC, at Paris, in 1939. This report, of only one page, discussed succinic acid as a secondary standard for combustion in a bomb at constant volume.

From the time of its establishment in 1930 until 1934, the Commission on Thermochemistry, IUPAC, had as its president, W. Swietoslawski, of Warsaw. From 1934 until World War II, the president was W. A. Roth, of Braunschweig and later of Freiburg im Breisgau. On its reestablishment after World War II, the Commission had as its president F. D. Rossini, of Washington and Pittsburgh, who served until 1953, when J. Coops, of Amsterdam, became the new president.

From the time of its establishment until 1953, L. J. P. Keffler, of Liverpool and later Brussels, served as the secretary of the Commission. In 1953, H. A. Skinner, of Manchester, became the new secretary of the Commission.

In 1951, upon reorganization of IUPAC into Sections, the existing Commission on Thermochemistry became the Subcommission on Experimental Thermochemistry under the Commission on Chemical Thermodynamics in the Section on Physical Chemistry.

After the change of officers in 1953, the Subcommission on Experimental Thermochemistry, IUPAC had the following composition:

*President:* J. Coops, Free University of Amsterdam, Amsterdam, Netherlands.

*Secretary:* H. A. Skinner, University of Manchester, Manchester, England.

*Members:* E. Calvet, University of Marseille, Marseille, France; L. J. P. Keffler, Brussels, Belgium; E. J. Prosen, National Bureau of Standards, Washington, D. C., U.S.A.; Frederick D. Rossini, Carnegie Institute of Technology, Pittsburgh, Pennsylvania, U.S.A.; Lennart Smith, University of Lund, Lund, Sweden; W. Swietoslawski, University of Warsaw, Warsaw, Poland.

*Expert Advisors:* Lars Bjellerup, University of Lund, Lund, Sweden;
J. D. Cox, National Chemical Laboratory, Teddington, England;
W. N. Hubbard, U. S. Bureau of Mines, Bartlesville, Oklahoma,
U.S.A.; R. S. Jessup, National Bureau of Standards, Washington,
D. C., U.S.A.; D. W. Scott, U. S. Bureau of Mines, Bartlesville,
Oklahoma, U.S.A.; Stig Sunner, University of Lund, Lund, Sweden;
K. van Nes, N.V. de Bataafsche Petroleum Maatschappij, Amster-
dam, Netherlands; Guy Waddington, U. S. Bureau of Mines, Bartles-
ville, Oklahoma, U.S.A.

After the meeting at Stockholm in 1953, the Subcommission on
Experimental Thermochemistry, IUPAC, suffered a great loss in the
death of L. J. P. Keffler, the original and long-time Secretary of the
Commission and Subcommission.

At its meeting at Amsterdam in 1949, the former Commission on
Thermochemistry embarked on the project of preparing a book which
would place before the scientific and technical world the best knowledge of the members and advisors of the Commission relative to experimental thermochemistry and the measurement of heats of chemical reactions. This book represents the culmination of that project.

Chapter 1, by Rossini, introduces and summarizes the principles
of modern thermochemistry. In Chapter 2, Rossini summarizes the
present status of the unit of energy and fundamental constants important in thermochemistry. Chapter 3, by Coops, Jessup, and van
Nes, presents a detailed account of experimental thermochemistry
for reactions in a bomb at constant volume, covering particularly the
determination of the energy equivalent of the calorimeter with
electrical energy and the use of benzoic acid as a primary standard
for determining the energy equivalent for combustions in a bomb.
In Chapter 4, Rossini discusses the thermochemistry of reactions in a
flame at constant pressure, including determination of the energy
equivalent of the calorimeter with electrical energy or with the primary standard reaction of hydrogen and oxygen to form water, and
the accurate determination of the amount of reaction. Chapter 5,
by Waddington, Hubbard, and Scott, presents a detailed discussion
of standard states and thermal corrections for combustions in a bomb
at constant volume. In Chapter 6, Prosen discusses the thermochemistry of combustion in a bomb of compounds containing carbon,
hydrogen, oxygen, and nitrogen, including evaluation of the Washburn correction to the standard heat of combustion for these sub-

stances. Chapter 7, by Waddington, Sunner, and Hubbard, presents a discussion of the combustion in a bomb of organic sulfur compounds, pointing out the advances made in this area in the past few years. In Chapter 8, Smith and Hubbard discuss the combustion in a bomb of organic chlorine compounds, emphasizing the importance of knowing the chemistry of the reaction occurring. Chapter 9, by Smith and Bjellerup, presents a discussion of the combustion in a bomb of organic bromine compounds, and Chapter 10 presents a similar discussion by Smith for organic iodine compounds. In Chapter 11, Skinner discusses the thermochemistry of reactions other than combustion, emphasizing the importance of this area of thermochemistry and the opportunities in it. Chapter 12, by Calvet, presents a detailed discussion of the microcalorimetry of slow phenomena, pointing out the utility of this method and technic for acquiring data not otherwise obtainable. In Chapter 13, Waddington discusses physicochemical standards for thermochemistry, and, in Chapter 14, Rossini presents a discussion of the evaluation of errors and the assignment of uncertainties to thermochemical data.

The authors of the several chapters of this book will feel amply repaid for their efforts if their contributions help workers engaged in thermochemical investigations to achieve better and more meaningful results.

On his part, the Editor wishes to express his thanks to the other authors of this book for their enthusiastic cooperation in the work. Also to be acknowledged is the great encouragement given to the preparation of this book by W. Albert Noyes, Jr., and E. W. R. Steacie, past Presidents, and M. Letort, President, of the Section on Physical Chemistry, and by R. Delaby, Secretary General, International Union of Pure and Applied Chemistry.

FREDERICK D. ROSSINI
*President*
*Commission on Chemical Thermodynamics*
*International Union of Pure and Applied Chemistry*

*January, 1956*
*Carnegie Institute of Technology*
*Pittsburgh, Pennsylvania, U.S.A.*

# Contributors

LARS BJELLERUP, *University of Lund, Lund, Sweden*

EDOUARD CALVET, *University of Marseille, Marseille, France*

J. COOPS, *Vrije Universiteit, Amsterdam, Netherlands*

W. N. HUBBARD, *U. S. Bureau of Mines, Bartlesville, Oklahoma, U.S.A.*

R. S. JESSUP, *National Bureau of Standards, Washington, D. C., U.S.A.*

K. VAN NES, *N. V. de Bataafsche Petroleum Maatschappij, Amsterdam, Netherlands*

E. J. PROSEN, *National Bureau of Standards, Washington, D. C., U.S.A.*

FREDERICK D. ROSSINI, *Carnegie Institute of Technology, Pittsburgh, Pennsylvania, U.S.A.*

D. W. SCOTT, *U. S. Bureau of Mines, Bartlesville, Oklahoma, U.S.A.*

H. A. SKINNER, *University of Manchester, Manchester, England*

LENNART SMITH, *University of Lund, Lund, Sweden*

STIG SUNNER, *University of Lund, Lund, Sweden*

GUY WADDINGTON, *U. S. Bureau of Mines, Bartlesville, Oklahoma, U.S.A.*

# Contents

# Introduction:  General Principles of Modern Thermochemistry*

FREDERICK D. ROSSINI

A thermochemical investigation is one in which the investigator aims to determine the quantity of energy associated with a unit amount of a given chemical reaction or physical process.  Important considerations include determination of the energy, determination of the amount of reaction, specification of the reaction or process, specification of the thermodynamic property, description of the thermochemical method, assignment of the temperature of the reaction or process, and corrections to standard or reference states.

**1. Specification of the reaction or process.**  In order to attach significance to the measured energy associated with a reaction or process, it is necessary to describe the given reaction or process adequately with respect to all factors which may influence the value of the energy.  Each such factor should be specified with a precision appropriate to its measure of influence on the value of the energy.  With the condition of each reactant and each product so specified, it becomes a simple matter to correct each to some specified reference state and thus obtain the value of the energy of the process with each substance in an appropriate reference state.  Such reference states, formally called standard states and denoted by a superscript circle on the thermodynamic symbol, as $\Delta H°$, may be ones realizable only in theory but are such that a given substance can be readily converted from the actual state to the appropriate standard state with the necessary auxiliary data.

* Most of this chapter is taken from reference (1), with permission of the publishers, John Wiley and Sons.

1

Unless the context provides a complete description of the reaction or process, as to the temperature, pressure, concentration, and so on, such information should be given explicitly in the writing of the chemical equation describing the process. In general, it is assumed that the molecular formula represents one gram-formula-weight of the given substance, as written, and that the numerical coefficient indicates the number of gram-formula-weights to be taken, with the number 1 not being written but understood. Following the formula of each substance are parentheses which may be used to inclose the information applicable to the substance which the parentheses follow. Within such parentheses should be given every bit of information needed to describe the thermodynamic state of the given substance. Whenever a given condition of temperature or pressure applies to every reactant or product, or to both the initial state and the final state of the reaction or process, it is usually simpler to state this condition along with the given thermodynamic property with which one is concerned. In such cases, the temperature in absolute degrees may be indicated by a numerical subscript on the symbol for the given property. Following are some examples:

$H_2O$(liquid, saturation pressure, 298.16°K)

$$= H_2O\text{(gas, saturation pressure, 298.16°K)};$$

$$\Delta H = x \text{ kcal/mole.} \tag{1}$$

$$H_2O\text{(liquid)} = H_2O\text{(gas)};$$

$$\Delta H_{298.16}\text{(saturation pressure)} = x \text{ kcal/mole.} \tag{2}$$

As may be seen from the preceding discussion, Equation 2 gives the same information as does Equation 1, but in a more condensed form. Similarly, the following two equations give identical information:

$HCl$(aqueous, 2 molal, 2 atm, 298.16°K)

+ $Ag$(crystal solid, 2 atm, 298.16°K)

= $AgCl$(crystal solid, 2 atm, 298.16°K)

$$+ \; {}^1\!/_2 H_2\text{(gas, 2 atm, 298.16°K)};$$

$$\Delta H = z \text{ kcal/mole.} \tag{3}$$

HCl(aqueous, 2 molal) + Ag(crystal solid)

$$= \text{AgCl(crystal solid)} + \frac{1}{2}\text{H}_2(\text{gas});$$

$$\Delta H_{298.16}(P = 2 \text{ atm}) = z \text{ kcal/mole}. \tag{4}$$

Normally, conditions of gravitational force, magnetic field, electric field, and so forth, are constant and no mention need be made of them. However, if during the process there are changes in such conditions that affect significantly the thermodynamic property, then the given conditions should be specified to the necessary precision.

**2. Specification of the thermodynamic property.** In addition to specifying adequately the given reaction or process and its components, it is important to specify the thermodynamic property which is measured, as the increment in energy, $\Delta E$, or the increment in heat content, $\Delta H$.

In the case of chemical reactions, the thermodynamic property of heat of reaction measured may usually be labeled as $\Delta E$ or $\Delta H$ depending upon whether the substances participating in the reaction are confined at constant volume or at constant pressure. Consider, for example, the reaction of a stoichiometric mixture of two diatomic gases, MX and $X_2$, to form the triatomic ideal gas, $MX_2$:

$$\text{MX(g)} + \frac{1}{2}\text{X}_2(\text{g}) = \text{MX}_2(\text{g}). \tag{5}$$

If the reaction takes place in a calorimeter in a closed bomb at constant volume, and if the total pressure of the reactant gases is $P$, then the reaction may be specified as follows, at the given temperature:

$$\text{MX}(\text{g}, P_{\text{MX}} = \tfrac{2}{3}P) + \tfrac{1}{2}\text{X}_2(\text{g}, P_{\text{X}_2} = \tfrac{1}{3}P)$$
$$= \text{MX}_2(\text{g}, P_{\text{MX}_2} = \tfrac{2}{3}P). \tag{6}$$

According to the first law, for any process,

$$\Delta E = q + w + u, \tag{7}$$

where $q$ is the heat energy, $w$ is the "$PV$" work energy, and $u$ is any other energy, each absorbed by the system during the process. But in this calorimetric experiment, $u$ is zero, and, since the volume is constant, $w$ is also zero. Hence, the calorimetrically measured heat energy absorbed, $q$, is equal to $\Delta E$, and for the reaction given by Equation 6, we may write,

$$\Delta E = q. \tag{8}$$

In general, the absorbed heat energy associated with any chemical reaction that takes place in a calorimeter in a vessel at constant volume may be placed equal to $\Delta E$ for the specified reaction or process taking place in the vessel.

If the reaction given by Equation 5 takes place in a calorimeter at constant pressure, with each reactant gas disappearing at the pressure, $P$, and the product gas appearing at the pressure, $P$, then the reaction may be specified as follows at the given temperature:

$$MX(g, P) + \tfrac{1}{2}X_2(g, P) = MX_2(g, P). \tag{9}$$

According to the first law, for any process,

$$\Delta E = q + w + u. \tag{10}$$

But in this calorimetric experiment, $u$ is zero. Since the system undergoes a change in volume and is subjected to a constant confining pressure, the "$PV$" work energy is

$$w = - \int P dV = -P \int dV = -P\Delta V. \tag{11}$$

Substituting in Equation 10 gives

$$\Delta E = q - P\Delta V. \tag{12}$$

Hence

$$\Delta E + P\Delta V = q,$$

and

$$\Delta E + \Delta(PV) = \Delta(E + PV) = q. \tag{13}$$

Finally, since we define

$$E + PV = H, \tag{14}$$

we may write

$$\Delta H = q. \tag{15}$$

That is, the calorimetrically measured heat energy absorbed, $q$, is equal to $\Delta H$, the increment in heat content for the given reaction.

In general, the absorbed heat energy associated with any chemical reaction that takes place in a calorimeter at constant pressure may be placed equal to $\Delta H$ for the specified reaction or process taking place.

For any specified reaction or process, the difference between the value of $\Delta E$ and $\Delta H$ may be evaluated from the relation

$$\Delta H = \Delta E + \Delta(PV). \tag{16}$$

In Equation 16, $\Delta(PV)$ is simply the sum of the product of pressure and volume for each of the products less the sum of the product of pressure and volume for each of the reactants, for the specified reaction or process. The value of $PV$ for liquid and solid substances will be small compared to the value of $PV$ for gaseous substances. For reactions in which all the reactants and products are liquids or solids, therefore, the difference between $\Delta E$ and $\Delta H$ will be relatively small. For reactions in which the number of moles of gaseous reactants is the same as the number of moles of gaseous products, the difference between $\Delta E$ and $\Delta H$ will also be relatively small. For other reactions, the difference between $\Delta E$ and $\Delta H$ will depend on the difference in the number of moles, $\Delta n$, of gaseous reactants and gaseous products.

In the case of the reaction given by Equation 5, wherein each of the substances involved is an ideal gas, the difference between $\Delta E$ and $\Delta H$ may be readily evaluated as follows:

$$\Delta H = \Delta E + \Delta(PV). \tag{17}$$

But

$$\Delta(PV) = (\Delta n)RT = -\tfrac{1}{2}RT. \tag{18}$$

Hence

$$\Delta H = \Delta E - \tfrac{1}{2}RT. \tag{19}$$

In general, for reactions involving only ideal gases, the difference between $\Delta E$ and $\Delta H$ is given by the relation

$$\Delta H = \Delta E + RT\Delta n, \tag{20}$$

where

$$\Delta n = \sum n_{\text{products}} - \sum n_{\text{reactants}}, \tag{21}$$

$n$ being the number of moles of gas.

In the case of processes such as those of transition, fusion, and vaporization, occurring in a calorimeter, the calorimetrically measured value of the heat energy is equivalent to $\Delta H$ if the process occurs at constant pressure and $\Delta E$ if the process occurs at constant volume.

Similarly, if the process is one of simply taking a given substance from one temperature to a slightly higher temperature, in order to determine the heat capacity of the given substance, as the ratio of the heat absorbed to the rise in temperature, the measured property will be the heat capacity at constant volume, $C_V$, if the process occurs at constant volume, and the heat capacity at constant pressure, $C_P$, if the process occurs at constant pressure. In any case, the property will be that for the substance in the physical state or states in which it actually exists in the calorimetric vessel in which it is contained.

**3. Thermochemical method.** The modern thermochemical method aims to determine as directly as possible the quantity of

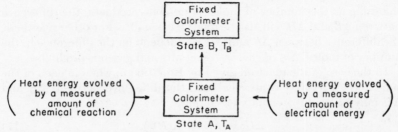

Figure 1. Schematic diagram of the thermochemical method of determining the heats of exothermal reactions.

energy associated with a unit amount of a given reaction or process. The thermochemical investigation consists essentially of two parts. One is the calorimetric part, which involves determination of the quantity of energy evolved or absorbed by the reaction or process. The other is the chemical part, which involves measurement of the amount of the given reaction or process. The desired result is the ratio, in appropriate units, of the quantity of energy to the amount of the given reaction or process.

**4. Calorimetric part of the thermochemical investigation.** For a chemical reaction or process that is exothermal, that is, one that evolves heat energy as it takes place, the method is schematically illustrated in Figure 1. Here, $A$ represents a fixed calorimeter system at the "standard" initial temperature $T_A$ and $B$ represents the same fixed calorimeter system at the "standard" final higher temperature $T_B$. In one kind of experiment, the heat evolved by a measured amount of the given chemical reaction or process is used to take the calorimeter system from its initial state $A$ and temperature, $T_A$, to its final state $B$ and temperature, $T_B$. In another kind of experiment, with the same calorimeter system at the same initial state, the heat evolved by a measured amount of electrical energy is used to take the calorimeter system from the same initial state $A$ and temperature, $T_A$, to the same final state $B$ and temperature, $T_B$. In this manner, there is obtained a direct equivalence between the measured amount of chemical reaction and the measured amount of electrical energy, using the fixed calorimeter system as the absorber and comparator of the two kinds of energy.

In actual practice it is easy to use a fixed calorimeter system but impracticable to try to obtain exactly the same rise of temperature in all experiments. Instead, with the fixed calorimeter system, the rise of temperature is made substantially the same in all experiments, and the small differences from one experiment to another are measured in order to effect the correction to the common or standard value of the rise of temperature. In most cases, the amount of electrical or chemical energy added to the calorimeter can be so regulated that the differences in the rise of temperature in the various experiments will be less than several per cent of the total rise. Since the small differences can be measured as precisely as necessary, the advantage of the substitutional nature of the method is retained, and the experimenter gains some needed flexibility in operation.

For the given calorimeter system it is convenient to determine a quantity called its energy equivalent,* which is the amount of electrical energy added to the fixed calorimeter system divided by the rise of temperature, the amount of energy added being regulated so that the actual rise of temperature differs little from the "standard" rise of temperature. The simple relation used in computing the energy equivalent of the calorimeter is

$$\text{(energy equivalent)} = \text{(electrical energy)}/\Delta t_e, \qquad (22)$$

where $\Delta t_e$ is the rise of temperature in the experiment with electrical

---

* The energy equivalent is substantially the same as that which in the early days was called the heat capacity of the calorimeter, but the latter designation is not recommended because it implies that the investigator has a knowledge of the actual physical boundaries of the material system to which the heat capacity is ascribed, and that the heat capacity of the calorimeter may be evaluated by a summation of the heat capacities of its component parts.

energy. From a series of such experiments, an average value of the energy equivalent is determined.

In a series of calorimetric reaction experiments, there is measured the amount of chemical reaction that produces, in the calorimeter, a rise of temperature substantially equal to the selected "standard" rise of temperature. The relation used to evaluate the "reaction equivalent" is

$$\text{(reaction equivalent)} = \Delta t_r/n, \tag{23}$$

where $\Delta t_r$ is the rise of temperature in the experiment with chemical energy (measured with the same thermometer over substantially the same range), and $n$ is the number of moles of reaction measured by the mass and molecular weights of the substance that is used to determine the amount of reaction. From a series of such experiments, an average value of the reaction equivalent is determined.

The experimental value of the change in energy or heat content for the given reaction, per mole, is then evaluated by the relation

$$-q = [(\text{electrical energy})/n][(\Delta t_r)/(\Delta t_e)]. \tag{24}$$

It will be noted from Equation 24 that the rises of temperature in the two kinds of experiments substantially cancel. It follows that the temperature need be known accurately, as distinguished from precision of differences, only to the extent required to specify the temperature to which the measured thermodynamic property is to be assigned.

Examples of exothermal reactions for which the decrease in energy or heat content may be measured in the above way are those of the following kinds: combustion of a gaseous, liquid, or solid substance in oxygen, as the combustion of gaseous ethane, or liquid normal heptane, or solid normal eicosane, in oxygen to form gaseous carbon dioxide and liquid water; solution of a gaseous, liquid, or solid substance in a liquid solvent, as the solution of hydrogen chloride in water to form aqueous hydrochloric acid, or the solution of liquid sulfuric acid in water to form aqueous sulfuric acid, or the solution of solid sodium hydroxide in water to form aqueous sodium hydroxide; neutralization, in the liquid phase, of an acid with a base, as the neutralization of aqueous hydrochloric acid with aqueous potassium hydroxide to form aqueous potassium chloride; reaction of a gaseous, liquid, or solid substance with a liquid to form an aqueous solution,

with or without a gaseous product or solid product, as the reaction of
solid potassium with liquid water to form aqueous potassium hydroxide and gaseous hydrogen; reaction of two gaseous substances to form
a gaseous product, as in the hydrogenation or chlorination of ethylene;
formation of a gaseous, liquid, or solid product from its elements,
gaseous, liquid, or solid, as in the formation of liquid water from
gaseous hydrogen and oxygen, or the formation of gaseous sulfur
dioxide from solid sulfur and gaseous oxygen, or the formation of
solid sodium chloride from solid sodium and gaseous chlorine, or the
formation of gaseous hydrogen chloride from gaseous hydrogen and
chlorine.

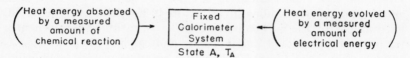

Figure 2. Schematic diagram of the thermochemical method of determining the
heats of endothermal reactions.

If the reaction or process is an endothermal one, that is, one that
absorbs heat energy as it takes place, then, in principle, the method is
simplified. In this case, a measured quantity of electrical energy is
added to the calorimeter system in an amount just sufficient to maintain the temperature constant, balancing the energy absorbed by the
reaction or process as it proceeds. This is illustrated schematically
in Figure 2. For this experiment, the initial and final states of the
calorimeter system are the same and the calorimeter neither absorbs
nor gives up energy. In this way, a direct equivalence (except for
sign) is obtained between the measured amount of electrical energy
and the measured amount of the given reaction or process.

Examples of endothermal reactions or processes for which the increase in energy or heat content may be measured isothermally in the
above way include any reactions of the kinds mentioned earlier which
may be endothermal, together with endothermal reactions of the
following types: decomposition of a gaseous substance into gaseous,
liquid, or solid products, as the decomposition of gaseous diborane
into solid boron and gaseous hydrogen; vaporization of a liquid substance to the gaseous state, as the vaporization of liquid water to
gaseous water; sublimation of a solid substance to the gaseous state, as

the sublimation of the solid octane, 2,2,3,3-tetramethylbutane; melting or fusion of a solid substance to the liquid state, as the melting or fusion of water ice to liquid water; transition of a solid substance from one stable crystalline form to another, as the transition of carbon tetrachloride from crystalline form II to crystalline form I.

When exothermal reactions are to be measured, and the investigator does not have available apparatus for measuring the electrical energy with adequate accuracy, there may be substituted for the experiments with electrical energy calibrating experiments with a similar chemical reaction the change in energy or heat content of which has previously been determined accurately in another laboratory. It is preferable that such calibrating reactions be ones which have been agreed upon by the leading investigators in the field, as represented, for example, by the Subcommission on Experimental Thermochemistry of the International Union of Pure and Applied Chemistry. Examples of the use of such calibrating reactions are the following: evaluation of the "energy equivalent" of a calorimeter system in which the reaction vessel is a closed bomb, using the combustion of standard benzoic acid under certain standardized conditions; evaluation of the "energy equivalent" of a calorimeter system in which the reaction vessel is one designed to burn gases in a flame at constant pressure, using the combustion of hydrogen in oxygen to form water; evaluation of the "energy equivalent" of a calorimeter system for measuring heats of solution of solids in water to form aqueous solutions, using the solution of a solid, the heat of solution of which has been previously accurately determined.

Similarly, for endothermal reactions, if the investigator does not have available apparatus for measuring electrical energy with adequate accuracy, it is possible to determine the ratio of the amount of the given reaction or process to the amount of a calibrating reaction or process associated with the same quantity of energy. This may be done either by ascertaining what amount of the calibrating reaction is needed to produce the same change (decrease) in the temperature of the calorimeter system, as is produced by a known amount of the given reaction, or by ascertaining what amount of the given reaction is brought about by identically the same, but not accurately measured, amount of electrical energy as is needed to bring about a known amount of the calibrating reaction.

In processes involving no chemical reaction as such, and where the substance under investigation does not change its state, as in the determination of the heat capacity of a liquid or a solid substance, the experiment involves measurement of the energy required to produce a measured change of temperature for the substance and the container. In such cases, the "energy equivalent" or heat capacity of the containing vessel must be accounted for. The most reliable way of doing this is to perform two sets of experiments, in one of which the calorimetric container is full of the substance under investigation and in the other of which the container contains only a small amount of the given substance. The difference in the two sets of experiments serves, in effect to determine the heat capacity of that amount of the given substance corresponding to the difference in mass of the two charges. With such a procedure, the container is under more nearly identical conditions than would be the case if the container were measured actually empty in the second set of experiments.

For any of the cases where a calibrating reaction or process is used, for energy either evolved or absorbed, it is possible, in principle, to devise a twin calorimeter arrangement, wherein the values of the "energy equivalent" of the two calorimeters are the same or have a known ratio one to the other. With such an apparatus, the given reaction and the calibrating reaction are run simultaneously, and the experiment serves, in effect, to determine the ratio of the amounts of the two reactions with which equal amounts of energy or heat content are associated.

**5. Chemical part of the thermochemical investigation.** In the chemical part of the thermochemical investigation, it is necessary first to establish that the actual reaction or process that occurs is the specified one, and second, to measure with the necessary accuracy the amount of the given reaction or process that occurs in each experiment for which the heat energy has been evaluated.

In the examination of the purity of the chemical reaction being studied, the investigator should demonstrate with reasonable certainty, by means of appropriate chemical or physical tests, that the reaction which actually occurs in the calorimetric reaction vessel is one that does not differ significantly from the theoretically pure reaction. Or, if there is a side reaction, the amount and effect of it must be evaluated with the necessary accuracy.

Having first decided that the reaction being studied is reasonably complete and clear cut, one can investigate the purity of the reaction as it actually occurs in the reaction vessel in the calorimeter, first by establishing the purity of the reacting substances, and second, by examining the products of the reaction for the presence of possible foreign substances. The permissible amounts of impurities in the reacting substances and the permissible amounts of side reactions depend to a large extent upon the method by which the amount of the reaction is determined and upon the amount of heat energy contributed by the side reactions involved.

One of the vital points in any thermochemical investigation is the method of determining the amount of chemical reaction that occurs in any given experiment. The method selected should be precise and accurate with respect to true mass and the amount should be accurately expressible in terms of moles. This latter requirement involves an accurate knowledge of the molecular weight of the substance whose mass determines the amount of reaction. Suppose, for example, the reaction being studied is

$$C_6H_{14}(\text{liq.}) + 9^1/_2O_2(g) = 6CO_2(g) + 7H_2O(\text{liq.}). \qquad (25)$$

In such a case, the amount of the reaction may be determined from the mass of hexane consumed, the mass of carbon dioxide formed, or the mass of water formed. For each mole of hexane consumed, the corresponding masses are hexane, 86.172 g, carbon dioxide, 264.060 g, and water, 126.112 g. If the atomic weight of each element involved is known without significant uncertainty, and if the true mass in grams is capable of being determined with about the same absolute uncertainty in each case, it is obvious that in this case the substance whose mass should determine the amount of reaction in moles is, in order of preference, carbon dioxide, water, hexane. If the mass of hexane is used, correction must be made for the small amount of water and air that may be dissolved in the sample.

Another point which needs consideration is that the determination of the amount of reaction from the mass of one substance, rather than that of another, may make permissible a greater amount of certain impurities in one of the reacting substances. An example of this situation is in the combustion of ethanol in oxygen,

$$C_2H_5OH(\text{liq.}) + 3^1/_2O_2(g) = 2CO_2(g) + 3H_2O(\text{liq.}). \qquad (26)$$

In this case, it would be unwise to determine the amount of reaction from the mass of the ethanol itself, or from the mass of water formed, without first establishing beyond reasonable doubt that the sample contained no water. On the other hand, the determination of the amount of reaction from the mass of carbon dioxide produced would make permissible the presence, in the ethanol, of a relatively large amount of water without introducing a significant error other than that of the heat of solution of the impurity of liquid water in the ethanol, which can be corrected for.

From the foregoing discussion, it is clear that the correction of values of molal heats of reaction by reason of changes in molecular weights must be done in each case with regard to the change in the molecular weight of the particular substance whose mass was used to determine the amount of reaction. If the molecular weight of this "determining" substance has not changed, no change in the value of the molal heat of reaction is necessary.

**6. Standard substances for thermochemistry.** Standard substances for use in thermochemical investigations are of two kinds. The first kind of standard is one which serves to permit transfer of the unit of energy from a national standardizing laboratory, or appropriate other laboratory with adequate facilities, to the given investigating laboratory when the latter does not have adequate facilities for calibration in terms of electrical energy. An example of this kind of standard is benzoic acid, the use of which for such purposes with bomb calorimeters is described in Chapter 3. Another example is the combustion of hydrogen in oxygen to form liquid water, the use of which for such purposes with constant pressure flame calorimeters is described in Chapter 4.

The second kind of standard is one used to control the chemical part of an investigation, that is, to permit the investigating laboratory to ascertain whether it has adequately mastered the analytical chemistry of the process, to check the purity of the reaction and to determine accurately enough how much of the reaction has taken place. Examples of possible standards for such purposes are discussed in Chapters 7, 8, 9, 10, and 13.

**7. Corrections to reference or standard states.** For purposes of intercomparison and tabulation of data on the energies or heats of reactions and processes, it is desirable that each substance participating in the given reaction or process be corrected to an appropriate reference or standard state. For example, with regard to energy or heat content, it is convenient and desirable to select for the reference state at the given temperature, say 25°C, the pure liquid or solid substance at an actual pressure of 1 atmosphere and the gas in the ideal state at 1 atmosphere.* Appropriate other reference states are required for aqueous and other solutions.

For every reaction or process that takes place in a calorimeter, it is imperative that significant data be recorded as to the phase, pressure, temperature, and concentration of each of the substances at the beginning and at the end of the reaction. A study of each reaction will indicate with what significance the various properties must be known and recorded.

Chapter 5 of this book discusses this problem in detail for combustions taking place in a bomb at constant volume.

**8. Variation of the heat of reaction with temperature.** When the value of the change in heat content, $\Delta H$, is known for a specified reaction or process at some temperature, the value at any other temperature may be readily calculated if there are known, for each of the individual reactants and products, the values of heat capacity, $C_P$, or of the heat content, $H$ (referred to some selected temperature), over the range of temperature for which the calculation is to be made.

Given the simple reaction,

$$M = N, \tag{27}$$

with the state of each substance being adequately specified. The change in heat content for this reaction at the given temperature, $T$, is equal to

$$\Delta H = H_N - H_M. \tag{28}$$

At constant pressure,

$$d(\Delta H)/dT = dH_N/dT - dH_M/dT. \tag{29}$$

Since, at constant pressure,

$$dH/dT = C_P, \tag{30}$$

it follows that

$$d(\Delta H)/dT = C_{P_N} - C_{P_M} = \Delta C_P. \tag{31}$$

---

* Thermodynamic reference and standard states are discussed in detail in Chapters 23 and 27 of reference (1).

Suppose that over a given range of temperature, $T_1$ to $T_2$,

$$C_{P_N} = a_N + b_N T + c_N T^2, \tag{32}$$

and

$$C_{P_M} = a_M + b_M T + c_M T^2. \tag{33}$$

Subtraction of Equation 33 from Equation 32 gives

$$\Delta C_P = (\Delta a) + (\Delta b)T + (\Delta c)T^2, \tag{34}$$

where

$$\Delta a = a_N - a_M, \tag{35}$$

$$\Delta b = b_N - b_M, \tag{36}$$

and

$$\Delta c = c_N - c_M. \tag{37}$$

Combination of Equations 31 and 34 gives, for constant pressure,

$$d(\Delta H)/dT = (\Delta a) + (\Delta b)T + (\Delta c)T^2. \tag{38}$$

Equation 38 may be readily integrated over the given range of temperature to give the value of $\Delta H$ at some temperature $T$ within the given range with reference to the value of $\Delta H$ at $T_1$:

$$\Delta H_T - \Delta H_{T_1}$$
$$= (\Delta a)(T - T_1) + \tfrac{1}{2}(\Delta b)(T^2 - T_1^2) + \tfrac{1}{3}(\Delta c)(T^3 - T_1^3). \tag{39}$$

Equation 39 serves to evaluate $\Delta H$ at the temperature $T$, between $T_1$ and $T_2$, when the value of $\Delta H$ at $T_1$ is known and when the values of the heat capacities of each of the reactants and products are known over the range of temperature $T_1$ to $T_2$. An equation similar to Equation 38 may be used when the value of $\Delta H$ is known at some other temperature within the given range $T_1$ to $T_2$, as at $T_3$:

$$\Delta H - \Delta H_{T_3}$$
$$= (\Delta a)(T - T_3) + \tfrac{1}{2}(\Delta b)(T^2 - T_3^2) + \tfrac{1}{3}(\Delta c)(T^3 - T_3^3). \tag{40}$$

In Equation 40, $T$ and $T_3$ have any values within the range of applicability of the equation, and $T$ may be lower than $T_3$. Equation 38 may be integrated without specific limits of temperature to give the relation

$$\Delta H = \Delta H_* + (\Delta a)T + \tfrac{1}{2}(\Delta b)T^2 + \tfrac{1}{3}(\Delta c)T^3, \tag{41}$$

where $\Delta H_*$ is the constant of integration required to make the equation valid over the range of applicability. In Equation 41, the values of the constants $\Delta a$, $\Delta b$, and $\Delta c$ are obtained from the equations for the heat capacity of each of the reactants and products, and $\Delta H_*$ is evaluated from the foregoing constants and the value of $\Delta H$ at a known temperature in the range $T_1$ to $T_2$. Although the substitution of $T = 0$ in Equation 41 makes $\Delta H_*$ appear formally to be the value for $0°$K, it must be remembered that Equation 41 is valid only over the range of temperature for which heat capacities, as given by Equations 32 and 33, are known, and within which range of temperature the actual value of $\Delta H$ is known at some one temperature.

Frequently, there are known for each of the reactants and products of a given reaction, values at various temperatures of the heat content, $H - H_0$, which is the heat content at a given temperature referred to the heat content at $0°$K. In such cases, the value of $\Delta H$ for other temperatures may be readily calculated from the value of $\Delta H$ at one temperature. Suppose that the value of $\Delta H$ at $25°$C is known. Then the actual value of $\Delta H$ at $0°$K is equal to

$$\Delta H_0 = \Delta H_{298.16} - \Delta(H_{298.16} - H_0) \tag{42}$$

where

$$\Delta(H_{298.16} - H_0)$$
$$= \Sigma(H_{298.16} - H_0)_{\text{products}} - \Sigma(H_{298.16} - H_0)_{\text{reactants}}. \tag{43}$$

The value of $\Delta H$ at any other temperature may be obtained from the relation

$$\Delta H = \Delta H_0 + \Delta(H - H_0), \tag{44}$$

where, as before,

$$\Delta(H - H_0) = \Sigma(H - H_0)_{\text{products}} - \Sigma(H - H_0)_{\text{reactants}}. \tag{45}$$

Equations 42 and 44 may be readily proved by considering the symbol $\Delta$ as an operator and multiplying it into each term inside the parentheses.

If there is need for them, equations corresponding to all the foregoing may be derived for the energy, $E$, the heat capacity at constant volume, $C_V$, and the energy content referred to $0°$K, $E - E_0$.

**9. Assignment of the temperature for the reaction or process.** For every reaction or process which is carried out in a calorimeter and for which a value of the change in energy or heat content is determined, it is important to assign with adequate accuracy the value of temperature to which the given thermodynamic property is to be ascribed. In the case of those experiments where each reactant enters the calorimeter, and each product leaves the calorimeter, on the average, at the mean temperature of the experiment, the value of the given thermodynamic property may usually be assigned to the mean of the initial and final temperatures of the calorimeter in the given experiment.

On the other hand, if the reaction takes place in a system such that all of the reactant material is in the calorimeter at the beginning of the experiment at the initial temperature, $T_A$, and all of the product material is in the calorimeter at the end of the experiment at the final temperature, $T_B$, one has a choice of using as the assigned temperature of the given property the initial temperature, $T_A$, the final temperature, $T_B$, or the mean temperature, $(T_A + T_B)/2$. If the energy equivalent of the calorimeter is taken as that of the final system, then the assigned temperature is the initial temperature. If the energy equivalent of the calorimeter is taken as that of the initial system, then the assigned temperature is the final temperature. If the energy equivalent of the calorimeter is taken as the mean of the initial and final systems, then the assigned temperature is the mean of the initial and final temperatures. Actually, also, the assigned temperature may be any intermediate temperature provided the appropriate fractions of the initial and final systems are used to evaluate the energy equivalent of the calorimeter.

An example of a reaction in which the foregoing points are important is as follows: Given the reaction of neutralization of aqueous sodium hydroxide with aqueous hydrochloric acid to form aqueous sodium chloride, with the reaction occurring at constant pressure in a calorimeter, with an initial temperature of 20°C and a rise of 5°C to give a final temperature of 25°C. The reaction may be written as follows:

$$(\text{NaOH} \cdot 100\text{H}_2\text{O})(\text{liq., } 20°\text{C}) + (\text{HCl} \cdot 100\text{H}_2\text{O})(\text{liq., } 20°\text{C})$$

$$= (\text{NaCl} \cdot 201\text{H}_2\text{O})(\text{liq., } 25°\text{C}). \quad (46)$$

One can proceed from the initial state to the final state in two simple ways.

The first way is given by the following two equations:

$(NaOH \cdot 100H_2O)(liq., 20°C) + (HCl \cdot 100H_2O)(liq., 20°C)$

$= (NaOH \cdot 100H_2O)(liq., 25°C) + (HCl \cdot 100H_2O)(liq., 25°C);$ (47)

$(NaOH \cdot 100H_2O)(liq., 25°C) + (HCl \cdot 100H_2O)(liq., 25°C)$

$= (NaCl \cdot 201H_2O)$ (liq., 25°C). (48)

It is clear that if the measured heat of the reaction is to be assigned to the final temperature, 25°C, the energy equivalent of the calorimeter must be determined in a separate experiment on the initial system, before reaction occurs, over the range of temperature 20° to 25°C.

The second way is given by the following two equations:

$(NaOH \cdot 100H_2O)(liq., 20°C) + (HCl \cdot 100H_2O)(liq., 20°C)$

$= (NaCl \cdot 201H_2O)(liq., 20°C);$ (49)

$(NaCl \cdot 201H_2O)(liq., 20°C) = (NaCl \cdot 201H_2O)(liq., 25°C).$ (50)

In this case, the heat of the reaction is to be ascribed to the initial temperature, 20°C, and the energy equivalent of the calorimeter must be determined in a separate experiment on the final system, after reaction occurs, over the range of temperature, 20° to 25°C.

A third way of going from the initial to the final state for the reaction under discussion is given by the following three equations:

$(NaOH \cdot 100H_2O)(liq., 20°C) + (HCl \cdot 100H_2O)(liq., 20°C) =$

$(NaOH \cdot 100H_2O)(liq., 22.5°C) + (HCl \cdot 100H_2O)(liq., 22.5°C);$ (51)

$(NaOH \cdot 100H_2O)(liq., 22.5°C) + (HCl \cdot 100H_2O)(liq., 22.5°C)$

$= (NaCl \cdot 201H_2O)(liq., 22.5°C);$ (52)

$(NaCl \cdot 201H_2O)(liq., 22.5°C) + (NaCl \cdot 201H_2O)(liq., 25°C).$ (53)

In this last case, the heat of the reaction is to be ascribed to the mean temperature, 22.5°C, and the energy equivalent of the calorimeter system must be determined in two separate experiments, one on the initial system over the range of temperature, 20° to 22.5°C, and one on the final system over the range of temperature, 22.5° to 25°C.

**10. Heats of formation.** The ideal table of heats of reaction is one which will permit calculation of the heat of every possible chemical reaction. Obviously it would be impractical to list in a table every chemical reaction and its corresponding change in heat content, but the same end is accomplished by listing for each chemical substance its heat of formation from its elements in selected reference states. It is evident that, by proper selection, the number of chemical reactions whose heats must be measured will be about the same as the number of substances listed in the table. Some saving in the number of reactions to be measured will occur because of the correlations of energy with molecular structure which are possible among certain organic compounds, particularly hydrocarbons.

The value of the heat of formation of a given substance from its elements may be the result of the determination of the heat of one reaction, as for the heat of formation of liquid water:

$$H_2(g) + \tfrac{1}{2}O_2(g) = H_2O(liq.). \tag{54}$$

For many other substances, however, the value will result from the measurement of the heats of a number of reactions, as for the heat of formation of crystalline sodium hydroxide:

$$Na(c) + H_2O(liq.) = NaOH(aq.) + \tfrac{1}{2}H_2(g); \tag{55}$$

$$H_2(g) + \tfrac{1}{2}O_2(g) = H_2O(liq.); \tag{56}$$

$$NaOH(c) = NaOH(aq.). \tag{57}$$

Addition of Equations 55 and 56 and subtraction of Equation 57 gives the desired result:

$$Na(c) + \tfrac{1}{2}O_2(g) + \tfrac{1}{2}H_2(g) = NaOH(c). \tag{58}$$

Similarly the heat of formation of carbon monoxide is evaluated from data on the following reactions:

$$CO(g) + \tfrac{1}{2}O_2(g) = CO_2(g); \tag{59}$$

$$C(c, graphite) + O_2(g) = CO_2(g). \tag{60}$$

Subtraction of Equation 59 from Equation 60 gives

$$C(c, graphite) + \tfrac{1}{2}O_2(g) = CO(g), \tag{61}$$

which is the desired result. In every case the reactions selected for measurement must be ones that can be made to proceed adequately and handled quantitatively in a calorimeter.

There are certain basic values in the table which will be used very frequently in the derivation of other values. These basic values, which should preferably be known with the highest accuracy, include the heats of formation of water, carbon dioxide, nitric acid, sulfuric acid, hydrogen chloride, hydrogen sulfide, etc. Because of this interdependence of many of the values of heats of formation, it is desirable that the basic values be carefully selected, and, when any change is made in any one of the basic values, corresponding changes should be made in all the values which depend upon it. It is for this same reason that the addition or subtraction of values of heats of formation from different tables is a procedure fraught with uncertainty.

For the primary table of heats of formation of the chemical compounds, it is necessary to have a selected reference temperature and a selected reference state for each substance. For each element, the heat of formation is given as zero for the selected reference state at the selected reference temperature.

## References

1. F. D. Rossini, *Chemical Thermodynamics*, John Wiley and Sons, Inc., New York, 1950.

# CHAPTER 2

# Unit of Energy; Fundamental Constants

FREDERICK D. ROSSINI

In this chapter are presented brief summaries of the present status of the unit of energy and fundamental constants from the standpoint of their applicability to thermochemistry. Additional details not given here may be found in reference (1) and the references given in that book.

**1. Unit of energy.** The basic unit of energy in modern experimental thermochemistry is the electrical joule, which is based upon the mean solar second as the unit of time and upon standards of electromotive force and resistance maintained at the several national standardizing laboratories. The working standards are saturated cadmium (Weston) cells and wire (usually manganin) resistance coils. When redefined in 1908, the units internationally agreed upon, specified then in terms of the mercury ohm and the silver voltammeter, were identical with the absolute units within the limits within which the latter could then be determined (2). Since that time, however, the accuracy of the absolute measurements has increased and more accurate determinations of the relations between the international units and the absolute units for the ohm and the ampere have been made (3–5).

All measurements of electrical energy made from about 1910 to 1948 by means of standard cells and resistances, with time in mean solar seconds, were actually in terms of international joules. Starting January 1, 1948, the National Bureau of Standards, along with the national standardizing laboratories of other countries, began certifying standard cells and resistances in absolute volts and absolute ohms, so that the resulting energy is measured in absolute joules (5).

**2. Joule versus calorie.** Notwithstanding the fact that practically all accurate calorimetric measurements made after about 1910 were actually based on electrical energy, directly or indirectly, most investigators continued until about 1930 to express their final results in such a way as to make it appear that the unit of energy was in some way still connected with the heat capacity of water. Actually, what they did was to convert their values, determined in international joules, into one or more of the several calories based on the heat capacity of water, usually for comparison with older values in the literature reported in calories. This procedure should have been reversed; that is, the older data should have been converted to the modern unit of energy. But the conversion to the older unit, the calorie, was favored because most chemists and physicists were reluctant to change from their habits of thinking of energy in terms of a unit the size of a calorie.

An important effort to accustom chemists and physicists to the use of the joule as the unit of energy was made by Washburn in connection with many (but not all) of the tabulations of chemical thermodynamic data in the International Critical Tables. This attempt to change over to the joule was not popular. It appeared then that the calorie would at least have to be retained as the name of the unit of heat energy. It was also realized that there would have to be separated from the new calorie every association with the heat capacity of water, else all the thermodynamic values would have to be changed every time someone determined the heat capacity of water with an accuracy greater than that already existing. It would also be necessary for the new calorie to have a size approximately equal to that of the traditional calorie.

The obvious solution was to have an artificial, conventional calorie, defined as equal to a given number of electrical joules, the unit in which the calorimetric measurements were actually made. The investigators would then report their results in terms of the unit in which the measurements are actually made, and, for the benefit of those who prefer to continue thinking of energy in terms of a unit having the name and size of the calorie, would also give the values in terms of the artificial calorie by using the conventional factor for the conversion.

**3. Thermochemical calorie.** The artificial, conventional calorie that was used after about 1930 in all the research laboratories in the

United States dealing with thermochemistry and chemical thermodynamics was defined completely by the relation

$$1 \text{ calorie } = 4.1833 \text{ international joules.} \tag{1}$$

Beginning January 1, 1948, this calorie was redefined in terms of
absolute joules, using the 1947 National Bureau of Standards relation
between the international and absolute electrical units (5), so that

$$1 \text{ calorie } = 4.1840 \text{ absolute joules.} \tag{2}$$

With this redefinition, the thermochemical calorie represents exactly the same quantity of energy as before, and all the values previously reported in terms of the thermochemical calorie remain unchanged.  As is obvious from the definition, the thermochemical
calorie is independent of the heat capacity of water.

The number 4.1833, which originally defined the thermochemical
calorie in terms of international joules, now has no particular significance, though for historical interest it may be mentioned that this
number arose from the quotient 4.185/1.0004, through the attempt to
hold to the factor 4.185 selected by the International Critical Tables
for the relation between the absolute joule and the 15° calorie and the
factor 1.0004 selected in 1930 as the then best ratio of the size of the
international joule to the absolute joule (3).

**4. Heat capacity of water.**  The present best values of the heat
capacity of water, in the range 0° to 100°C, appear to be those of Osborne, Stimson, and Ginnings (6).  These values may be used to
convert to joules such thermal data reported in the literature as may
have been obtained in terms of the heat capacity of water at a given
temperature.

**5. Fundamental constants.**  Many of the calculations of thermochemistry involve fundamental constants the values of which enter
into the final results reported.  In order that the values of such constants shall not affect the comparison of results reported by different
investigators, and in order to maintain maximum consistency in
communication of results from different laboratories in different countries, it is desirable to have a set of recommended fundamental constants available for use by all such laboratories.

Fundamental constants may for convenience and simplicity be
classified as (a) basic constants, the values of which are determined
by experimental measurements, (b) derived constants, the values of

which are obtained by applying physical relations to the basic constants, and (c) defined constants, the values of which are fixed by definition.

## TABLE 1
### Values of Basic Constants

| Name | Symbol | Value | Units |
|---|---|---|---|
| Velocity of light | $c$ | $\left.\begin{array}{c} 2.997902 \\ \pm 0.000013 \end{array}\right\} \times 10^{10}$ | cm/sec |
| Planck constant | $h$ | $\left.\begin{array}{c} 6.62377 \\ \pm 0.00027 \end{array}\right\} \times 10^{-27}$ | erg sec/molecule |
| Avogadro constant | $N$ | $\left.\begin{array}{c} 6.02380 \\ \pm 0.00016 \end{array}\right\} \times 10^{23}$ | number of molecules/ mole |
| Faraday constant | $\mathfrak{F}$ | $96,493.1\} \pm 1.0$ | coulombs/equivalent |
| Absolute temperature[a] of the "ice" point, 0°C | $T_{0°C}$ | $273.160 \pm 0.010$ | °K |
| Pressure–volume product for one mole of a gas at 0° and zero pressure | $(PV)_{T_{0°C}}^{P=0}$ | $2271.16 \pm 0.04$ | joules/mole |

[a] The corresponding value of the triple point of water, which is 0.0100°C, would be 273.170 ± 0.010°K.

## TABLE 2
### Values of Derived Constants

| Name | Symbol relation | Value | Units |
|---|---|---|---|
| Electronic charge | $e = \mathfrak{F}/N$ | $\left.\begin{array}{c} 1.601864 \\ \pm 0.000036 \end{array}\right\} \times 10^{-19}$ | coulomb |
| Gas constant | $R = \dfrac{(PV)_{T_{0°C}}^{P=0}}{T_{0°C}}$ | $8.31439 \pm 0.00034$ | joules/deg mole |
| Boltzmann constant | $k = R/N$ | $\left.\begin{array}{c} 1.380257 \\ \pm 0.000067 \end{array}\right\} \times 10^{-16}$ | erg/deg molecule |
| Constant relating wave number and energy | $Z = Nhc$ | $11.96171 \pm 0.00026$ | joule cm/mole |
| Second radiation constant | $c_2 = hc/k$ | $1.438676 \pm 0.000091$ | cm deg |
| Einstein constant relating mass and energy | $Y = c^2$ | $\left.\begin{array}{c} 8.987416 \\ \pm 0.000081 \end{array}\right\} \times 10^{13}$ | joules/g |

TABLE 3

Values of Defined Constants

| Name | Symbol | Values | Units |
|---|---|---|---|
| Standard gravity | $g_0$ | 980.665 | cm/sec$^2$ |
| Standard atmosphere | atm | 1,013,250 | dynes/cm$^2$ |
| Standard millimeter of mercury pressure | mm Hg | 1/760 | atm |
| Calorie (thermochemical) | cal | 4.1840 | joules |

TABLE 4

Values of Certain Auxiliary Relations[a]

1 sec (mean solar) = 1.00273791 sidereal sec
1 joule = 0.999835 ± 0.000052 international joule (NBS)
1 ohm = 0.999505 ± 0.000015 international ohm (NBS)
1 amp = 1.000165 ± 0.000025 international amp (NBS)
1 volt = 0.999670 ± 0.000029 international volt (NBS)
1 coulomb = 1.000165 ± 0.000025 international coulomb (NBS)
1 watt = 0.999835 ± 0.000052 international watt (NBS)
1 liter = 1,000.028 ± 0.004 cm$^3$

[a] All electrical units are absolute unless otherwise indicated.

With regard to the basic and derived constants, it may happen that a given pair of constants related by physical laws may change places from one category to the other, depending upon the relative accuracy with which the values of the two constants may be determined experimentally. The more accurately determined constant is placed in the basic list, leaving the other one to be derived from the value of the first constant with the appropriate physical relation. Occasionally, the two constants may be measurable with about the same accuracy and the preference of one over the other becomes arbitrary. In such cases, appropriate mathematical treatment may be utilized to treat both as nonindependent basic constants.

The fundamental units in terms of which the measurements of the basic constants are made are those of length, mass, and time.

Additional details regarding the fundamental constants, with appropriate other references, are given in reference (1).

The most recently published list of recommended constants for physical chemistry is that of the U. S. National Research Council Committee on Physical Chemistry (7). Tables 1, 2, 3, 4, and 5, all

## TABLE 5
### Values of Various Constants Expressed in Different Units

| Constant | Values[a] | Units[b] |
|---|---|---|
| $(PV)_{T_0 {}^\circ C}^{P=0}$ | 2271.16 | joules/mole |
| | 22,414.6 | cm³ atm/mole |
| | 22.4140 | liter atm/mole |
| $\mathfrak{F}$ | 96,493.1 | coulombs/equivalent |
| | 23,062.4 | cal/volt equivalent |
| $e$ | $1.601864 \times 10^{-19}$ | coulombs |
| | $1.601864 \times 10^{-20}$ | e.m.u. |
| | $4.80223 \times 10^{-10}$ | e.s.u. |
| $R$ | 8.31439 | joules/deg mole |
| | 1.98719 | cal/deg mole |
| | 82.0567 | cm³ atm/deg mole |
| | 0.0820544 | liter atm/deg mole |
| $Z$ | 11.96171 | joule cm/mole |
| | 2.858917 | cal cm/mole |
| $Y$ | $8.987416 \times 10^{13}$ | joules/g |
| | $2.148044 \times 10^{13}$ | cal/g |
| 1 cal | 4.1840 (exact) | joules |
| | 4.18331 | int. joules |
| | 41.2929 | cm³ atm |
| | 0.0412917 | liter atm |

[a] See the preceding tables regarding the uncertainties.
[b] All electrical units are absolute unless otherwise indicated.

taken from the report of the U. S. National Research Council Committee on Physical Chemistry (7) give, respectively, the values of the six basic constants, the values of six derived constants, the values of four defined constants, the values of certain auxiliary relations, and the values of various constants expressed in different units.

## References

1. F. D. Rossini, *Chemical Thermodynamics*, John Wiley and Sons, Inc., New York, 1950.
2. International Congress on Electrical Units and Standards, London, 1908.
3. *Natl. Bur. Standards Tech. News Bull.* **156** (1930).
4. H. L. Curtis, *J. Research Natl. Bur. Standards* **33**, 235 (1944).
5. *Natl. Bur. Standards Circ.* **C459** (1947).
6. N. S. Osborne, H. F. Stimson, and D. C. Ginnings, *J. Research Natl. Bur. Standards* **23**, 238 (1939).
7. F. D. Rossini, F. T. Gucker, Jr., H. L. Johnston, L. Pauling, and G. W. Vinal, *J. Am. Chem. Soc.* **74**, 2699 (1952).

# CHAPTER 3

# Calibration of Calorimeters for Reactions in a Bomb at Constant Volume

J. Coops, R. S. Jessup, and K. van Nes

**1. Introduction.** The energy equivalent of a bomb-calorimetric system can be determined by either of two methods: (a) by determining the temperature rise of the system produced by the addition of a measured quantity of electrical energy, or (b) by determining the temperature rise produced by combustion in the bomb of a weighed quantity of a standard substance, the heat of combustion per unit mass of which has been accurately determined in terms of electrical energy. The first of these two methods yields the more direct determination of the energy equivalent in terms of electric energy units. However, it has the disadvantage that it is more difficult and time-consuming than the second method, and requires more elaborate and costly apparatus. The second method, on the other hand, requires no other apparatus than that which will be needed in any case for measurements of heats of combustion. The second method is almost as satisfactory as the first in all respects, since there is available a standard substance, benzoic acid, the heat of combustion of which has been determined in several different laboratories, with the results of the six most recent determinations covering a total range of 0.02 per cent.

The present chapter will discuss both methods of determining the energy equivalent of a bomb-calorimeter. As both methods involve the determination of the temperature rise, this subject will be discussed first in Section 2 of this chapter. The procedures peculiar to the calibration of a calorimeter by means of standard benzoic acid and by means of electrical energy will be discussed in Sections 3 and

27

4, respectively. The discussion will be restricted to stirred-liquid calorimeters enclosed by jackets which are maintained at constant temperature. Detailed descriptions of calorimeters of this type will be found in numerous papers (1,5,9,11,20–24,26,36,37–39).

**2. Determination of the corrected temperature rise.** (a) *Stirring of the Calorimetric Liquid.* It is necessary that the calorimetric liquid be stirred adequately throughout the course of an experiment. The heat developed by the stirring must be corrected for in calculating the results of an experiment, and since the method generally used for making the correction is based on the assumption that the rate of production of heat by stirring is constant, it is necessary that the rate of stirring be kept constant. Stirring may be produced by a screw propeller in a tube (1,18), or by a centrifugal pump (10). The ring stirrer formerly used almost universally has been shown (1) to be considerably less effective than the screw propeller.

The rate of stirring should be sufficient to insure the desired uniformity of temperature, but not high enough to produce excessive amounts of heat. According to White (18) the rate of temperature rise produced by stirring should not be much more than 0.0001 deg per minute, but accurate results have been obtained (10) with a rate as high as 0.0005 deg per minute when the speed of the stirrer is controlled within sufficiently narrow limits.

(b) *Observations of Temperature and Time.* The type of calorimetric experiment considered here is ordinarily divided into three periods: an initial period in which the temperature change of the calorimeter is due entirely to heat transfer between calorimeter and surroundings (thermal leakage) and heat of stirring; a main period in which the principal part of the temperature rise takes place as a result of the addition of electrical energy, or of combustion taking place in the bomb; and a final period in which the temperature change of the calorimeter is again due entirely to thermal leakage and heat of stirring.

The relation between the temperature, $\theta$, of the calorimeter and time, $t$, in an experiment in which combustion takes place in the bomb is illustrated by the curve in Figure 1, where the parts $ab$, $be$, and $eh$ of the curve represent the temperature-time relations in the initial, main, and final periods, respectively. The horizontal lines at the top represent the temperature of the jacket, $\theta_j$, and the convergence temperature, $\theta\infty$, of the calorimeter, that is, the temperature which the calorimeter would attain in an infinite time if $\theta_j$ and the rate of stirring remained constant.

The length of the initial and final periods is usually 10 to 20 min each, and during these periods measurements of temperature are made as precisely as possible at equal time intervals of 1 or 2 min. The length of the main period depends partly upon the lag of the bomb, but chiefly upon the time of heating in an electrical calibration experiment and almost entirely upon the lag of the bomb in a combustion experiment. It should be taken long enough so that the final

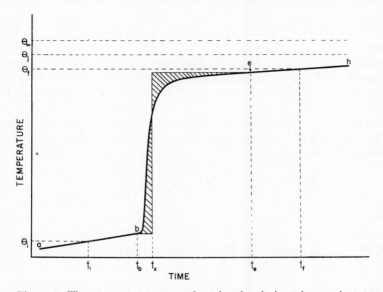

Figure 1. Time-temperature curve for a bomb-calorimetric experiment.

steady rate of change of temperature is attained at the end of this period. In the case of a combustion experiment the length of the main period should be greater by a factor of 10 than the time required for the temperature rise to attain two thirds of its final value (10). The frequency and precision of the temperature measurements during the main period should be sufficient to permit the evaluation of the correction for thermal leakage with the desired accuracy. It will not ordinarily be difficult in an electrical calibration experiment to determine the temperatures during the main period with a precision of

0.001 or 0.002°, which will usually be sufficient. In a combustion experiment the same precision should be attainable after the first 1 or 2 min. To obtain an accuracy of the order of 0.01 per cent in the corrected temperature rise, temperatures in the main period should be read (or at least be obtainable by interpolation) at intervals of not more than 15 sec (15).

(c) *Observed and Corrected Temperature Rise.* If we let $\theta_b$ and $\theta_e$ denote the temperature of the calorimeter at the beginning and end, respectively, of the main period, then the observed temperature rise of the calorimeter may be taken as $(\theta_e - \theta_b)$. This must be corrected for heat of stirring and thermal leakage in order to obtain the temperature rise resulting from the addition of electrical energy, or from reactions which take place in the bomb. This correction is calculated from the observations of time and temperature (Figure 1), on the assumption that the rate, $u$, of the temperature rise of the calorimeter due to heat of stirring is constant, and the rate of temperature rise due to thermal leakage is proportional to the difference between the temperatures of calorimeter and jacket (Newton's law of cooling). The total rate of temperature rise due to heat of stirring and thermal leakage is then given by

$$\frac{d\theta}{dt} = u + k(\theta_j - \theta), \tag{1}$$

where $k$ is the "cooling constant" of the calorimeter.* Another expression which is equivalent to Equation 1 is obtained by noting that $d\theta/dt = 0$ when $\theta = \theta_\infty$. Then from Equation 1

$$\theta_j = \theta_\infty - u/k.$$

*In Equation 1, the first term is a constant which represents the rate of temperature change of the calorimeter due to heat of stirring, and the second term represents the rate of temperature change due to heat transfer between calorimeter and jacket. Actually, the temperature of the jacket may not be exactly equal to the effective temperature of the environment of the calorimeter, and in this case $u$ does not exactly represent the heat of stirring. Thus, if the temperature of the room is lower than that of the jacket, and if thermometer leads or heater leads extend out into the room without being brought into sufficiently intimate thermal contact with the jacket, then the effective temperature of the environment will be somewhat lower than the temperature of the jacket. This does not affect the validity of using Equation 1, however, in the manner described in Section 2c to calculate the correction for thermal leakage and heat of stirring

*Footnote continued on next page*

Substituting this expression for $\theta_j$ in Equation 1, we obtain

$$d\theta/dt = k(\theta_\infty - \theta). \tag{2}$$

The constants $u$ and $k$, or $\theta_\infty$ and $k$, can be calculated from the data of the initial and final periods. Thus if $g_i$ and $g_f$ represent the values of $d\theta/dt$ at the mean temperatures $\theta_i$ and $\theta_f$ of the initial and final periods, respectively, we obtain from Equations 1 and 2:

$$k = \frac{g_i - g_f}{\theta_f - \theta_i} \tag{3}$$

$$u = g_f + k(\theta_f - \theta_j) \tag{4}$$

$$\theta_\infty = \frac{g_f}{k} + \theta_f = \frac{g_i\theta_f - g_f\theta_i}{g_i - g_f}. \tag{5}$$

A third expression for $d\theta/dt$ which does not involve $u$, $\theta_j$, or $\theta_\infty$ may be obtained by combining

$$g_f = u + k(\theta_j - \theta_f)$$

with Equation 1, or by combining

$$g_f = k(\theta_\infty - \theta_f)$$

with Equation 2. In either case we obtain

$$\frac{d\theta}{dt} = g_f + k(\theta_f - \theta). \tag{6}$$

The correction, $\Delta\theta$, which must be added to the observed temperature rise, $(\theta_e - \theta_b)$, to eliminate the effect of heat of stirring and thermal leakage can be obtained by integration of any one of the Equations 1, 2, and 6. The resulting expressions for $\Delta\theta$ are, respectively, the following Equations 7, 8, and 9:

*Footnote continued from preceding page*

The only requirement that the constants $u$ and $\theta_j$ must satisfy is that they be so chosen that Equation 1 correctly represents $d\theta/dt$ as a linear function of $\theta$. Thus, instead of Equation 1 we could use the equally correct equation

$$\frac{d\theta}{dt} = \alpha + k(\beta - \theta),$$

where $\beta$ has any constant value whatever, and where

$$\alpha = u - k(\beta - \theta_j).$$

$$\Delta\theta = -u(t_e - t_b) - k \int_{t_b}^{t_e} (\theta_j - \theta)\mathrm{d}t$$
$$= -[u + k(\theta_j - \theta_m)](t_e - t_b) \tag{7}$$

$$\Delta\theta = -k \int_{t_b}^{t_e} (\theta_\infty - \theta)\mathrm{d}t$$
$$= -k(\theta_\infty - \theta_m)(t_e - t_b) \tag{8}$$

$$\Delta\theta = -g_f(t_e - t_b) - k \int_{t_b}^{t_e} (\theta_f - \theta)\mathrm{d}t$$
$$= -[g_f + k(\theta_f - \theta_m)](t_e - t_b). \tag{9}$$

In these expressions $\theta_m$ represents the average temperature of the wall of the calorimeter in the main period.

No simple analytical expression for the relation between temperature and time in the main period of a combustion experiment has been found, and the value of $\theta_m$ must be found by graphical or numerical integration. The Regnault-Pfaundler method may be used when $n$ temperatures, $\theta_r$, are measured (or obtained by interpolation between observed values) at equal time intervals, $\Delta t$, during the main period. The average temperature is then given by

$$\theta_m = \left\{ \sum_{r=2}^{n-1} \theta_r + \frac{\theta_b + \theta_e}{2} \right\} \frac{\Delta t}{t_e - t_b}$$
$$= \left\{ \sum_{r=2}^{n-1} \theta_r + \frac{\theta_b + \theta_e}{2} \right\} \frac{1}{n - 1}. \tag{10}$$

Sufficiently accurate results have been obtained with Equation 10 with equal time intervals of not more than 15 sec, and this equation was found to give somewhat better results than Simpson's rule (15). The maximum permissible value of the equal time intervals may differ somewhat for different calorimetric systems. The more rapidly $\mathrm{d}\theta/\mathrm{d}t$ changes, the smaller must be the time interval between readings.

In accordance with the above discussion, the corrected temperature rise is given by the equation

$$\Delta\theta_{\mathrm{corr.}} = \theta_e - \theta_b + \Delta\theta, \tag{11}$$

where $\Delta\theta$ can be obtained from any one of the Equations 7, 8, or 9, and where $\theta_m$ can be obtained from Equation 10.

The precision of the value of $(\theta_e - \theta_b)$ can be markedly increased if all the observations of the initial and final periods are used to eliminate random errors in the observed values of $\theta_b$ and $\theta_b$. This can be done in several ways, for example, by plotting the values of temperature versus time,* drawing smooth curves through the points, and reading corrected values of $\theta_b$ and $\theta_e$ from the curves.

Corrected values of $\theta_b$ and $\theta_e$ can also be obtained, somewhat more objectively, by the method of least squares. Thus, to the extent that the curves of $\theta$ versus $t$ of the initial and final periods can be considered linear, the corrected values can be calculated (15) from the relation

$$\theta_{\text{corr.}} = 1/n \sum_{r=1}^{n} \theta_r \pm [(n-1)/2]g, \tag{12}$$

where $\theta_r$ represents the $r$th temperature reading of the initial (or final) period, made in a series of $n$ observations at equally spaced times and $g$ represents the average change in temperature per interval for that period, calculated from

$$g = 6 \frac{(n-1)(\theta_n - \theta_1) + (n-3)(\theta_{n-1} - \theta_2) + \cdots}{n(n^2 - 1)}. \tag{13}$$

The plus sign before the last term in Equation 12 is used in calculating $\theta_b$ from the data of the initial period while the minus sign is used in calculating $\theta_e$ from the data of the final period.

Some objection may be raised to the use of Equations 12 and 13 on the ground that they assume that the curve of $\theta$ versus $t$ in the initial (or final) period is a straight line, whereas it is actually an exponential curve, since it represents a solution of Equation 2. The error is relatively small, however, and the effect of the error is eliminated if the same method of calculation is used with periods of the same length in both the calibration experiments and in measurements of heats of combustion; and if the values of $\theta_b$, $\theta_e$, and $\theta_\infty$ are approximately the same in both types of experiment (see Appendix 1).

The graphical method which may be used to obtain $\theta_b$ and $\theta_e$ has the advantage that if one of the points is in error by a large amount, this fact is immediately evident, and the point can be given less weight in drawing the curve. The use of Equations 12 and 13 has the advantage of automatically giving the best values of $\theta_b$ and $\theta_e$ corresponding to linear representations of the data. If it is desired, all

* The plotting should be done in such a manner as to obtain sufficient sensitivity in the plot.

the experimental values of $\theta$ in the rating periods can be compared with values calculated by an obvious application of Equations 12 and 13, so that any large error in these experimental values can be detected.

Dickinson's method (1) of obtaining the corrected temperature rise consists in finding a time $t_x$ such that

$$-g_b(t_x - t_b) - g_e(t_e - t_x) = k \int_{t_b}^{t_e} (\theta - \theta_\infty)\mathrm{d}t = \Delta\theta.$$

Dickinson showed that this condition will be satisfied if the two crosshatched areas in Figure 1 are equal. The method of finding $t_x$ consists in plotting the $\theta$-versus-$t$ curve on coordinate paper, and finding by trial a $t_x$ such that the crosshatched areas of Figure 1 are equal, as determined by counting squares. This procedure is correct, but is so laborious that Dickinson proposed and used approximate methods of finding $t_x$ for both electrical calibration and combustion experiments. Such approximate methods may be expected to yield a somewhat lower precision than the more exact methods, which should be used where the highest possible accuracy is required.

As stated previously, the methods described for finding the corrected temperature rise in a calorimetric experiment are based on the assumption that the rate of temperature change due to thermal leakage and heat of stirring in an isothermally jacketed calorimeter is a linear function of the calorimeter temperature. The user of a calorimeter should determine the range of validity of this assumption for his calorimetric system by experiment (15,16). It has been found that the assumption is valid over the range of temperature differences usually encountered in bomb calorimetry (1,15,16,17), provided the following conditions are satisfied: (a) no insulating material other than air can be used in the space between calorimeter and jacket; (b) the thickness of the air space between calorimeter and jacket must not exceed about 12 mm (for a 3° maximum temperature difference between calorimeter and jacket); and (c) evaporation of water from the calorimeter must be reduced to a minimum. Evaporation from the calorimeter may be reduced by keeping the temperature of the calorimeter always below that of the jacket and keeping the jacket space as tightly closed as possible (1,5,16,11), or by reducing to a minimum the area of the surface from which water can evaporate (9).

As discussed in Chapter 1, the scale of temperature used in bomb calorimetric measurements is unimportant, provided calibration experiments and measurements of heats of combustion are made over the range from the same initial to the same final temperature. Thus, instead of temperature one may make use of the resistance of a given platinum resistance thermometer as measured with a given Wheatstone bridge (5), or of an arbitrary scale on a sufficiently sensitive mercurial thermometer (11,17). This implies that the relation between the standard temperature scale and the scale actually used in the calorimetric measurements is sufficiently near to linear so that Newton's law holds with sufficient accuracy in terms of both scales. This condition is satisfied for the temperature scales commonly used in bomb calorimetric measurements.

**3. Determination of the energy equivalent with benzoic acid.** (*a*) *Definitions.* If a quantity of energy, $Q$, is added to a fixed calorimetric system, and if the corrected temperature rise of the system is $\Delta\theta_{\text{corr.}} = \theta_e - \theta_b + \Delta\theta$, then the energy equivalent, $\mathcal{E}$, of the system is defined by the expression

$$\mathcal{E} = \frac{Q}{\Delta\theta_{\text{corr.}}}. \tag{14}$$

When the temperature rise of a bomb calorimeter is produced by combustion (and other reactions) taking place in the bomb, the situation is somewhat different from that implied in the preceding paragraph. The differences are: (*a*) the calorimetric system is not fixed, since the reactants in the bomb are replaced by products of the combustion reaction, so that the energy equivalent of the system changes, in general; (*b*) the change in energy of the system corresponding to the corrected temperature rise, $\Delta\theta_{\text{corr.}} = \theta_e - \theta_b + \Delta\theta$, is zero, since $\Delta\theta$ corrects for the effect of any energy added or removed; and (*c*) the combustion (and other reactions) in the bomb take place over a range of temperature. However, it is easily shown (see Appendix 2) that the energy equivalent, $\mathcal{E}_i$, of the fixed initial system and the energy equivalent, $\mathcal{E}_f$, of the fixed final system are given by

$$\mathcal{E}_i = \frac{Q_{(\theta_e + \Delta\theta)}}{\Delta\theta_{\text{corr.}}}, \tag{15}$$

and

$$\mathcal{E}_f = \frac{Q_{(\theta_b)}}{\Delta\theta_{\text{corr.}}}, \tag{16}$$

where $Q_{(\theta)}$ represents the quantity of heat which would have been evolved by the system if the reactions in the bomb had taken place at the constant temperature $\theta$. Thus if $m_s$ grams of benzoic acid were burned in the bomb, the values of the energy equivalents of the initial and final systems would be given by

$$\mathcal{E}_i = \frac{m_s(-\Delta E_{B(\theta_e + \Delta\theta)}) + q_i + q_n - q_c}{\Delta\theta_{\text{corr.}}}, \tag{17}$$

and

$$\mathcal{E}_f = \frac{m_s(-\Delta E_{B(\theta_b)}) + q_i + q_n - q_c}{\Delta\theta_{\text{corr.}}}, \tag{18}$$

where $-\Delta E_{B(\theta)}$ represents the heat of combustion per gram of benzoic acid at the temperature $\theta$, and under the conditions of the actual bomb process; $q_i$ is the energy used to ignite the charge, $q_n$ is the energy produced by the formation of nitric acid in the bomb at the temperature $\theta$, and $q_c$ is the quantity of heat which would have been produced by the combustion in the bomb of any soot found in the crucible at the end of the experiment.

In the use of the bomb calorimeter to measure heats of combustion, neither $\mathcal{E}_i$ nor $\mathcal{E}_f$ as determined with benzoic acid is applicable, since in such measurements the combustible material in the initial system will be something other than benzoic acid, and consequently the products of combustion in the final system will be different from those formed when benzoic acid is burned. For this reason it is convenient to reduce the results of determinations of energy equivalent to the basis of a standard calorimeter system which does not involve benzoic acid or its products. In the use of the calorimeter to measure heats of combustion, the energy equivalent, $\mathcal{E}_s$, of the standard calorimeter system can be corrected by addition of a term, $\mathcal{E}_c$, which is equal to the excess over $\mathcal{E}_s$ of the energy equivalent of the system as actually used in the measurements.

The definition of the standard calorimeter system can be made arbitrarily in a number of different ways. Thus, one may take the system with an empty bomb, or with the bomb containing those substances common to all experiments. For example, $\mathcal{E}_{st}$ may be taken as the energy equivalent of the system with specified masses of water in the calorimeter vessel and in the bomb, with the bomb containing the crucible and firing fuse, and a specified quantity of oxygen, but no benzoic acid or other combustible material (5,16). If $\mathcal{E}_i$ is the value of the energy equivalent of the initial system obtained in an experiment with benzoic acid, then the value, $\mathcal{E}_{si}$, of the energy equivalent of the standard initial calorimeter system would be given by

$$\mathcal{E}_{si} = \mathcal{E}_i - \mathcal{E}_{ci}, \qquad (19)$$

where $\mathcal{E}_{ci}$ would be calculated from the specific heat of benzoic acid and the mass used in the experiment, and the specific heats and differences in mass of any other materials present in different amounts in the initial calorimeter system as used, and in the standard initial system.

Similarly, $\mathcal{E}_{sf}$ may be taken as the energy equivalent of the system with a specified mass of water in the calorimeter vessel, and with the bomb empty (13). Then if $\mathcal{E}_f$ represents the energy equivalent of the final system as determined with benzoic acid, the energy equivalent of the standard final calorimetric system would be given by

$$\mathcal{E}_{sf} = \mathcal{E}_f - \mathcal{E}_{cf}, \qquad (20)$$

where $\mathcal{E}_{cf}$ would be calculated from the heat capacities of the crucible, oxygen, carbon dioxide, and water in the bomb at the end of the experiment with benzoic acid, and the specific heats and differences in mass of any other materials present in different amounts in the standard calorimeter system and the system as actually used.

(b) *Benzoic Acid as a Calorimetric Standard Substance.* This substance has been chosen as a calorimetric standard substance (6) because it (a) can be obtained in a stable solid modification, (b) can be purified relatively easily, (c) is not noticeably volatile at ordinary room temperatures, (d) does not absorb moisture from the atmosphere, (e) burns quantitatively in the bomb, and (f) can be compressed into briquets.

At the present time, the National Bureau of Standards in Washington, D. C., is the only source of benzoic acid with a certified value for its heat of combustion, based on a direct comparison with electric energy. The standard sample benzoic acid is of a high degree of purity and uniformity, and its heat of combustion has been found to be identical, within the accuracy of the measurements, with specially purified benzoic acid of purity better than 99.99 mole per cent (6). It seems improbable, therefore, that the heat of combustion of more highly purified material would differ significantly from that of the present standard sample material.

It is recommended that standard sample material from the National Bureau of Standards be used for the calibration of bomb calorimeters if possible. Where this is not possible, it is recommended that a sufficient amount of benzoic acid of high purity and uniformity be standardized by comparison with benzoic acid from the National Bureau of Standards, and that the material so standardized be used for the calibration of bomb calorimeters.

The present certified value for the heat of combustion of the benzoic acid distributed by the National Bureau of Standards is $26.433_8$ absolute kilojoules per gram mass (weight *in vacuo*) with an estimated uncertainty of 0.01 per cent, when the sample is burned under the following conditions:

(a) The combustion reaction is referred to 25°C.
(b) The sample is burned in a bomb of constant volume in pure oxygen at an initial pressure of 30 atm at 25°C.
(c) The number of grams of sample burned is equal to three times the internal volume of the bomb in liters.
(d) The number of grams of water placed in the bomb before combustion is equal to three times the internal volume of the bomb in liters.

No unnecessary departure should be made from the above standard conditions. The heat of combustion of the standard sample benzoic acid under conditions differing by small amounts from the standard conditions specified by (a), (b), (c), and (d) above will be obtained by multiplying the value given above by the factor (6)

$$f = 1 + 10^{-6}[20(P - 30) + 42(m_s/V - 3) + 30(m_w/V - 3)$$
$$- 45(\theta - 25)], \quad (21)$$

where $P$ is the initial pressure in atmospheres of the oxygen at the temperature, $\theta$, to which the reaction is referred, $m_s$ is the mass in grams of sample burned, $m_w$ is the mass in grams of water placed in the bomb, and $V$ is the internal volume of the bomb in liters.

Equation 21, being linear in the variables $P$, $m_s/V$, etc., is strictly applicable only for relatively small departures from the standard conditions. It has been calculated that in the range of variables:

$20 < P < 40$ atm, $2 < m_s/V < 4$ g/liter, $2 < m_w/V < 4$ g/liter, $20° < \theta < 30°$, the maximum error in the values of $f$ given by this equation is of the order of $15 \times 10^{-6}$. For larger departures from the standard conditions the error may be expected to increase rather rapidly, and if such larger departures are necessary, the value of the heat of the bomb process for the actual conditions should be calculated using the methods described by Washburn (2). (See also Chapter 5.) It may be noted that the calculation of the heat of the bomb process under any particular set of conditions assumes that equilibrium between the gas and liquid phase is attained in the bomb. Data on the rate of approach to equilibrium will be found in reference (11).

TABLE 1

Results of the Six Most Recent Determinations of the Heat of Combustion of Benzoic Acid

| Investigator | Heat of combustion under standard conditions, abs. kj/g |
|---|---|
| Jessup and Green (16,6) | $26.432_0$ |
| Jessup (6) | $26.433_8$ |
| Prosen and Rossini (27) | $26.434_7$ |
| Coops, van Nes, and Schaafsma (13) | $26.437$ |
| Challoner, Gundry, and Meetham (38) | $26.436$ |
| Coops and Adriaanse (39) | $26.435$ |

The heat of combustion of benzoic acid in terms of electric energy units has been determined in a number of independent investigations during the past 35 years. The reports of most of the older investigations do not give sufficient data to permit the results to be reduced unambiguously to the basis of the standard conditions specified above. The results of the last six investigations, for which complete data are given, are in excellent agreement with each other as will be seen from Table 1, where the results reported by the various investigators have been reduced, where necessary, to the basis of the value $1.320$ g/cm$^3$ for the density of benzoic acid (8), and expressed in terms of absolute joules. It will be seen from Table 1 that the total spread of the six values is a little less than 0.02 per cent, whereas the total spread for the last five values is slightly more than 0.01 per cent.

*(c) Summary of Procedure.**

### Preliminary operations

(i) The benzoic acid sample is compressed into a pellet and weighed to 0.01 mg in the crucible in which it is to be burned.

(ii) The firing fuse is connected to the leads in the bomb.

(iii) A fixed amount of water is placed in the bottom of the bomb. The crucible with the weighed pellet of benzoic acid is put in place, and the bomb is closed.

(iv) The bomb is filled with a known quantity of purified oxygen and tested for leaks.

(v) The calorimeter vessel is carefully wiped and filled with a weighed quantity of water, the temperature of which is adjusted to a suitable value beforehand, and placed in the jacket. The bomb with firing leads attached is put in place in the calorimeter vessel, which is then closed. The jacket is closed and the thermometer is inserted in the calorimeter.

### Observations of temperature of calorimeter

(i) The stirrer is started and the calorimeter is heated to slightly below the starting temperature. After a long enough wait for the establishment of a steady rate of temperature change, the observations of the initial period are begun. These consist of observations, over a fixed time interval, of temperatures at equally spaced times.

(ii) At the end of the initial period the charge is fired, and the observations of temperature and time of the main period are begun immediately.

(iii) After a steady rate of temperature change is again established, the observations of temperature and time of the final period are made.

### Examination of completeness of combustion and determination of amount of nitric acid formed

(i) After removal of the bomb from the calorimeter, the bomb gases are tested for carbon monoxide.

(ii) The interior of the bomb is examined for soot. If any soot is found outside the crucible, the experiment is rejected. Otherwise, the

---

* The numbering of the items in this section is the same as the numbering of the corresponding items in the more detailed description of procedure in Section 3d.

whole internal surface of the bomb is washed with distilled water, and the amount of nitric acid formed is determined by titration.

(iii) The weight of any soot found in the crucible is determined.

### Calculation of results

(i) The observed rise in temperature $(\theta_e - \theta_b)$ is calculated from the data of the initial and final periods.

(ii) The correction $\Delta\theta$ for thermal leakage and heat of stirring is determined.

(iii) The corrections for ignition energy, formation of nitric acid, and unburned soot are determined.

(iv) The value of the heat of combustion of benzoic acid under the conditions of the experiment is calculated.

(v) The values of $\varepsilon_i$ (or $\varepsilon_f$) and of $\varepsilon_{si}$ (or $\varepsilon_{sf}$) are calculated.

(vi) The value to be used for $\varepsilon_{si}$ or $\varepsilon_{sf}$ is determined by averaging.

(d) *Details of Procedure.*

### Preliminary operations

(i) The benzoic acid sample is compressed into a pellet, the weight of which is adjusted within 0.01 g of the value required to give the standard temperature rise of the calorimeter. The standard temperature rise should preferably be so chosen that the mass of benzoic acid will satisfy condition (c) of Section 3b. The pellet of benzoic acid is weighed to 0.01 mg in the crucible in which it is to be burned, the weights having been calibrated in terms of the standard of mass, and the corrections found in the calibration are applied to the observed weight. The corrected weight in air is reduced to weight *in vacuo*, using the value 1.320 g/cm³ for the density of benzoic acid at 25°C, the density of the weights used, and a value for the density of air at the temperature, relative humidity, and barometric pressure at the time the weighing is made.

(ii) Any one of three different methods of firing the charge may be used. All three methods make use of an electric current, which may be taken conveniently from a small transformer with a secondary voltage of 6 to 10. In the first method, a fine platinum wire (0.08 mm diameter, 5 cm long) is fused by the electric current; in the second, an iron wire is ignited by the current; and in the third, a fixed platinum wire is heated sufficiently by the current to ignite a small piece of cotton thread.

When the first method is used, the platinum wire is attached to heavier platinum leads and placed in contact with the charge of benzoic acid. The firing energy, determined in blank experiments, has been found to be negligible (25).

In the second method, iron wire of about 0.13 mm diameter is used. Some investigators have used a 2-cm length of the wire which is wound into a helix and attached to platinum leads. All of the wire is burned, and the ignition energy is determined in blank experiments in which only the iron is burned (6,16). Other investigators have used a 5-cm length of iron wire wound into a helix near the middle, and attached to heavy platinum leads. Ignition energy was determined in blank experiments. The iron wire is not all burned with this variation of the method, but the unburned portion in each experiment is weighed and the results corrected to the basis of a standard mass of iron burned, using for the energy of combustion of iron (to form $Fe_2O_3$) the value 7.5 j/mg (34).

In the third method, the fixed platinum wire is heated to ignite a weighed cotton thread which, in turn, ignites the charge of combustible. A thread weighing only about 0.5 mg has been found to be sufficient, so that variation in moisture content can be ignored. One end of the thread is placed under the charge of benzoic acid, so that the thread must be weighed first. The heat of combustion of the cotton thread and the electrical energy used for ignition are determined in separate experiments (9). In a variation of this method a small piece of ashless filter paper is used instead of the cotton thread (26).

(iii) A fixed amount of distilled water (3 g per liter of bomb volume in accordance with condition (d) of Section 3b) is placed in the bomb, the fuse wire is attached to the firing leads, the crucible containing the charge is placed in position, and the bomb is closed.

(iv) The air present in the bomb is removed by flushing with pure oxygen, either by passing the oxygen continuously through the bomb for a sufficient length of time, or by alternately filling the bomb with oxygen under pressure and releasing the pressure. The oxygen used should not contain more than 1 per cent nitrogen. It should be freed from combustible impurities, for example by passing the oxygen slowly over a glowing platinum spiral (9) or through a bed of copper oxide maintained at a temperature of at least 500°C (5). The oxygen thus prepared can be freed from products of combustion by passing it through an absorbent for carbon dioxide (quicklime or Ascarite) and subsequently through a drying agent.

The bomb is filled with the purified oxygen at a known temperature in such a way that the pressure at 25°C will be 30 atm in accordance with condition (b), Section 3b.

After filling with oxygen the bomb is tested for leaks, because gas bubbles will cause evaporation of water from the calorimeter vessel with a considerable loss of heat. Testing for leaks can be carried out by placing the bomb in a volatile solvent such as ether. The last traces of solvent are conveniently removed by evacuation under a bell jar.

(v) Evaporation of water on the surface of the calorimeter vessel or on the jacket may give rise to irregular transfer of heat between the vessel and jacket. To eliminate this source of error the surfaces of the vessel and jacket should be wiped thoroughly and systematically before each experiment.

The calorimeter is filled with water at a temperature somewhat below the standard starting temperature of the experiment. The temperature should preferably be the same as that of the air in the balance case to avoid errors in weighing as a result of convection currents in the air. The weight is adjusted to the standard value within about 0.02 g. The adjustment may be made by use of a drop funnel inside the balance case, and by allowing the excess to evaporate if too much is added. To accelerate the evaporation a drying agent may be placed in the balance case. When the standard weight is reached, the calorimeter is placed in the jacket. The bomb, with firing leads connected to it, is placed in the calorimeter vessel, which is then closed. The jacket is closed and the thermometer is put in place in the calorimeter. The effect of evaporation after the calorimeter is weighed should be reduced by carrying out the operations just described as rapidly and as nearly in the same manner as possible in all experiments.

## Observations of temperature

(i) The stirrer is started, the temperature of the jacket is measured, and the calorimeter vessel and contents are heated to slightly below the desired starting temperature. This can be done conveniently by means of a heating coil which is a permanent part of the system (5,9). When a steady state has been attained, and the standard starting temperature is reached, the observations of temperature and time of the initial period are made.

(ii) The charge is fired, and the observations of temperature and time of the main period are begun immediately. These may be made at equal time intervals, as indicated previously, although if a resistance thermometer is used it will usually be more convenient to observe the times at which previously selected values of resistance are reached, at least during the first few minutes after firing the charge. The resistances should be so spaced as to permit accurate evaluation of the correction, $\Delta\theta$, in accordance with the methods outlined in Section 2 of this chapter.

(iii) When a steady rate of change of temperature has again been attained, the observations of temperature and time of the final period are made, after which the temperature of the jacket is again measured.

*Examination of completeness of combustion and determination of amount of nitric acid formed*

(i) After the bomb is removed from the calorimeter, the bomb gases are tested for carbon monoxide. This may be done by means of Winkler's reagent (3), or by Shepherd's colorimetric method (19). The presence of carbon monoxide usually means that an excessive amount of soot is deposited in the bomb.

(ii) When the bomb is opened, the interior is inspected for soot. If soot is found anywhere outside the crucible the experiment is rejected. If no soot is found, the internal surface of the bomb is washed out with distilled water, and the amount of nitric acid in the washings is determined by titration against a $0.1\ N$ alkali solution, using methyl orange as indicator.

(iii) It is probably better to reject an experiment if a significant amount of soot is left in the crucible. If the amount of soot is small, however, the amount may be determined by burning out the soot in a stream of carbon dioxide–free oxygen (or air), absorbing the resulting carbon dioxide in a dilute alkali solution, and titrating the excess alkali against a dilute acid solution, using phenolphthalein as indicator. The amount of soot may also be determined from the loss in weight of the dried crucible when it is heated to a sufficiently high temperature to burn out the soot. This method is likely to give too high results, however, because of loss in weight of the crucible.

## Calculation of results

(i) Corrected values of the temperatures $\theta_b$ and $\theta_e$ are obtained from the data of the initial and final periods, respectively, either graphically or by means of Equation 12, using values of $g_i$ and $g_f$ determined as described under (ii) below.   The difference, $(\theta_e - \theta_b)$, is taken as the observed temperature rise.

(ii) Values of the initial and final rates, $g_i$ and $g_f$, are calculated by means of Equation 13.   Values of the constants, $k$ and $u$ (or $k$ and $\theta_\infty$) are calculated by means of Equations 3 and 4 (or 3 and 5), respectively.

The mean temperature, $\theta_m$, during the main period is obtained by suitable integration of the temperature-time curve during this period, for example, by means of Equation 10.

The correction, $\Delta\theta$, for thermal leakage and heat of stirring is calculated by means of any one of Equations 7, 8, and 9.   The corrected temperature rise is then given by Equation 11.

(iii) If the ignition energy, $q_i$, is determined entirely by blank experiments, as when ignition is by fusion of a platinum wire, or by means of an iron wire which is burned completely, the value to be used for $q_i$ is simply the mean of the results of the blank experiments.

If iron wire is used, but is not completely burned, the mean value derived from blank experiments for the ignition energy corresponding to a standard mass of iron burned must be corrected for any difference between the standard mass and the mass actually burned in the experiment, using the value 7.5 j/mg for the heat of combustion of iron.

If ignition is by means of a cotton thread (or piece of filter paper) which is ignited by a heated platinum wire, the value of $q_i$ is the mean value of the electrical energy as determined in blank experiments, plus the product of the mass and heat of combustion of the cotton thread (or filter paper).

The correction, $q_n$, for the heat produced by the formation of nitric acid in the bomb at 25°C is calculated using the value 59 kj per mole of nitric acid formed.   This value was used in deriving the value of heat of combustion certified by the National Bureau of Standards for its standard sample benzoic acid; therefore, it should be used in calculating the results of determinations of the energy equivalent with benzoic acid, regardless of what value may be selected as best to use in calculating the results of measurements of heat of combustion.

The correction, $q_c$, for unburned soot is equal to the product of the mass of soot and its heat of combustion, which may be taken as 32.8 j/mg.

(iv) The factor, $f$, is calculated by inserting in Equation 21 the appropriate values of $P$, $m_s/V$, $m_w/V$, and the temperature to which the reaction is to be referred ($\theta_b$ or $\theta_e + \Delta\theta$) corresponding to the actual conditions in the experiment. The value for the heat of combustion of benzoic acid to be used for this experiment is then obtained by multiplying the value which is applicable under the standard conditions (a, b, c, d in Section 3b) by the value for the factor $f$ for this experiment.

(v) With the above data the value of $\mathcal{E}_i$ (or $\mathcal{E}_f$) resulting from the experiment is calculated by means of Equation 17 (or Equation 18).

The values of $\mathcal{E}_{si}$ and $\mathcal{E}_{sf}$ are then calculated by means of the equations

$$\mathcal{E}_{si} = \mathcal{E}_i - \mathcal{E}_{ci}$$
$$= \mathcal{E}_i - 10^{-3}D[1.21m_s + 21.0\Delta n_{O_2} + 0.136\Delta m_{Pt} + 4.18\Delta m_w] \tag{22}$$

and

$$\mathcal{E}_{sf} = \mathcal{E}_f - \mathcal{E}_{cf}$$
$$= \mathcal{E}_f - 10^{-3}D[21.0n_{O_2} + 4.18m_w + 2.28m_s + 0.136m_{Pt}], \tag{23}$$

where $D$ = number of degrees centigrade (Celsius) equivalent to one unit of the temperature scale used,

$n_{O_2}$ = the number of moles of oxygen initially present in the bomb,

$\Delta n_{O_2}$ = the excess of the number of moles of oxygen initially present over that in the standard initial calorimeter system,

$m_s$ = mass of benzoic acid in grams,

$m_{Pt}$ = mass of the platinum crucible in grams,

$m_w$ = mass of water initially present in bomb in grams,

$\Delta m_{Pt}, \Delta m_w$ = excess of mass of platinum, or water, in bomb over that of standard initial calorimeter system.

In the above equations $\mathcal{E}_{si}$, $\mathcal{E}_{sf}$, etc., are expressed in kilojoules per unit of the temperature scale used.

Strictly speaking, Equation 23 does not represent the true energy equivalent of the standard calorimeter system with the bomb empty, since a small term representing the energy of vaporization of water in the bomb has been omitted.   No error will be introduced, however, if this term is also omitted in calculating the value of $\mathcal{E}_f$ to be used for measurements of heats of combustion.

If the calorimetric system as used in determining $\mathcal{E}_i$ (or $\mathcal{E}_f$) differs from the corresponding standard calorimeter system in any respect other than in a difference in the contents of the bomb, Equations 22 and 23 must be modified accordingly.   The terms representing $\mathcal{E}_{ci}$ and $\mathcal{E}_{cf}$ in these equations apply only to measurements in which the material burned in the bomb is benzoic acid.

(vi) The value to be used for $\mathcal{E}_{si}$ or $\mathcal{E}_{sf}$ should be the arithmetic mean of five to eight acceptable experiments.

**4. Determination of the energy equivalent with electrical energy.**
(a) *General Principles.*   As stated in the introduction to this chapter, the most direct method of determining the energy equivalent of a bomb calorimeter in terms of electric energy units is by determining the temperature rise produced in the calorimetric system by a measured quantity of electric energy.   The procedure in such a determination is the same as in an experiment with benzoic acid, except that no combustion takes place in the bomb, and that during the main period energy is supplied to the calorimeter electrically, and the quantity of energy so supplied is measured.   The energy is supplied by passing current from a storage battery through a heating coil immersed in the water of the calorimeter.   The quantity of energy supplied to the calorimeter is determined in terms of the mean solar second as the unit of time, and the absolute ohm and absolute volt as units of resistance and electromotive force, respectively, by measurements of the time, $\Delta t$, during which the heating current flows; the potential drop $e$, across the heating coil;  and the potential drop across a standard resistor in series with the heating coil, which gives the ratio, $e/r$, of electromotive force to resistance.   The value for the energy equivalent of the calorimeter derived from such measurements is given, in absolute joules per unit of the temperature scale used, by the expression

$$\mathcal{E} = \frac{(e^2/r)\,\Delta t}{\Delta\theta_{\text{corr.}}}, \tag{24}$$

where $\Delta\theta_{corr.}$ is the corrected temperature rise of the calorimeter determined as described in Section 2 of this report.

Equation 24 gives the energy equivalent of the actual calorimeter system used in the experiment. For example, if the bomb contained only the crucible and the standard quantities of water and oxygen, then Equation 24 would give the energy equivalent, $\mathcal{E}_{si}$, of the standard initial system. If the system differed in any respect from the standard initial system, the value of $\mathcal{E}_{si}$ would be obtained by correcting the value of $\mathcal{E}_i$ given by Equation 24 for any difference in the standard calorimeter system and the system actually used.

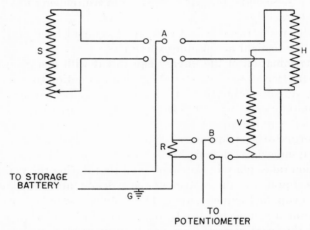

Figure 2. Power-measuring circuit. S, stabilizing resistance; A, switch operated by timing device; H, heater in calorimeter; R, standard resistor; G, connection to ground; V, volt box.

If the energy equivalent of the final system as used is desired, the calibration experiment would be made with the bomb containing the products of combustion of some substance burned in the bomb, together with the crucible, the excess oxygen, and the water initially placed in the bomb. Equation 24 would then give the energy equivalent, $\mathcal{E}_f$, of the actual final system, and the value of the energy equivalent of the standard final system would be given by Equation 23 if the substance burned in the bomb was benzoic acid, and by an analogous expression if some other substance was burned in the bomb.*

* See footnote in Section 4c, p. 51.

A diagram of a suitable circuit for supplying and measuring the electric power is illustrated in Figure 2. Current from a storage battery flows through either a stabilizing resistance, S, or the heater, H, in the calorimeter depending upon which way the switch, A, is thrown. The resistance, S, is adjusted to approximate equality with H so that the current drawn from the storage battery changes by only a small amount when A is thrown so as to divert the current from S to H. If the circuit is grounded at G to metal plates placed under the potentiometer, galvanometer, volt box, etc., the electromotive force tending to cause leakage through the measuring circuit will not exceed that actually measured by the potentiometer, i.e., it will be a small fraction of the potential drop across the heating coil.

The current leads to the heater should be in intimate thermal contact with both calorimeter and jacket, and the potential leads should be connected to the current leads at points midway between the calorimeter and the jacket.

Convenience in making alternate measurements of potential drop across the heater and across the standard resistor can be achieved by choosing the volt-box ratio and the resistances of heating coil and standard resistor so that the potentiometer reading is nearly the same in both cases (1). Equal convenience is afforded by the use of a double potentiometer. Adjustment of the resistance of the power-supply network can be made so as to minimize the effect of the rapid change in resistance of the heater at the beginning of a heating period (35).

Detailed descriptions of methods of electrical calibration of bomb calorimeters will be found in numerous publications (1,7,13,23,24, 38,39).

(b) *Apparatus.* As indicated in Figure 2, the additional apparatus required for electrical calibration of the calorimeter includes a standard resistor, a volt box, and a potentiometer, together with a suitable galvanometer and a standard cell. Some device, such as a chronograph, will also be required for accurate measurement of the time of electrical heating.

The standard resistor, volt box, potentiometer, and standard cell should be calibrated by a recognized standardizing laboratory. The calibrations of the standard resistor, volt box, and potentiometer should be made at different temperatures so as to determine temperature coefficients and, preferably, should be repeated at intervals so as to determine any seasonal or secular variation in these instruments. If this is not feasible, calibrations should at least be made immediately preceding and following the determinations of the energy equivalent of the calorimeter. The volt box should be calibrated at the voltages to which it will be subjected in use.

The standard cell used with the potentiometer may be either a saturated or an unsaturated cadmium cell. Since the saturated cell has a large temperature coefficient, whereas the unsaturated cell exhibits hysteresis when subjected to varying temperature (28), either type of cell should be maintained at a constant temperature (29) when in use, and at the same temperature when being calibrated. The cell should also be calibrated immediately before and after the measurements of energy equivalent of the calorimeter.

The calibration of a potentiometer can be checked at the time of each experiment by means of an auxiliary storage battery and two standard resistors (4). The resistors are connected in series with each other and with the battery, and the current is adjusted so that the potential drop across one of the resistors is balanced against the standard cell. The potential drop across the other resistor is then measured by means of the potentiometer.

Measurement of the time of electrical heating may be made by means of a chronograph which records the times at which the current is diverted from S to H and vice versa (Figure 2). Automatic methods of making the chronograph records have been described by Jaeger and Von Steinwehr (24) and by Dickinson (1). Methods of actuating the switch, A (Figure 2), by signals from a standard clock have been described by White (30), by Osborne, Stimson, and Fiock (31), and by Johnston (32). A timing device consisting of a switch operated by signals from a standard clock, together with a chronograph to record the lag in the operation of the switch, has been described by van Nes, (13). Electronic time recording with the aid of a crystal vibrator is described by Coops, Adriaanse, and van Nes (39).

(c) *Experimental Procedure.*

### Preliminary operations

The preliminary operations are the same as those summarized in Section 3c and described in detail in Section 3d, with the following exceptions:

(i) When a determination of the energy equivalent of the initial calorimetric system is to be made, no benzoic acid is placed in the bomb.

(ii) When a determination of the energy equivalent ($\mathcal{E}_f$) of the final calorimetric system is to be made the benzoic acid (or other combustible material) placed in the bomb is burned before starting the operaations under Sections 3c and 3d.*

(iii) Temperatures of the volt box, standard resistor, and potentiometer are recorded.

### Observations of temperature of calorimeter

The procedure in the temperature measurements is practically the same as that described in Section 3d, the only difference being that because of the more nearly linear character of the temperature-time curve in the main period of an experiment with electrical energy, temperature measurements during the main period need not be made as frequently in such an experiment as in a combustion experiment.

### Determination of the quantity of electrical energy supplied to the calorimeter

At the beginning of the main period, the switch, A (Figure 2), is thrown so as to divert the current from the stabilizing resistance, S, to the heater, H, in the calorimeter, the time at which the switch is thrown being determined by means of a chronograph or by having the switch thrown by a suitable timing device actuated by signals from the standard clock.

During the main period alternate readings are made at equal time intervals, by means of the potentiometer, of the potential drop across the standard resistor, and of a known fraction (determined by the volt-box ratio) of the potential drop across the heater in the calorimeter.

At the end of the main period the switch is thrown so as to divert the current from the heater in the calorimeter to the stabilizing resistance, and the time of throwing the switch is again determined.

---

* It would be possible, of course, to determine the energy equivalent ($\mathcal{E}_{sf}$) of the standard final calorimeter system directly, by making the measurements with the bomb empty. The procedure described in the text has the advantage that the effect of evaporation of water, including the change in density of water vapor arising from dissolved gases and nitric acid, is automatically accounted for in the measurements.

## Calculation of results

The method of calculating the corrected temperature rise, $\Delta\theta_c$, of the calorimeter is the same as that described in Section 3d.

The individual observed values of the potential drop across the heating coil (products of potentiometer readings and nominal volt-box ratio) are averaged. The mean value thus obtained is corrected for errors in the potentiometer and for any departure of the volt-box ratio* from its nominal value to obtain the corrected mean potential drop, $e$, across the heating coil. The individual observed values of potential drop across the standard resistor are averaged, and the mean value is divided by the resistance of the standard resistor, corrected for errors in the potentiometer and for the current through the volt box to obtain the corrected mean value of $e/r$.

The time, $\Delta t$, during which the heating current flowed through the calorimeter heater is determined from the chronograph record or from the recorded times at which the particular timing device used was operated.

The energy equivalent of the calorimeter, as used in the experiment, is calculated from the corrected values of $e$, $e/r$, $\Delta t$, and $\Delta\theta_{corr}$. by means of Equation 24. If the bomb contained the crucible and the standard quantities of oxygen and water, and the system was otherwise identical with the standard initial system, then the result obtained is $\mathcal{E}_{si}$, the energy equivalent of the standard initial system. If the bomb contained the products of combustion of some substance plus excess oxygen, etc., then the result obtained is $\mathcal{E}_f$, the energy equivalent of the actual final calorimeter system. The value of $\mathcal{E}_{sf}$, is then obtained by means of a relation analogous to Equation 23.

* If the resistance of the leads from the heater to the volt box is a significant fraction of the total resistance of the volt box, a correction for this lead resistance should be applied to the volt-box ratio as determined by the standardizing laboratory.

## References

1. H. C. Dickinson, *Bull. Natl. Bur. Standards* **11**, 189 (1914).
2. E. W. Washburn, *J. Research Natl. Bur. Standards* **10**, 525 (1933).
3. L. W. Winkler, *Z. anal. Chem.* **102**, 99 (1935).
4. N. S. Osborne, H. F. Stimson, and D. C. Ginnings, *J. Research Natl. Bur. Standards* **23**, 197, 261 (1939).

5. E. J. Prosen and F. D. Rossini, *J. Research Natl. Bur. Standards* **27**, 289 (1941).
6. R. S. Jessup, *J. Research Natl. Bur. Standards* **29**, 247 (1942).
7. E. J. Prosen and F. D. Rossini, *J. Research Natl. Bur. Standards* **33**, 255 (1944).
8. R. S. Jessup, *J. Research Natl. Bur. Standards* **36**, 421 (1946).
9. J. Coops, K. van Nes, A. Kentie, and J. W. Dienske, *Rec. Trav. Chim. Pays-Bas* **66**, 113 (1947).
10. J. Coops and K. van Nes, *Rec. Trav. Chim. Pays-Bas* **66**, 131 (1947).
11. S. Sunner, Dissertation, University of Lund, Carl Bloms Boktryckerie, Lund, Sweden, 1949.
12. F. D. Rossini *et al.*, *Natl. Bur. Standards Circular* **461** (1947).
13. K. van Nes, Thesis, Vrije Universiteit, Amsterdam, 1951.
14. G. T. Furukawa, R. E. McCoskey, and G. J. King, *J. Research Natl. Bur. Standards* **47**, 256 (1951).
15. J. Coops and K. van Nes, *Rec. Trav. Chim. Pays-Bas* **66**, 161 (1947).
16. R. S. Jessup and C. B. Green, *J. Research Natl. Bur. Standards* **13**, 469 (1934).
17. J. Coops and K. van Nes, *Rec. Trav. Chim. Pays-Bas* **66**, 142 (1947).
18. W. P. White, *The Modern Calorimeter*, Reinhold Publishing Corporation, New York, 1928.
19. M. Shepherd, *Anal. Chem.* **19**, 77 (1947).
20. L. J. P. Keffler, *J. Phys. Chem.* **33**, 37 (1929).
21. T. W. Richards and R. H. Jesse, *J. Am. Chem. Soc.* **32**, 268 (1910).
22. W. A. Roth and P. Chall, *Z. Elektrochem.* **38**, 94 (1932).
23. W. A. Roth, O. Doepke, and H. Banse, *Z. physik. Chem.* **133**, 431 (1928).
24. W. Jaeger and H. von Steinwehr, *Z. physik. Chem.* **135**, 305 (1928).
25. E. J. Prosen, National Bureau of Standards, Unpublished data.
26. H. M. Huffman and E. L. Ellis, *J. Am. Chem. Soc.* **57**, 41 (1935).
27. E. J. Prosen and F. D. Rossini, *J. Research Natl. Bur. Standards* **33**, 439 (1944).
28. J. H. Park, *J. Research Natl. Bur. Standards* **10**, 89 (1933).
29. E. F. Mueller and H. F. Stimson, *J. Research Natl. Bur. Standards* **13**, 699 (1934).
30. W. P. White, *Physical Review* **31**, 686 (1910).
31. N. S. Osborne, H. F. Stimson, and E. F. Fiock, *J. Research Natl. Bur. Standards* **5**, 411 (1930).
32. H. L. Johnston, *J. Optical Soc. Am. & Rev. Sci. Insts.* **17**, 381 (1928).
33. J. F. Masi, The NBS-NACA Tables of Thermal Properties of Gases, Tables 13.24 (1949) and 13.26 (1951).
34. F. D. Rossini *et al.*, *Natl. Bur. Standards Circular* **500** (1952).
35. H. J. Hoge, *Rev. Sci. Insts.* **20**, 59 (1949).
36. P. B. Aitken, Helen L. Boxall, and L. G. Cook, *Rev. Sci. Insts.* **25**, 967 (1954).
37. W. N. Hubbard, C. Katz, and G. Waddington, *J. Phys. Chem.* **58**, 142 (1954).
38. A. R. Challoner, H. A. Gundry, and A. R. Meetham, *Trans. Royal Soc. London*, **A247**, 553 (1955).
39. J. Coops, N. Adriaanse, and K. van Nes, *Rec. Trav. Chim. Pays-Bas*, in press.

## Appendix 1. Relation between Temperature and Time in the Initial (or Final) Period

As stated in Section 2c, Equations 12 and 13 are based on the assumption that the temperature-time curve in the initial (or final) period is linear, whereas this curve actually represents an exponential function. It is possible to take account of the exponential character of such a curve by expanding the exponential function in powers of $t$ and neglecting powers higher than the second. The solution of Equation 2 can be written

$$\theta = \theta_\infty + Ae^{-kt}$$
$$= \theta_\infty + A(1 - kt + \tfrac{1}{2}k^2t^2 \ldots),$$

where $A$ is a constant of integration. Differentiation with respect to $t$, and putting $t = t_i$ yields

$$\left(\frac{d\theta}{dt}\right)_{t=t_i} = g_i = -Ak(1 - kt_i)$$

so that

$$A = -\frac{g_i}{k(1 - kt_i)}.$$

The solution of Equation 2 for $\theta$ in the initial period can then be written to a high degree of approximation in the form

$$\theta = \alpha + \beta t + \gamma t^2,$$

where

$$\gamma = \tfrac{1}{2}k^2A = -\frac{kg_i}{2(1 - kt_i)}.$$

The constant $\gamma$ can be determined much more accurately from the above formula than by direct application of the method of least squares to the data of the initial period. Using the value of $\gamma$ determined in this way, the corrected value of $\theta_b$ is given by

$$\theta_b = \frac{1}{n} \sum_{r=1}^{n} (\theta_r - \gamma t_r^2) + \frac{n-1}{2}\beta + \gamma t_n^2 \tag{12a}$$

and the values of $\beta$ and $\alpha$ derived by the method of least squares are given by

$$\beta =$$ (13a)

$$6\,\frac{(n-1)(\theta_n - \gamma t_n{}^2 - \theta_1 + \gamma t_1{}^2) + (n-3)(\theta_{n-1} - \gamma t_{n-1}{}^2 - \theta_2 + \gamma t_2{}^2) + \ldots}{n(n^2-1)}$$

and

$$\alpha = \frac{1}{n}\sum_{r=1}^{n}(\theta_r - \gamma t_r{}^2) - \frac{n-1}{2}\beta - \beta t_1$$

Similar formulas could easily be derived for the final period.

Equations 12a and 13a, when applied to the data of an initial period of 10 min with $(\theta_\infty - \theta_i) = 3°$ and with $k = 0.002$, yielded a value of $\theta_b$ which was lower by $0.000072°$ than the value obtained by means of Equations 12 and 13. For an initial period of 20 min the discrepancy would be about five times as great. However, it is evident that if the values of $\theta_b$, $\theta_e$, and $\theta_\infty$ are approximately the same in calibration experiments as in measurements of heats of combustion, and if the rating periods are of the same length in both types of experiment, then the error in $(\theta_e - \theta_b)$ resulting from linear representations of the rating period data will be practically the same in both types of experiment, and will therefore have no appreciable effect on the final result of the measurements of heats of combustion. If the above conditions are satisfied the use of Equations 12 and 13 instead of the more complicated Equations 12a and 13a will be entirely justified.

## Appendix 2. Derivation of Equations for Evaluating the Energy Equivalent

Consider the calorimetric system consisting initially of calorimeter vessel, bomb, thermometer, water, etc., and the contents of the bomb, including reactants plus water and excess oxygen. The quantity of heat evolved by this system, in the process in which the combustion reaction takes place and the temperature changes from $\theta_b$ to $\theta_e + \Delta\theta$, is zero, since $\Delta\theta$ corrects for the effect of heat gained or lost by the system. Also, since the external pressure of the atmosphere is constant, the net quantity of heat evolved by the system will be zero for any process by which the system goes from its initial state at $\theta_b$ to its final state at $\theta_e + \Delta\theta$. We may, for example, consider the process in which (a) the initial system is heated from $\theta_b$ to $\theta_e + \Delta\theta$, and (b) the combustion reaction takes place and a quantity of heat, $Q_{(\theta_e + \Delta\theta)}$, is removed from the system so that its final temperature is again $\theta_e + \Delta\theta$. Since the net quantity of heat evolved by the system in this process is zero, the quantity of heat added to the initial system to raise its temperature from $\theta_b$ to $\theta_e + \Delta\theta$ is equal to the quantity of heat $Q_{(\theta_e + \Delta\theta)}$ removed in order to reduce the final temperature to $\theta_e + \Delta\theta$, or

$$Q_{(\theta_e + \Delta\theta)} = \mathcal{E}_i(\theta_e - \theta_b + \Delta\theta) = \mathcal{E}_i\Delta\theta_{\text{corr.}},$$

where $\mathcal{E}_i$ is the energy equivalent of the initial system. Similarly it can be shown that

$$Q_{(\theta_b)} = \mathcal{E}_f(\theta_e - \theta_b + \Delta\theta) = \mathcal{E}_f\Delta\theta_{\text{corr.}},$$

where $\mathcal{E}_f$ is the energy equivalent of the final system, and $Q_{(\theta_b)}$ is the quantity of heat which would be evolved by the system if combustion were started at the temperature $\theta_b$ and the temperature after combustion were reduced to the initial temperature, $\theta_b$.

It follows from the above discussion that an experiment in which benzoic acid is burned in the bomb, and the resulting corrected temperature rise is $\Delta\theta_{\text{corr.}} = \theta_e - \theta_b + \Delta\theta$ yields for the energy equivalent of the initial system

$$\mathcal{E}_i = \frac{Q_{(\theta_e + \Delta\theta)}}{\Delta\theta_{\text{corr.}}}, \tag{15}$$

and for the energy equivalent of the final system

$$\mathcal{E}_f = \frac{Q_{(\theta_b)}}{\Delta\theta_{\text{corr.}}}, \tag{16}$$

## Appendix 3. Notation

$D$ = number of degrees Celsius equivalent to one unit of the temperature scale used.

$e$ = potential drop across heating coil in calorimeter.

$\mathcal{E}_i, \mathcal{E}_f$ = total energy equivalent of the calorimetric system as used; the subscripts $i$ and $f$ refer to the initial and final systems, respectively.

$\mathcal{E}_{si}, \mathcal{E}_{sf}$ = energy equivalent of the standard initial or final system.

$\mathcal{E}_{ci}, \mathcal{E}_{cf}$ = difference between the energy equivalents of the standard and actual initial or final system.

$g_i, g_f$ = rate of change of calorimeter temperature at midpoint of initial or final period.

$m_s$ = mass of benzoic acid burned in an experiment.

$m_w$        = mass of water placed in bomb.

$n_{O_2}$      = number of moles of oxygen present in bomb before combustion.

$P$          = initial pressure of oxygen in bomb at temperature to which combustion reaction is referred.

$r$          = resistance of electric heating coil in calorimeter.

$q_c$         = correction for unburned carbon.

$q_i$         = energy used for ignition.

$q_n$         = correction for energy of formation of nitric acid in bomb.

$\theta_i, \theta_f$      = mean temperatures of calorimeter in initial and final periods, respectively.

$\theta_b, \theta_e$      = temperatures of calorimeter at beginning and end, respectively, of main period.

$\theta_j$         = temperature of jacket.

$\theta_\infty$         = convergence temperature of calorimeter.

$\Delta\theta$         = correction for thermal leakage and heat of stirring.

$\Delta\theta_{corr.}$     = $\theta_e - \theta_b + \Delta\theta$ = corrected temperature rise of calorimeter.

$t_i, t_f, t_b, t_e$   = times corresponding to $\theta_i, \theta_f, \theta_b, \theta_e$, respectively.

$\Delta t$         = time of heating in an electrical calibration experiment.

$-\Delta E_B$     = heat of combustion of benzoic acid under conditions of bomb process.

$V$          = internal volume of bomb.

## Appendix 4. Numerical Data

### Benzoic Acid

Specific heat at 25°C                     1.21 j g$^{-1}$ deg$^{-1}$ (14)

Density at 25°C                           1.320 g ml$^{-1}$ (8)

### Oxygen

Equation of state

$n_{O_2} = [PV/0.08206T][1 + (890 - 11.3\theta)10^{-6}P]$ (2)

where $P$   = pressure in atmospheres

$T$   = temperature in degrees Kelvin

$\theta$   = temperature in degrees centigrade (Celsius)

$V$   = volume in liters

$n_{O_2}$   = number of moles of oxygen

Specific heat at constant volume at 25°C., $C^\circ_V = 20.96$ j mole$^{-1}$ deg$^{-1}$ (12)

### Carbon

Heat of combustion                        33 kj g$^{-1}$

## Carbon Dioxide

Specific heat at 25°C, at constant volume, and at a pressure of 4 atm

29.7 j mole$^{-1}$ deg$^{-1}$ (33)

## Water

| | |
|---|---|
| Specific heat of liquid at 25°C | 4.1795 j g$^{-1}$ deg$^{-1}$ (4) |
| Specific heat of vapor under saturation conditions at 25°C | 1.815  j g$^{-1}$ deg$^{-1}$ (4) |
| Energy of vaporization at 25°C | 2299.88 j g$^{-1}$ (4) |
| Specific volume of vapor at 20°C | 57836 cm$^3$ g$^{-1}$ |
| 25°C | 43401 cm$^3$ g$^{-1}$ (4) |
| 30°C | 32929 cm$^3$ g$^{-1}$ |

## Nitric Acid

Energy of formation in bomb at 25°     59* kj mole$^{-1}$ (6)

## Cotton

Energy of combustion                    16.24 kj g$^{-1}$ (9)

## Iron

Energy of combustion (to form $Fe_2O_3$)     7.5 kj g$^{-1}$ (12)

## Platinum

Specific heat                    0.136 j g$^{-1}$ deg$^{-1}$ (34)

* For use only in calibration experiments with benzoic acid (see p. 45).

# CHAPTER 4

# Calibrations of Calorimeters for Reactions in a Flame at Constant Pressure*

## Frederick D. Rossini

**1. Introduction.** The energy equivalent of a calorimeter for performing reactions in a flame at constant pressure may be determined either (*a*) directly with electrical energy or (*b*) indirectly by measuring a "standard" reference reaction which has been accurately measured in terms of electrical energy in another laboratory adequately equipped for such measurements. In either case, the general principles governing the method are those outlined in Chapter 1.

**2. Apparatus.** The apparatus required for measuring heats of reaction in a flame at constant pressure is the same as that described in Chapter 3 for measuring heats of reaction in a bomb at constant volume except that in place of the calorimetric bomb there is used a glass reaction vessel accommodating a flame at constant pressure, with appropriate inlet tubes for the reacting gases and an appropriate exit tube for the issuing gases.

Figure 1 gives a schematic diagram of the apparatus used by Rossini for the combustion of hydrogen and oxygen to form water. All the parts through which the hydrogen and oxygen gases travel are of Pyrex laboratory glass. A, B, C, and D are each the entrance to a set of three purifying tubes containing in sequence (*a*) Ascarite, a solid mixture of asbestos and sodium hydroxide, for removing carbon dioxide or other acidic components; (*b*) magnesium perchlorate for removing water vapor; and (*c*) phosphorus pentoxide, for removing

* The material in this chapter is largely from Rossini (1,2,3), modified as appropriate by later experience, with additional references given at the proper places in the text.

the last traces of water vapor. For the experiments in which hydrogen was burned in oxygen, A and C were attached, respectively, to cylinders of pure compressed hydrogen and oxygen used in the reaction. D was connected to an extra cylinder of oxygen used to flush out the system and, after the conclusion of the calorimetric observations, to vaporize the water collected as liquid in the reaction vessel

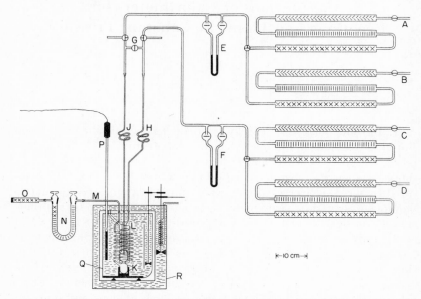

Figure 1. Schematic diagram of the calorimetric apparatus for the reaction of hydrogen and oxygen to form water. From Rossini (1). The letters have the following significance: A, B, C, D, purifying tubes; E, F, flow meters; G, stopcocks; J, H, inlet tubes to calorimeter; M, exit tube from calorimeter; N, absorption tube; O, guard tube; P, platinum thermometer; Q, calorimeter can; R, jacket.

so that it would be absorbed outside the calorimeter in the absorption tube N. For the experiments in which oxygen was burned in excess hydrogen, the connections to A and C were reversed and to D was connected an extra cylinder of hydrogen replacing the extra cylinder of oxygen already mentioned and being used for the same purpose. Train B was a spare. The two mercury flow meters, E and F, served to indicate the rate of flow of gas. The two three-way stopcocks at

G permitted wasting of either gas, while the connecting stopcock allowed flushing of both inlet tubes with one gas. The coils on the inlet tubes, J and H, served to permit easy assembly. The heating coil L served to impart electrical energy to the calorimeter. The

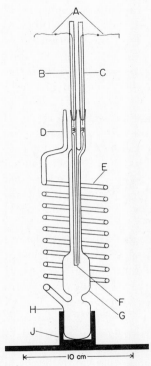

Figure 2. Reaction vessel for combining hydrogen and oxygen to form water. From Rossini (1). The letters have the following significance: A, leads of the spark circuit; B, C, inlet tubes; D, exit tube; E, cooling coil; F, burner tube; G, reaction chamber; H, condensing chamber; J, supporting frame.

reaction vessel and its supporting frame are shown at K. The calorimeter can Q also contained a stirrer and the platinum resistance thermometer P. The tube M served as an exit connection between the reaction vessel and the absorption tube N. The latter was followed by a guard tube O.

**3. The reaction vessel and its operation.** The reaction vessel for combining hydrogen and oxygen quietly in a flame at constant pressure is shown in Figure 2. This vessel was made of Pyrex laboratory glass, except for the burner tube, which was silica glass, with a graded seal, silica-to-Pyrex, about 5 cm from the tip F. The glass vessel was supported in the brass metal frame J. The platinum wire leads at A were sealed through the two inlet tubes, B and C, and continued down into the inlet tubes of the reaction vessel, where the continuity was broken by a gap of about 2 mm. Two other pieces of platinum wire, coiled at the top to assure rigidity in the tubes, extended down into the reaction chamber, one outside and one inside the burner tube.

The spark which ignited the gas issuing from the burner tube jumped across the gap at the tip F. The flame, about 5 mm long, burned quietly at F in the reaction chamber G. The water produced in the reaction formed as a vapor in G, condensed, and collected as a liquid in the chamber below. The excess gas, plus a small amount of water vapor with which it was saturated, passed from the condensing chamber at H, through the cooling coil E, and out through the exit D.

In an actual combustion experiment, the entire reaction vessel was first flushed out with the excess gas, oxygen, or hydrogen. When for example, the excess gas was oxygen, the entire reaction vessel was flushed with oxygen, and the flow of oxygen adjusted to a value in excess of that required stoichiometrically. Then the rate of flow of hydrogen, flowing through the waste tube, was adjusted. At a given moment, the hydrogen was switched into the burner tube B. One or two seconds later, the spark-coil switch was closed and the spark, jumping across the gap at F, was operated for a measured number of seconds, 2 to 6. This ignited the hydrogen, and the flame burned quietly in an atmosphere of oxygen.

**4. Determination of the purity and amount of reaction in the formation of water.** The amount of reaction is determined from the mass of water formed in the combustion. The reacting gases, hydrogen and oxygen, are required to contain no other reacting gases in order to be suitable for such experiments. Inert and nonreacting gases do not affect the results. To control the purity of the reaction, appropriate examination of the purity of the water formed can be made, and foreign gases can be looked for in the gaseous product.

The total mass of water formed from hydrogen and oxygen in each experiment is

$$m_{H_2O} = m_a + m_b + m_c, \tag{1}$$

where $m_a$ is the mass of water remaining as liquid in the condensing chamber of the reaction vessel at the conclusion of the calorimetric experiment, $m_b$ is the mass of water existing as vapor in the reaction vessel at the conclusion of the calorimetric experiment, and $m_c$ is the mass of water carried from the calorimetric reaction vessel into the absorption tube N (Figure 1) during the reaction period by the excess gas. With the apparatus shown in Figure 1, and the procedure described in detail in reference (1), the average values of the several amounts of water were as follows: $m_a$, 2.85 g; $m_b$, 0.0012 g; $m_c$, 0.010 g. A quantity of water equal to $m_c$ was collected in the absorption tube N (Figure 1) during the time of the calorimetric experiment. At the end of the calorimetric experiment, a flow of the excess gas of about 0.5 liter per minute was sent through the system in order to carry all the water remaining in the reaction vessel as $m_a$ and $m_b$ into the absorption tube N. In this way, all of the water formed in the combustion can be transported from the reaction vessel into the absorption tube N without loss or gain.

For the absorption of water, the absorption tube is charged with appropriate layers of magnesium perchlorate and phosphorus pentoxide, each bounded by a layer of asbestos fiber.

The apparent increase in mass of the absorption tube after it receives all of the water formed in a given combustion experiment requires correction to the true mass of water. The following considerations hold: after the absorption tube has been properly charged and prepared for absorption of water, with the inlet and outlet closed, the mass of the entire absorption tube and contents consists of the following: the glass of the absorber, the lubricant on the main ground-glass plugs controlling the inlet and outlet, the absorbent magnesium perchlorate, the absorbent phosphorus pentoxide, three layers of asbestos, and the gas filling the void space in the tube. The void space in the tube may be of the order of 50 cm³. During the absorption of water in the absorption tube, the mass of the solid absorbent increases by the mass of water absorbed. However, the volume of the magnesium perchlorate, into which all but a very small quantity of the water is absorbed, increases on absorption of water to form a hydrate.   This increase in volume of the solid absorbent results in a decrease in the volume of the void space inside the absorption tube, and a consequent decrease in mass of the gas filling the void space.   The mass of the gas filling the void space is a function of the molecular weight of the gas, the volume of the void space, and the temperature and pressure at which the gas is closed off in the tube.

For each gram of water absorbed, magnesium perchlorate increases in volume 0.60 cm$^3$ (1).   With the confined gas at 25°C and 1 atm, the mass of this volume of gas would be 0.00079 g for oxygen, 0.00071 g for air, 0.00010 g for helium, and 0.00005 g for hydrogen.   With the air in the balance case having a density of 0.0012 g/cm$^3$, the correction for the buoyancy of brass weights is $-0.00014$ g/g.   Accordingly, with brass weights, air in the balance case having a density of 0.0012 g/cm$^3$, and oxygen at 25°C and 1 atm inside the absorption tube, at the times of the two weighings of the absorption tube, before and after the absorption of the water, the true mass of water absorbed is

$$\Delta m_{H_2O} = (1 + 0.00079 - 0.00014)\Delta m_{tube} = 1.00065 \Delta m_{tube}, \quad (2)$$

where $\Delta m_{tube}$ is the observed increase in mass of the absorption tube. For the same conditions, except with air, helium, and hydrogen inside the absorption tube, the corresponding relations are as follows:

For air inside the absorption tube,

$$\Delta m_{H_2O} = 1.00057 \Delta m_{tube}. \quad (3)$$

For helium inside the absorption tube,

$$\Delta m_{H_2O} = 0.99996 \Delta m_{tube}. \quad (4)$$

For hydrogen inside the absorption tube,

$$\Delta m_{H_2O} = 0.99991 \Delta m_{tube}. \quad (5)$$

For different values of density of the weights used, or of the air in the balance case, or of the gas inside the absorption tube, appropriate changes in the above factors can be made.

For modern thermochemical investigations, where an overall precision of 1 in 10,000 is approached, it is clearly advantageous to weigh the absorption tube with hydrogen or helium inside of it, in order to avoid the large correction associated with the use of air or oxygen inside the tube.   In the writer's laboratory, it has become standard practice to flush out all absorption tubes, before weighing, with hydrogen gas or helium gas.   Our more recent practice is to use helium gas for safety reasons.   The operation of flushing out an absorption tube with hydrogen or helium can be performed repeatedly without changing the weight of the absorption tube more than about 0.00010 g.   With the total change in mass being 2 or 3 g, this permits adequate precision.

**5. Determination of the amount of reaction when carbon dioxide is a product of the reaction.**   For the absorption of carbon dioxide formed in the combustion of hydrocarbons, or of compounds of carbon, hydrogen, and oxygen, or of these with nitrogen, the absorption tube is charged with appropriate layers of Ascarite, magnesium perchlorate, and phosphorus pentoxide, each bounded by a layer of asbestos fiber.   In the case of compounds containing nitrogen, the possible formation and absorption of nitrogen oxides must be considered.

For each gram of carbon dioxide absorbed by the Ascarite, the solid absorbent increases in volume by $0.45$ cm$^3$ (2).   For the same conditions as discussed above, the appropriate relations giving the true mass of carbon dioxide absorbed are as follows:

For oxygen inside the absorption tube,

$$\Delta m_{CO_2} = (1 + 0.00059 - 0.00014)\Delta m_{tube} = 1.00045\Delta m_{tube}. \quad (6)$$

For air inside the absorption tube,

$$\Delta m_{CO_2} = 1.00039\Delta m_{tube}. \quad (7)$$

For helium inside the absorption tube,

$$\Delta m_{CO_2} = 0.99994\Delta m_{tube}. \quad (8)$$

For hydrogen inside the absorption tube,

$$\Delta m_{CO_2} = 0.99990\Delta m_{tube}. \quad (9)$$

As in the case of the determination of the true mass of water, the determination of the true mass of carbon dioxide is best effected by having the absorption tube always filled with the same light gas (helium or hydrogen) at the times of weighing, to obtain the maximum precision and accuracy.

An improved form of tube for absorbing water or carbon dioxide is shown in Figure 3 (5).

**6. Determination of the corrected "temperature" rise.**   It is usually desirable to operate with a jacket at constant temperature maintained slightly above the final temperature of the experiment. For an apparatus of the kind shown in Figure 1, with the amount of reaction indicated previously, the standard temperature rise in the given investigation can be selected at some value between 2 and 4

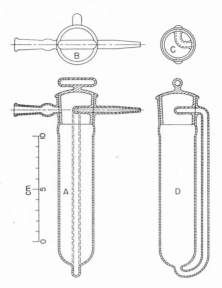

Figure 3. Details of the improved absorption tube. From Prosen and Rossini (5). A, B, and D are, respectively, front section, top view, and side section of the absorption tube, and C is a bottom view of the stopper The gas enters at the left, passes through the cap through a right angle turn, leaves the body of the tube at the top, and passes downward through the side tube. At the bottom, the gas reenters the body of the tube and passes upward through, in order, layers of Ascarite, anhydrous magnesium perchlorate, and phosphorus pentoxide separated by layers of shredded asbestos.

deg. In the experiments reported in reference (1), the time-temperature curves for the experiments with electrical energy and those with chemical energy were very much alike, as shown in Figure 4.

In each experiment, the observations of temperature at given times are divided into three periods: the "fore" period, 0 to 20 min; the "reaction" period, 20 to 40 min; and the "after" period, 40 to 60 min. In Figure 4, curve S-1 represents the data of an experiment with electrical energy and curve S-C represents the data of an experiment with chemical energy from the combustion of hydrogen and oxygen to form water.    These curves show how very much alike are the time-temperature curves in the two kinds of experiments.    With such a procedure, full advantage is taken of the substitution method and any unknown constant error in determining the true temperature rise is essentially completely eliminated.

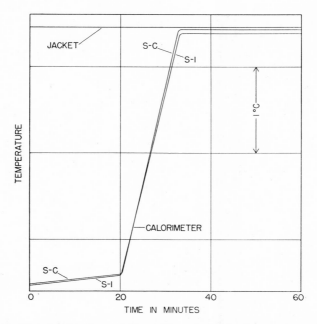

Figure 4. Plot showing the variation of the calorimeter temperature with time. From Rossini (1).   The scale of ordinates gives the temperature and the scale of abscissas gives the time in minutes.   Curve S-1 represents the results of an experiment with electrical energy and curve S-C the results of an experiment with chemical energy.

If the two kinds of experiment (those with electrical energy and those with chemical energy) are performed under similar conditions, as with the same calorimeter system, nearly the same total temperature rise, the same rate of change of temperature, the same average temperature, etc., the determination of the true corrected temperature rise becomes somewhat of a formality.   However, in order to note differences in operational features of the various experiments, it is desirable to make detailed calculations of the corrections to be applied to the observed temperature rise to obtain the corrected temperature rise. For this purpose, the corrections to be applied are of two kinds: the first is a correction which is independent of the difference in temperature between the calorimeter and the jacket, being constant with time; the second is a correction which is directly proportional to the difference in temperature between the calorimeter and the jacket. The first correction is a combination of the energy given to the calorimeter by the stirrer and the energy removed from the calorimeter by the evaporation of a small amount of water. The second correction consists, in large measure, of the flow of energy from the jacket to the calorimeter water, which is at a lower temperature. In the following equations, $u$ is the constant rate, in ohms per minute, at which the temperature of the calorimeter increases (or decreases) and is chiefly due to the input of energy by stirring and the removal of energy by evaporation; $k$ is the proportionality factor, in ohms per minute ohm, which measures the rate at which heat flows from the jacket to the calorimeter per unit difference in temperature between the jacket and the calorimeter; $R$ is the temperature of the calorimeter in ohms; $R_j$ is the constant temperature of the jacket in ohms; $Z$ is the time; and numerical subscripts indicate the given time.

From the observations of the "fore" period:

$$u + \left( R_j - \frac{R_0 + R_{20}}{2} \right) k = \frac{R_{20} - R_0}{20} \text{ ohms/min.} \qquad (10)$$

From the observations of the "after" period:

$$u + \left( R_j - \frac{R_{40} + R_{60}}{2} \right) k = \frac{R_{60} - R_{40}}{20} \text{ ohms/min.} \qquad (11)$$

These equations can be solved for $u$ and $k$. Since the coefficient of $k$ in Equation 11 is small, and since the value of $u$ is small compared to the value of the entire second term in Equation 10, the value of $u$ is essentially determined from Equation 11 and that of $k$ from Equation 10.

The total value of the first correction is

$$U = 20\,u \text{ ohms,} \qquad (12)$$

and that of the second correction is

$$K = k \ (Area) \text{ ohms},\tag{13}$$

where $(Area)$ is the area, in ohm-minutes, represented as the area between the temperature of the calorimeter and the temperature of the jacket and the time between 20 and 40 min, as may be seen from the time-temperature curves in Figure 4.

The observed temperature rise is

$$\Delta R = R_{40} - R_{20} \text{ ohms}.\tag{14}$$

The corrected temperature rise is

$$\Delta R_c = \Delta R - U - K \text{ ohms}.\tag{15}$$

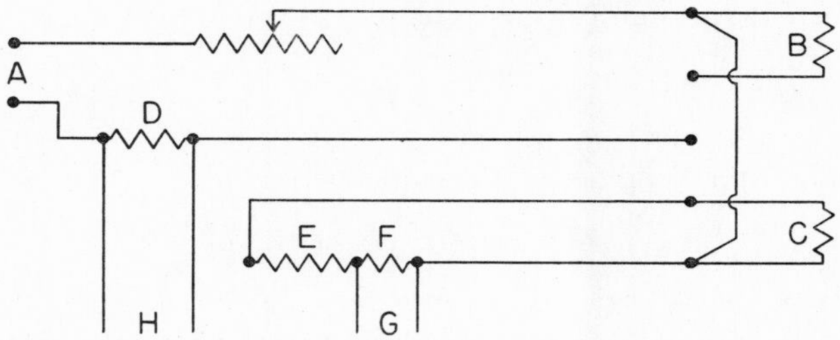

Figure 5. Diagram of the circuit for electrical energy. From Rossini (1). The letters have the following significance: A, storage battery of 70 volts; B, external stabilizing resistance, or spill coil; C, calorimeter resistance heater; D, E, F, standard resistors of 0.1, 10,000 and 10 ohms, respectively; G, H, leads to the potentiometer.

As discussed in reference (4), it is unnecessary to express the temperature rise in degrees, and more convenient to let it remain expressed as the increase in resistance in ohms of the given platinum resistance thermometer at the mean temperature of the experiment, as measured on the given resistance bridge.

**7. Determination of the energy equivalent of the calorimeter system with electrical energy.**   The system for providing and measuring electrical energy includes the heating coil in the calorimeter proper, a precision potentiometer, an accurate device for measuring the time of input of electrical energy, a stable source of electrical power (as from a battery of lead storage cells), a standard cell, and three appropriate standard resistances arranged in the proper circuit.   Figure

5 shows a diagram of the circuit for electrical energy described in reference (1).

The input of electrical power into the calorimeter is determined by measuring (a) the potential drop $e_C$, across the heating coil of the calorimeter, and (b) the potential drop, $e_F$, across a standard resistance through which passed the same current as through the heating coil (less a small calculable amount which flowed through the potential coils in parallel with the heating coil). In the circuit described in reference (1) shown in Figure 5, the three standard resistances had values of 0.1, 10, and 10,000 ohms, respectively, for $r_D$, $r_F$, and $r_E$; the calorimeter heater had a resistance, $r_C$, of about 70 ohms; power was supplied from a storage battery of 70 volts; and the "spill" coil B had a resistance the same as that of the calorimeter coil C.

The current through the calorimeter coil C is*

$$i_C = (e_D/r_D)[1 - r_C/(r_E + r_F + r_C + r_L)] = (e_D/r_D) - (e_F/r_F),$$
(16)

and the potential drop across the calorimeter coil C is

$$e_C = (e_F/r_F)(r_E + r_F + r_L).$$
(17)

In the foregoing equations, $r_L$ represents the small resistance of the copper leads joining the resistances E and F with C. It is to be noted that with a sufficiently large value of $r_E$, the value of $r_L$ may not be significant. The electrical power, $i_C e_C$, is thus given in terms of the two measured potential drops, $e_D$ and $e_F$, and appropriate combination of the resistances $r_E$, $r_F$, and, if significant, $r_L$:

$$i_C e_C = (e_F/r_F)(r_E + r_F + r_L)[(e_D/r_D) - (e_F/r_F)].$$
(18)

If the measured potential drops $e_D$ and $e_F$ vary during the time of input of electrical energy, an appropriate mean value of the product should be evaluated according to Equation 18. Multiplication of this mean value of the electrical power by the time, $Z$, of input of electrical energy gives the amount of the electrical energy for the given experiment.

In the later experiments described in reference (1), the time of input of electrical energy was 780 sec and was measured with a timing de-

---

* A typographical error occurs in line 2 of page 13 of reference (1), in which the denominator of the fraction inside the parentheses, written as $r_E + r_F$, should be $r_E + r_F + r_C$.

vice having a precision of better than 0.01 sec.  With all of the standard resistances and the coils of the potentiometer appropriately calibrated, the measurement of electrical power can be readily made with high precision.  Additional details regarding measurements with electrical energy, and the apparatus and procedure, are giving in Chapter 3 of this book.   Details of the experimental procedure may be found in references (1,2,3,4,6).

From the value of the electrical energy, $eiZ$, and the corrected temperature rise, each experiment with electrical energy yields a value of the standard energy equivalent of the calorimeter, $E_s$, as

$$\mathcal{E}_s = (eiZ)/\Delta R_c. \tag{19}$$

In Equation 19, $\mathcal{E}_s$ is the energy equivalent, in joules/ohm, over the standard interval of temperature, of the standard calorimeter system, obtained as the ratio of the quantity of electrical energy to the corresponding value of the corrected temperature rise, $\Delta R_c$.

**8. Determination of the energy equivalent of the calorimeter system with the reaction of hydrogen and oxygen to form water.**   When the necessary instruments for measuring electrical power and time are not available, it is recommended that the energy equivalent of the calorimeter system be determined using the reaction of hydrogen and oxygen to form water.

In the preceding section, $\mathcal{E}_s$ and $\Delta R_c$ have been defined.   Let $m_{H_2O}$ be the mass, in grams, of water formed in the reaction of hydrogen and oxygen in the given experiment;   $q_i$ the energy, in joules, introduced into the calorimeter in the ignition process, consisting of sparking, igniting the flame, and extinguishing the flame, but not including any part of the heat of combustion; $q_g$ the net energy, in joules, introduced into the calorimeter by gases entering or leaving at a temperature different from the mean temperature of the calorimeter;   $-q_v$ the energy, in joules, removed from the calorimeter by the process of evaporating such water as leaves or remains in the calorimeter in the gaseous state;   and $q_r$ the energy, in joules, introduced into the calorimeter by the heat of the chemical reaction.

The total energy, $q$, in joules, introduced into the calorimeter in an experiment is

$$q = (\mathcal{E}_s)(\Delta R_c) = q_r + q_v + q_g + q_i, \tag{20}$$

Solving for $\mathcal{E}_s$, one obtains

$$\mathcal{E}_s = (q_r + q_v + q_g + q_i)/\Delta R_c. \tag{21}$$

For the calibrating reaction of hydrogen and oxygen to form water,

$$q_r = (-\Delta H)_{H_2O}m_{H_2O}/M_{H_2O}, \tag{22}$$

where $(-\Delta H)_{H_2O}$ is the calibrating reference value, in joules/mole, of the heat of formation of liquid water from gaseous hydrogen and oxygen at 1 atm at the given temperature, $m_{H_2O}$ is the true mass of water formed in the reaction, and $M_{H_2O}$ is the molecular weight of water to which the given value of $(-\Delta H)_{H_2O}$ applies.

The energy equivalent, $\mathcal{E}_s$, is thus evaluated from the measured quantities $m_{H_2O}$, $\Delta R_c$, $q_v$, $q_g$, and $q_i$:

$$\mathcal{E}_s = \left[\frac{(-\Delta H)_{H_2O}m_{H_2O}}{M_{H_2O}} + q_v + q_g + q_i\right]\Big/\Delta R_c. \tag{23}$$

The former Commission on Thermochemistry of the International Union of Chemistry, in its reports issued in 1934 and 1936 (10,11), accepted as the standard for reactions in a flame at constant pressure the reaction of hydrogen and oxygen to form water, and recommended for calibration purposes the data reported by Rossini (1,3). The value there reported now requires correction to the present accepted molecular weight of water, 18.0160 g (13), and to absolute joules (10) (see Chapters 1 and 13). Making these corrections (12), the following value is obtained as the standard calibrating value for the reaction of gaseous hydrogen and gaseous oxygen to form liquid water, all at 1 atm pressure:

$$(-\Delta H)_{H_2O} \text{ at } 25°C = 285,828 \pm 40 \text{ absolute joules/mole.} \tag{24}$$

The corresponding values at 20°C and 30°C are:

$$(-\Delta H)_{H_2O} \text{ at } 20°C = 285,988 \pm 40 \text{ absolute joules/mole;} \tag{25}$$

$$(-\Delta H)_{H_2O} \text{ at } 30°C = 285,668 \pm 40 \text{ absolute joules/mole.} \tag{26}$$

The value of $-\Delta H°$ for the reaction of forming liquid water from gaseous hydrogen and oxygen, with each substance in its thermodynamic standard reference state (14), differs from the above values only by a small amount, 3.6 j/mole (12).

Details regarding the evaluation of $q_g$, $q_i$, and $q_v$ are given in references (1,2,4,6). The magnitudes of these quantities, in terms of the total energy in one experiment are, approximately, as follows: $q_g$, 0 to 0.2 per cent; $q_i$, 0.1 per cent; $q_v$, 0.2 to 1 per cent. Additional details and description of the experimental processes, including that for ignition, are given in references (1,2,4,6).

**9. Determination of the heat of a reaction occurring in a flame at constant pressure.** Reaction vessels suitable for reactions in a flame at constant pressure have been described for the following reactions: hydrogen in oxygen, or oxygen in hydrogen, to form water (1); carbon monoxide in oxygen to form carbon dioxide, and methane in oxygen to form carbon dioxide and water (2); gaseous methanol, or gaseous ethanol, in oxygen to form carbon dioxide and water (7); oxygen in gaseous sulfur to form gaseous sulfur dioxide (8); chlorine in hydrogen to form hydrogen chloride (9); gaseous hydrocarbons ($C_2$ to $C_5$) in oxygen to form carbon dioxide and water (4,6).

With the energy equivalent of the calorimeter system having been determined with electrical energy or with the standard reaction of hydrogen and oxygen, as described in the preceding sections, the calorimeter system is ready for measuring the heat of other reactions. It is important that the reaction vessel used in the experiments to evaluate the energy equivalent be the same as that used in the experiments on the reactions for which the heat of reaction is to be evaluated.

In the given reaction experiment, the quantities measured are $\Delta R_c$, $q_g$, $q_i$, $q_v$ (if water is formed in the reaction), and $m_x$. Here, $m_x$ is the mass of the substance (usually taken as one of the products) that is to determine the amount of reaction in a given experiment.

It is convenient to define the quantity

$$B = q_r / \mathcal{E}_s m_x. \tag{27}$$

The total energy absorbed by the calorimeter is

$$q = \mathcal{E}_s \Delta R_c = q_r + q_v + q_g + q_i. \tag{28}$$

But

$$q_r = (-\Delta H)_x m_x / M_x. \tag{29}$$

where the three symbols on the right side represent, respectively, the heat of reaction per mole, the mass of the substance that measures the amount of reaction, and $M_x$ is the molecular weight of the substance $x$, taken stoichiometrically in accordance with the value of $(-\Delta H)_x$. Then, from Equations 27 and 28,

$$B\mathcal{E}_s m_x = \mathcal{E}_s \Delta R_c - (q_v + q_g + q_i) \tag{30}$$

or

$$B = \frac{\Delta R_c}{m_x}\left[1 - \frac{q_v + q_g + q_i}{\mathcal{E}_s \Delta R_c}\right]. \tag{31}$$

Thus, the quantity $B$ can be completely evaluated for each experiment from quantities which are experimentally measured. With the average value of $B$ from a series of experiments on a given reaction determined, the value of the heat of the given reaction is given by

$$(-\Delta H)_x = B\mathcal{E}_s M_x, \tag{32}$$

where $M_x$ is the appropriate stoichiometrical molecular weight.

## References

1. F. D. Rossini, *J. Research Natl. Bur. Standards* 6, 1 (1931).
2. F. D. Rossini, *J. Research Natl. Bur. Standards* 6, 39 (1931).
3. F. D. Rossini, *J. Research Natl. Bur. Standards* 7, 329 (1931).
4. F. D. Rossini, *J. Research Natl. Bur. Standards* 12, 735 (1934).
5. E. J. Prosen and F. D. Rossini, *J. Research Natl. Bur. Standards* 33, 255 (1944).
6. E. J. Prosen, F. W. Maron, and F. D. Rossini, *J. Research Natl. Bur. Standards* 42, 269 (1949).
7. F. D. Rossini, *J. Research Natl. Bur. Standards* 8, 119 (1932).
8. J. R. Eckman and F. D. Rossini, *J. Research Natl. Bur. Standards* 3, 597 (1929).
9. F. D. Rossini, *J. Research Natl. Bur. Standards* 9, 679 (1932).
10. First Report from the Standing Commission for Thermochemistry, International Union of Chemistry, Paris, 1934.
11. Appendix to the First Report from the Standing Commission for Thermochemistry, International Union of Chemistry, Paris, 1936.
12. F. D. Rossini, *J. Research Natl. Bur. Standards* 22, 407 (1939).
13. E. Wichers, *J. Am. Chem. Soc.* 76, 2033 (1954).
14. F. D. Rossini, *Chemical Thermodynamics*, John Wiley and Sons, New York, 1950.

# CHAPTER 5

# Standard States and Corrections for Combustions in a Bomb at Constant Volume

W. N. Hubbard, D. W. Scott, and Guy Waddington

**1. Introduction.** The energy evolved when the combustion of a substance takes place in a bomb calorimeter may differ significantly from the decrease in internal energy for the combustion reaction under standard conditions. This fact was emphasized by Washburn (1) in 1933 in a paper entitled "Standard States for Bomb Calorimetry." Washburn treated in detail the corrections that must be applied to bomb calorimetric data in order that investigators may obtain values of the standard change of internal energy. In high-precision combustion calorimetry, it has become standard practice to apply the corrections proposed by Washburn. They are usually referred to as the "Washburn corrections" or collectively as the "Washburn reduction."

Washburn's treatment applied to the combustion of compounds that contain only carbon, hydrogen, and oxygen, that is, to compounds of the general formula, $C_aH_bO_c$. In 1933 it was only for such compounds that bomb calorimetric data were being obtained with accuracy high enough to make the corrections to standard states significant. However, in the two decades since the publication of Washburn's paper, great improvements have been made in techniques for determining heats of combustion of compounds that contain elements other than carbon, hydrogen, and oxygen, e.g., compounds that also contain sulfur, nitrogen, or one of the halogens. For these classes of compounds, data are now being obtained, or are likely to be obtained in the near future, that must be corrected to standard states if full advantage is to be taken of their accuracy. It has, therefore,

75

become increasingly necessary for investigators to consider the corrections to standard states for these other classes of compounds to which Washburn's original treatment did not apply.  In 1951 Prosen (2) extended the Washburn corrections to apply to nitrogen compounds of the general formula, $C_aH_bO_cN_d$.  More recently, Hubbard, Scott, and Waddington (3) extended the Washburn corrections to apply to sulfur compounds of the general formula, $C_aH_bO_cS_d$ and made a critical selection of the numerical values that enter into the corrections to take advantage of more accurate experimental data that have become available since 1933.  Extensions of the Washburn corrections to apply to halogen compounds have not been published heretofore.

The purpose of this chapter is to consider the correction to standard states of bomb calorimetric data for sulfur, nitrogen, and halogen compounds, the general formulas of which are $C_aH_bO_cS_d$, $C_aH_bO_cN_d$, $C_aH_bO_cCl_d$, $C_aH_bO_cBr_d$, and $C_aH_bO_cI_d$.  The corrections for these classes of compounds include the simpler corrections for compounds of the general formula, $C_aH_bO_c$, as limiting cases when $d$ is zero, and for compounds of the general formula, $C_aH_b$, as limiting cases when both $c$ and $d$ are zero.  Washburn's original treatment referred the combustion reactions to a temperature of 20 °C.  In recent years there has been an increasing tendency to conduct combustion experiments at higher temperatures and to refer the combustion reactions to 25 °C.  In recognition of this tendency, in the treatment of Hubbard, Scott, and Waddington (3) the combustion reactions were all referred to a standard temperature of 25 °C.  In this chapter, the treatment has been expanded in order that the corrections may be applied at any temperature between 20 and 30 °C.

The Washburn corrections for sulfur compounds are selected to illustrate the general method of handling these corrections for four-element compounds and are, therefore, discussed in the greatest detail.  They are treated in the next section of this chapter, and the treatment there essentially follows that of Hubbard, Scott, and Waddington (3).  The subsequent sections of this chapter discuss the modifications that must be made in the Washburn corrections for sulfur compounds to make them applicable to nitrogen, chlorine, bromine, and iodine compounds.

**2. Organic sulfur compounds of the general formula, $C_aH_bO_cS_d$.**
(a) *General Considerations.*  The calorimetric determination of the

heat of combustion of an organic sulfur compound takes place as follows. The substance, oxygen (in excess), nitrogen, and water are introduced into a combustion bomb. (The nitrogen may be merely an impurity in the oxygen, or it may be introduced deliberately to catalyze the oxidation of sulfur to the +6 oxidation state.) The substance is caused to react with the oxygen to produce carbon dioxide, water, and sulfuric acid. Side reactions that produce nitric and nitrous acids may occur simultaneously. After the reaction is complete, the bomb contains carbon dioxide, water, sulfuric acid, the oxygen not consumed in the reaction, nitrogen, and possibly nitric and nitrous acids. The process just described takes place in a bomb calorimeter. The increase in temperature of the calorimeter is measured, and, by suitable calibration of the calorimeter, this increase in temperature is related to the heat liberated by the process. The heat liberated is equal to the decrease in internal energy of the contents of the bomb when they are converted from the particular state in which they exist before the combustion reaction to the particular state in which they exist after the combustion reaction, i.e., the heat liberated is the change in internal energy for the actual bomb process. In practice, by the application of appropriate calorimetric corrections, this is reduced to the change in internal energy for the isothermal bomb process.

The quantity which an investigator wishes to obtain from bomb calorimetric data is not the change in internal energy for the isothermal bomb process but the change in internal energy for an idealized combustion reaction. This is defined as the reaction, isothermally at a given temperature, $t_h$, of a unit quantity of substance in its standard state with an equivalent amount of pure oxygen gas and the necessary amount of pure liquid water, both of which are in their standard states, to produce the stoichiometric amounts of pure carbon dioxide and an aqueous sulfuric acid solution of a designated concentration, both of which are in their standard states. The equation of the reaction is:

$$C_aH_bO_cS_d(\text{c or liq.}) + (a + b/4 - c/2 + 3d/2)O_2(g)$$
$$+ (nd - b/2 + d)H_2O(\text{liq.}) = aCO_2(g) + d(H_2SO_4 \cdot nH_2O)(\text{liq.}).$$

The change in internal energy associated with this process is called the "energy of the idealized combustion reaction," and is designated $\Delta Ec^\circ$.

The idealized combustion reaction is conveniently regarded as occurring in a series of processes, one of which is the actual bomb process and the remainder of which are imaginary. The first process starts with the substance, oxygen (in excess), nitrogen, and water, all in their standard states at $t_h$. These are placed in the combustion bomb, and equilibrium is established at $t_h$, except that the substance is not allowed to mix with the other materials. The phases that result are: (a) whatever phases constitute the substance; (b) a gaseous phase consisting of oxygen, nitrogen, and water vapor; and (c) a liquid phase consisting of water saturated with dissolved oxygen and nitrogen. The next process consists of bringing these initial contents of the bomb from their equilibrium state at $t_h$ to their equilibrium state at the initial temperature, $t_i$, of the actual bomb process. The next process is the actual bomb process, in which the actual initial contents of the bomb are converted to the actual final contents of the bomb, and the temperature increases from $t_i$ to $t_f$, the final temperature of the actual bomb process. Two phases result, namely, (a) a gaseous phase consisting of oxygen, carbon dioxide, nitrogen, and water vapor; and (b) a liquid phase consisting of an aqueous solution of sulfuric, nitric, and nitrous acids saturated with dissolved oxygen, carbon dioxide, and nitrogen. The next process consists of bringing these final contents of the bomb from their equilibrium state at $t_f$ to their equilibrium state at $t_h$. In the final process, the nitric and nitrous acids are decomposed into nitrogen, oxygen, and water; all of the oxygen, carbon dioxide, and nitrogen are removed from the bomb, separated from each other, and brought individually to their standard states at $t_h$; all the water and sulfuric acid is removed from the bomb as an aqueous sulfuric acid solution under 1 atm pressure; and this solution is adjusted to the designated concentration by the isothermal addition or removal of liquid water in its standard state at $t_h$. The net change in this series of processes is just the idealized combustion reaction. The sum of the changes in internal energy for all the processes is, therefore, the energy of the idealized combustion reaction, $\Delta Ec^\circ$. The actual bomb process and the processes immediately preceding and following it constitute the isothermal bomb process, for which the change in internal energy is obtained calorimetrically. The changes in internal energy for the other two processes are the Washburn corrections, the addition of which to the experimentally determined change in internal energy for the isothermal bomb process gives the desired quantity, $\Delta Ec^{\circ}$. The calculation of the Washburn corrections then consists of computing the changes in internal energy for these other imaginary processes.

The standard states are defined in a manner consistent with current thermodynamic usage. The definitions are: (a) for oxygen, nitrogen, and carbon dioxide, the pure substances in the ideal gas state at 1 atm pressure; (b) for the substance, the material in a thermodynamically defined state (solid or liquid) under a pressure of 1 atm; (c) for water, the pure liquid under a pressure of 1 atm; and (d) for the aqueous sulfuric acid solution, the liquid at a defined concentration (which is selected to be approximately that obtained in the actual combustion experiment) under a pressure of 1 atm.

The presentation adopted in this chapter was determined by several considerations. One was that all the corrections that must be applied to the original calorimetric data should be included. Some of these corrections are calorimetric, some are thermochemical, and only the rest are those usually regarded as the Washburn corrections. However, all these different kinds of corrections are not strictly independent, and there may be ambiguity about the classification of certain corrections and uncertainty about the order in which they are to be applied. These difficulties are removed if all the corrections are included in one consistent treatment. A second consideration was that the treatment should be as complete and rigorous as is practical. This consideration led to the inclusion of terms that are negligible for the experimental conditions and attainable precision that the authors consider usual in combustion calorimetry. However, these terms are included so that an investigator who uses different experimental conditions or who obtains increased precision may determine the magnitude of these terms and decide whether or not they are negligible for his purpose. A third consideration was that all the terms should be kept separate and not be combined into a single complex expression, as was done by Washburn. Keeping the terms separate has several advantages: (a) the individual terms are more easily examined to determine whether they are significant or negligible; (b) when a more reliable experimental value for a quantity which enters the treatment becomes available, the term or terms that contain this quantity may be conveniently revised without disturbing the rest of the treatment; (c) many of the terms of this treatment for organic sulfur compounds also apply, either unchanged or with slight modifications, to the treatments for organic nitrogen and halogen compounds. These terms, if kept separate, can be readily transferred to the treatments for these other classes of compounds in later sections of this chapter.

A fourth consideration was that the treatment should be presented in a way that is adaptable for use by other investigators. The rather long calculations involved in applying all of the corrections to the original calorimetric data are conveniently carried out on a computation form. The presentation is, therefore, given as the items which make up such a computation form, interspersed with explanatory text. These items, 100 in number, consist of the input data (experimental values, molecular weights, physical constants, auxiliary energy quantities, etc.) and the quantities that the investigator must calculate from them to obtain the desired quantity, $\Delta Ec^\circ$, which is item 100. The items are so ordered that the calculation of each one depends only on the numerical values obtained for prior items, and they are so designed that the numerical operations are conveniently performed with a desk calculator. Items 1–67, which relate to the description of the initial and final states of the isothermal bomb process, items 68–80, which relate to energy factors and calorimetric data, and items 81–100, which relate to the changes in internal energy, are treated in the next three subsections. As an illustration of the use of the method, and as a means of illustrating the magnitude of the various terms, a numerical example of the calculations is given. This numerical example is selected from a series of experiments carried out to determine the heat of combustion of 3-methylthiophene (4). In the application of the corrections, $t_h$ is 25 °C.

(b) *Initial and Final States.* The substance is defined as all of the material that undergoes combustion and consists of the compound whose heat of combustion is being determined and any other combustible materials added for any purpose, e.g., the auxiliary material and the fuse. The first 18 items of the computation sheet list the formula (chemical or empirical), mass $m$, molecular weight $M$, number of moles $n$, density $\rho$, and volume $V$ of each of the materials that comprise the substance. Primes are used to distinguish different materials. In the numerical example, the compound is 3-methylthiophene, the auxiliary material is a hydrocarbon oil, the empirical formula of which is $CH_{1.891}$, and the fuse is filter paper, the empirical formula of which is $CH_{1.686}O_{0.843}$. Starred item numbers denote input data, and unstarred item numbers denote calculated quantities.

| | | |
|---|---|---|
| (1*) | Formula of compound, $C_{a'}H_{b'}O_{c'}S_{d'}$ | $C_5H_6S$ |
| (2*) | $m'$, mass of compound | 0.85715 g |
| (3*) | $M'$, molecular weight of compound | 98.164 g mole$^{-1}$ |
| (4) | $n' = m'/M'$ | 0.00873182 mole |
| (5*) | $\rho'$, density of compound | 1.02 g ml$^{-1}$ |
| (6) | $V' = m'/1000\rho'$ | 0.0008 liter |
| (7*) | Formula of auxiliary material, $C_{a''}H_{b''}O_{c''}S_{d''}$ | $CH_{1.891}$ |
| (8*) | $m''$, mass of auxiliary material | 0.05354 g |
| (9*) | $M''$, molecular weight of auxiliary material | 13.916 g mole$^{-1}$ |
| (10) | $n'' = m''/M''$ | 0.0038474 mole |
| (11*) | $\rho''$, density of auxiliary material | 0.87 g ml$^{-1}$ |
| (12) | $V'' = m''/1000\rho''$ | 0.0001 liter |
| (13*) | Formula of fuse, $C_{a'''}H_{b'''}O_{c'''}S_{d'''}$ | $CH_{1.686}O_{0.843}$ |
| (14*) | $m'''$, mass of fuse | 0.00410 g |
| (15*) | $M'''$, molecular weight of fuse | 27.197 g mole$^{-1}$ |
| (16) | $n''' = m'''/M'''$ | 0.0001508 mole |
| (17*) | $\rho'''$, density of fuse | 1.5 g ml$^{-1}$ |
| (18) | $V''' = m'''/1000\rho'''$ | 0.0000 liter |

In the numerical example, $c'$, $c''$, $d''$, and $d'''$ are zero.

Items 19–25 list the subscripts, $a$, $b$, $c$, and $d$, of the empirical formula $C_aH_bO_cS_d$, and the mass, $m(\text{Sub.})$, molecular weight, $M(\text{Sub.})$, and the number of moles, $n(\text{Sub.})$, of the total substance that undergoes combustion. The subscripts $a$, $b$, $c$, and $d$ are defined so that $n(\text{Sub.})$ is always unity.

| | | |
|---|---|---|
| (19) | $a = n'a' + n''a'' + n'''a'''$ | 0.0476573 |
| (20) | $b = n'b' + n''b'' + n'''b'''$ | 0.0599206 |
| (21) | $c = n'c' + n''c'' + n'''c'''$ | 0.0001271 |
| (22) | $d = n'd' + n''d'' + n'''d'''$ | 0.0087318 |
| (23) | $m(\text{Sub.}) = m' + m'' + m'''$ | 0.91479 g |
| (24) | $M(\text{Sub.}) = 12.010a + 1.008b + 16.000c + 32.066d$ | 0.91479 g mole$^{-1}$ |
| (25) | $n(\text{Sub.}) = m(\text{Sub.})/M(\text{Sub.})$ | 1.00000 mole |

Items 26–36 deal with the amounts of $O_2$, $N_2$, and $H_2O$ in the bomb, and the distribution of these compounds between the gaseous and liquid phases, in the initial state of the isothermal bomb process. Except for stoichiometry, the $N_2$ is treated as though it were $O_2$. This approximation is justified because (a) $N_2$ and $O_2$ have similar physical properties, (b) the mole fraction of $N_2$ in the bomb gases is small (less than 0.03 in current practice), and (c) the errors from treating $N_2$ as $O_2$ in the initial state are nearly compensated by similar errors from

so treating it in the final state, since $N_2$ is present in nearly the same amount and condition in both states.

In the equations to follow, *superscripts i* and *f* are used to designate the initial and final states, respectively, of the *isothermal* bomb process. (*Subscripts i* and *f* are reserved to designate the initial and final states of the *actual* bomb process.) The material to which a symbol applies and the state of that material are given parenthetically after the symbol. The abbreviations used include the chemical formulas of single compounds and the following other abbreviations: Sub., total substance; gas., gaseous mixture of $O_2$, $N_2$, and $H_2O$ vapor (and $CO_2$ in the final state); soln., aqueous solution of $H_2SO_4$, $HNO_3$, and $HNO_2$; vap., vapor; liq., liquid; diss., dissolved; and tot., total.

The next three items list the volume of the bomb, $V(Bomb)$; the volume of $H_2O$ added to the bomb, $V^i(H_2O \text{ tot.})$; and the initial pressure at $t_h$, $P^i(gas.)$. The volume of the bomb is defined as the internal volume, exclusive of the volume occupied by the crucible, electrodes, and other noncombustible accessories. In the numerical example, 10.03 ml of water is introduced into the bomb, the volume of which is 0.3471 liter, and the bomb, which contains air at atmospheric pressure, is charged to a total pressure of 30.00 atm (at 25 °C).

| | | |
|---|---|---|
| (26*) | $V(Bomb)$ | 0.3471 liter |
| (27*) | $V^i(H_2O \text{ tot.})$ | 0.01003 liter |
| (28*) | $P^i(gas.)$ | 30.00 atm |

The density, $\rho(H_2O)$, and molecular weight, 18.016 g mole$^{-1}$, of $H_2O$ are used to calculate the mass and number of moles of total $H_2O$ in the bomb.

| | | |
|---|---|---|
| (29) | $m^i(H_2O \text{ tot.}) = \rho(H_2O)V^i(H_2O \text{ tot.})$ | 10.00 g |
| (30) | $n^i(H_2O \text{ tot.}) = m^i(H_2O \text{ tot.})/18.016$ | 0.5551 mole |

The volume occupied by the gaseous phase is obtained by subtracting the volume of liquid $H_2O$ and of substance from the volume of the bomb. The volume of liquid $H_2O$ differs from $V^i(H_2O \text{ tot.})$ only by the amount vaporized into the gaseous phase, an amount which is insignificant in this calculation.

| | | |
|---|---|---|
| (31) | $V^i(gas.) = V(Bomb) - V^i(H_2O \text{ tot.}) - V' - V'' - V'''$ | 0.3362 liter |

The concentration of saturated $H_2O$ vapor in gases at various pressures, $C_W$, may be represented by the equation given by Washburn [Equation 105 in reference (1)], $C_W = C_0 + \alpha P$. The term, $C_0$, is the concentration of saturated $H_2O$ vapor in the absence of other gases (5). $P$ is the pressure of other gas, which, for the pressure range of interest here, does not differ significantly from the total pressure. The constant $\alpha$ is determined by the nature of the gas phase. Unfortunately experimental data are still unavailable for the evaluation of $\alpha$ for $O_2$, and it is necessary to assume, as Washburn did, that $\alpha$ is the same for $O_2$ as for $N_2$ or air. However, the data used by Washburn for the concentration of $H_2O$ vapor in $N_2$ and air (6) have been superseded by more recently determined data (7). The values of $\alpha$ selected here are based on the smoothed data of Deaton and Frost (7b) for air at 400 lb in.$^{-2}$ gauge (28.1 atm absolute). The number of moles of water in the gaseous phase, $n^i(H_2O$ vap.$)$, is calculated from the equation:

(32)   $n^i(H_2O$ vap.$) = [C_0 + \alpha P^i(\text{gas.})] V^i(\text{gas.})/18.016$          0.000475 mole

in which $C_0$ and $\alpha$ have the following values:

|  | $C_0$, g liter$^{-1}$ | $\alpha$, g liter$^{-1}$ atm$^{-1}$ |
|---|---|---|
| 20° | 0.01729 | 0.00006 |
| 25° | 0.02304 | 0.00008 |
| 30° | 0.03037 | 0.00010 |

The number of moles, $n^i(H_2O$ liq.$)$, of liquid water is obtained by difference.

(33)   $n^i(H_2O$ liq.$) = n^i(H_2O$ tot.$) - n^i(H_2O$ vap.$)$          0.5546 mole

The equation of state, $PV = nRT[1 - (890 - 11.3t)10^{-6}P]$, (in which $t$ is the temperature in °C) fits the $PVT$ data of $O_2$ (8) for $t = 20$ to 30° and $P = 20$ to 40 atm to a sufficiently good approximation. Since $N_2$ is treated as though it were $O_2$ and the concentration of $H_2O$ is too small to affect the $PVT$ behavior significantly, this equation is used to calculate the number of moles of the gaseous mixture, $n^i(\text{gas.})$.

(34)   $n^i(\text{gas.}) =$

$$\frac{P^i(\text{gas.})V^i(\text{gas.})}{0.082054(t_h + 273.2)[1 - (890 - 11.3\ t_h)10^{-6}P^i(\text{gas.})]}$$          0.4199 mole

The solubility of $O_2$ in aqueous $H_2SO_4$ solutions will be discussed subsequently. The limiting value of the solubility in water, obtained from the following table, is used to calculate the number of moles of $O_2 + N_2$ dissolved in the liquid $H_2O$.

$K*(O_2)$, moles of dissolved $O_2$ per liter $H_2O$ per atm $O_2$ pressure

$P^i$(gas.), atm

| | 20 | 30 | 40 |
|---|---|---|---|
| 20° | 0.00133 | 0.00129 | 0.00126 |
| 25° | 0.00120 | 0.00117 | 0.00114 |
| 30° | 0.00107 | 0.00105 | 0.00102 |

(35) $n^i[(O_2 + N_2)$ diss.]

  = $0.01807K*(O_2)n^i(H_2O$ liq.$)[P^i$(gas.) $- P^i(H_2O$ vap.$)]$  0.000351 mole

For use in item 35, values of the partial pressure of water vapor, $P^i(H_2O$ vap.$)$, are 0.02, 0.03, and 0.04 atm at 20°, 25°, and 30°C.

The total number of moles of $O_2 + N_2$ is calculated next.

(36) $n^i[(O_2 + N_2)$tot.$]$ $= n^i$(gas.) $- n^i(H_2O$ vap.)

              $+ n^i[(O_2 + N_2)$ diss.]  0.4198 mole

Items 37–67 deal with the compounds present in the bomb in the final state of the isothermal bomb process, and their distribution between the gaseous and aqueous phases. The substance has reacted with $O_2$ according to the net equation:

$$C_aH_bO_cS_d + (a + b/4 - c/2 + 3d/2)O_2 = aCO_2 + (b/2 - d)H_2O + dH_2SO_4.$$

Side reactions may have occurred according to the net equations:

$$1/2N_2 + 5/4O_2 + 1/2H_2O = HNO_3$$

and

$$1/2N_2 + 3/4O_2 + 1/2H_2O = HNO_2.$$

The extent of these side reactions is determined experimentally by chemical analysis of the final bomb solution.* In the numerical example, it was found that 0.00069 mole of $HNO_3$ and 0.000005 mole of $HNO_2$ were formed.

(37*) $n^f(HNO_3)$              0.00069 mole
(38*) $n^f(HNO_2)$             0.000005 mole

The number of moles of $H_2SO_4$ produced in the combustion is calculated by stoichiometry.

(39) $n^f(H_2SO_4) = dn$(Sub.)         0.008732 mole

---

* The corrections for iron wire discussed by Washburn are omitted from this treatment.

The number of moles of $H_2O$ in the liquid phase is given rigorously by

$$n^i(H_2O \text{ tot.}) + (b/2 - d)n(\text{Sub.}) - {}^1\!/_2 n^f(HNO_3) - {}^1\!/_2 n^f(HNO_2) - n^f(H_2O \text{ vap.}).$$

However the final term (which is small compared to the first two terms) is not known at this stage of calculation. If the $H_2SO_4$ solution in the final state is relatively dilute, the number of moles of $H_2O$ vapor do not differ greatly in the initial and final states, and it is a satisfactory approximation to substitute $n^i(H_2O \text{ vap.})$ for $n^f(H_2O \text{ vap.})$. The validity of this approximation may be verified after item 67 is calculated.

(40)  $n^f(H_2O \text{ liq.}) = n^i(H_2O \text{ tot.}) + (b/2 - d)n(\text{Sub.}) - {}^1\!/_2 n^f(HNO_3)$
$\qquad\qquad\qquad - {}^1\!/_2 n^f(HNO_2) - n^i(H_2O \text{ vap.})$        0.5755 mole

The mass of solution is obtained by summing the masses of the constituents.

(41)  $m^f(\text{soln.}) = 18.016 n^f(H_2O \text{ liq.}) + 98.1 n^f(H_2SO_4)$
$\qquad\qquad\qquad + 63 n^f(HNO_3) + 47 n^f(HNO_2)$        11.27 g

The concentrations, in weight per cent, of $H_2SO_4$ and of the combined nitrogen acids are calculated next.

(42)  wt.$\%(H_2SO_4) = 9808 n^f(H_2SO_4)/m^f(\text{soln.})$        7.60%
(43)  wt.$\%(HNO_3 + HNO_2)$
$\qquad\qquad = [6302 n^f(HNO_3) + 4702 n^f(HNO_2)]/m^f(\text{soln.})$        0.39%

Density data for $H_2SO_4$ and $HNO_3$ solutions individually (9a) may be represented, for the concentration ranges of interest here, by $\rho = \rho_0 + 0.0066$ wt.$\%(H_2SO_4)$ and $\rho = \rho_0 + 0.0054$ wt.$\%(HNO_3)$ g ml$^{-1}$ in which equations $\rho_0$, the density of pure water, is 0.9982, 0.9970 and 0.9957 at 20°, 25°, and 30°C.

In calculating the density and volume of the aqueous solution, two approximations are made: (a) that $H_2SO_4$ and $HNO_3$ increase the density of $H_2O$ additively according to weight per cent, and (b) that the small amount of $HNO_2$ may be treated as though it were $HNO_3$. The second approximation will be made repeatedly throughout this subsection.

(44)  $\rho^f(\text{soln.}) = \rho_0 + 0.0066$ wt.$\%(H_2SO_4)$
$\qquad\qquad\qquad + 0.0054$ wt.$\%(HNO_3 + HNO_2)$        1.049 g ml$^{-1}$
(45)  $V^f(\text{soln.}) = m^f(\text{soln.})/1000\rho^f(\text{soln.})$        0.01074 liter

The normality of $H_2SO_4$ and of the combined nitrogen acids, and the molar ratio of $H_2O$ to $H_2SO_4$ are calculated in the next three items.

(46)    $N(H_2SO_4) = 2n^f(H_2SO_4)/V^f(\text{soln.})$                                    $1.626N$

(47)    $N(HNO_3 + HNO_2) = [n^f(HNO_3) + n^f(HNO_2)]/V^f(\text{soln.})$     $0.065N$

(48)    $n^f(H_2O \text{ liq.})/n^f(H_2SO_4)$                                                       $65.91$

The volume of the gaseous mixture is obtained by difference.

(49)    $V^f(\text{gas.}) = V(\text{Bomb}) - V^f(\text{soln.})$                          0.3364 liter

The number of moles of $CO_2$ produced in the combustion process is calculated from stoichiometry.

(50)    $n^f(CO_2 \text{ tot.}) = an(\text{Sub.})$                                            0.047657 mole

The solubility of $CO_2$ in aqueous $H_2SO_4$ is read from a smooth curve through a large scale plot of the values (for $t_h$) given below. The values in the table are based on the data of Markham and Kobe (10), Kobe and Williams (11), Geffcken (12), and Sunner (13). The data of Geffcken (12) show that $HNO_3$, on a normality basis, *increases* the solubility of $CO_2$ in aqueous solutions approximately half as much as $H_2SO_4$ *decreases* it. The independent variable is therefore selected to be $N(H_2SO_4) - \frac{1}{2}N(HNO_3 + HNO_2)$. An extrapolation to negative values of this variable is included to cover cases in which nitrogen acids are present and $H_2SO_4$ is not. The solubility constant, $K(CO_2)$, is defined as the number of moles of $CO_2$ dissolved in 1 liter of solution at unit fugacity of $CO_2$ gas.

$$N(H_2SO_4) - \frac{1}{2}N(HNO_3 + HNO_2)$$

| | −0.5 | 0.0 | 0.5 | 1.0 | 1.5 | 2.0 | 2.5 | 3.0 | 3.5 | 4.0 |
|---|---|---|---|---|---|---|---|---|---|---|
| | | | | | $K(CO_2) \times 10^4$ | | | | | |
| 20° | 409.6 | 390.2 | 373.1 | 357.7 | 345.1 | 335.9 | 328.0 | 320.9 | 313.8 | 307.9 |
| 25° | 356.5 | 340.5 | 326.9 | 314.5 | 304.5 | 297.0 | 290.8 | 285.0 | 279.2 | 274.2 |
| 30° | 308.9 | 296.0 | 285.5 | 275.8 | 268.1 | 262.2 | 257.5 | 252.9 | 248.2 | 244.0 |

(51)    $K(CO_2)$                                              0.0303 mole liter$^{-1}$ atm$^{-1}$

In the computation of the number of moles of $CO_2$ dissolved in the aqueous phase, it is necessary to take account of (*a*) the fugacity of the $CO_2$ gas in the presence of the $O_2$ gas, and (*b*) the total pressure on the aqueous phase. It is convenient to treat the $CO_2$ and $O_2$ as ideal gases and then use a fictitious solubility constant, $K^*(CO_2)$, that includes corrections for fugacity and total pressure.* The fictitious solubility constant is obtained by multiplication of the actual solubility constant by a factor, $D(CO_2)$. Values of $D(CO_2)$ are tabulated below as a function of temperature, the final pressure, $P^f(\text{gas.})$, and the mole fraction of $CO_2$, $x(CO_2)$. At this stage of the computation, only approximate estimates of $x(CO_2)$ and $P^f(\text{gas.})$ are required; the estimated values may be checked after accurate values have been calculated in items 63 and 65.

| | 20°C $P^f$(gas.), atm | | | 25°C $P^f$(gas.), atm | | | 30°C $P^f$(gas.), atm | | |
| --- | --- | --- | --- | --- | --- | --- | --- | --- | --- |
| $x(CO_2)$ | 20 | 30 | 40 | 20 | 30 | 40 | 20 | 30 | 40 |
| 0.0 | 0.908 | 0.865 | 0.824 | 0.914 | 0.873 | 0.834 | 0.920 | 0.882 | 0.845 |
| 0.1 | 0.894 | 0.845 | 0.798 | 0.900 | 0.854 | 0.810 | 0.908 | 0.865 | 0.824 |
| 0.2 | 0.880 | 0.825 | 0.774 | 0.887 | 0.836 | 0.787 | 0.896 | 0.848 | 0.802 |

In the numerical example, the estimated values are 0.12 for $x(CO_2)$ and 28 atm for $P^f(\text{gas.})$.

(52) $D(CO_2)$ — 0.859

(53) $K^*(CO_2) = D(CO_2)K(CO_2)$ — 0.0260 mole liter$^{-1}$ atm$^{-1}$

(54) $n^f(CO_2 \text{ diss.})$

$$= \frac{0.082054(t_h + 273.2)K^*(CO_2)V^f(\text{soln.})/V^f(\text{gas.})}{1 + 0.082054(t_h + 273.2)K^*(CO_2)V^f(\text{soln.})/V^f(\text{gas.})} \, n^f(CO_2 \text{ tot.})$$

0.000949 mole

(55) $n^f(CO_2 \text{ gas}) = n^f(CO_2 \text{ tot.}) - n^f(CO_2 \text{ diss.})$ — 0.046708 mole

The number of moles of $O_2 + N_2$ in the final state is calculated next.

(56) $n^f[(O_2 + N_2)\text{tot.}] = n^i[(O_2 + N_2) \text{ tot.}]$
$- (a + b/4 - c/2 + 3d/2)n(\text{Sub.}) - {}^7/_4 n^f(HNO_3)$
$- {}^5/_4 n^f(HNO_2)$ — 0.3429 mole

The solubility of $O_2$ in aqueous $H_2SO_4$ solution is read from a large scale plot of the values given below, which are based on the data of Geffcken (12) for 15° and 25°C. As $HNO_3$ decreases the solubility of $O_2$ approximately half as much as $H_2SO_4$, on a normality basis, the

* The equation of state of item 65 was used in the computation of the fugacity of $CO_2$ gas in the presence of $O_2$ gas. A value of 33 ml for the partial molal volume of $CO_2$ in aqueous solution was used in computing of the effect of total pressure.

independent variable is selected to be $N(H_2SO_4) + \frac{1}{2}N(HNO_3 + HNO_2)$. The solubility constant, $K(O_2)$, is defined as the number of moles of $O_2$ dissolved in 1 liter of solution at unit fugacity of $O_2$ gas.

$$N(H_2SO_4) + \frac{1}{2}N(HNO_3 + HNO_2)$$

|  | 0.0 | 0.5 | 1.0 | 1.5 | 2.0 | 2.5 | 3.0 | 3.5 | 4.0 |
|---|---|---|---|---|---|---|---|---|---|
|  | | | | $K(O_2) \times 10^4$ | | | | | |
| 20° | 13.98 | 13.07 | 12.39 | 11.78 | 11.21 | 10.66 | 10.12 | 9.62 | 9.22 |
| 25° | 12.60 | 11.81 | 11.26 | 10.77 | 10.31 | 9.85 | 9.39 | 8.95 | 8.61 |
| 30° | 11.22 | 10.55 | 10.14 | 9.77 | 9.42 | 9.05 | 8.66 | 8.29 | 8.01 |

(57)  $K(O_2)$                                 0.00106 mole liter$^{-1}$ atm$^{-1}$

The solubility of $O_2 + N_2$ in the aqueous solution is handled in much the same way as that of $CO_2$. Values of $D(O_2)$ are tabulated below.*

| | 20° | | | 25° | | | 30° | | |
|---|---|---|---|---|---|---|---|---|---|
| | $P^f$(gas.), atm | | | $P^f$(gas.), atm | | | $P^f$(gas.), atm | | |
| $x(CO_2)$ | 20 | 30 | 40 | 20 | 30 | 40 | 20 | 30 | 40 |
| 0.0 | 0.949 | 0.924 | 0.900 | 0.951 | 0.928 | 0.905 | 0.954 | 0.932 | 0.910 |
| 0.1 | 0.945 | 0.918 | 0.892 | 0.947 | 0.922 | 0.897 | 0.951 | 0.927 | 0.904 |
| 0.2 | 0.941 | 0.912 | 0.885 | 0.944 | 0.917 | 0.890 | 0.947 | 0.922 | 0.897 |

(58)  $D(O_2)$                                                         0.926

(59)  $K^*(O_2) = D(O_2)K(O_2)$                    0.00098 mole liter$^{-1}$ atm$^{-1}$

(60)  $n^f[(O_2 + N_2)$ diss.]

$$= \frac{0.082054(t_h + 273.2)K^*(O_2)V^f(\text{soln.})/V^f(\text{gas.})}{1 + 0.082054(t_h + 273.2)K^*(O_2)V^f(\text{soln.})/V^f(\text{gas.})} n^f[(O_2 + N_2) \text{ tot.}]$$

0.000262 mole

(61)  $n^f[(O_2 + N_2) \text{ gas}] = n^f[(O_2 + N_2) \text{ tot.}]$
      $- n^f[(O_2 + N_2) \text{ diss.}]$                          0.3426 mole

The number of moles of gaseous mixture is calculated next. As in item 40, $n^t(H_2O$ vap.) is used as an approximation for $n^f(H_2O$ vap.).

(62)  $n^f(\text{gas.}) = n^f[(O_2 + N_2) \text{ gas}] + n^f(CO_2 \text{ gas}) + n^i(H_2O \text{ vap.})$

0.3898 mole

* The equation of state of item 65 was used in the computation of the fugacity of $O_2$ gas in the presence of $CO_2$ gas. A value of 31 ml for the partial molal volume of $O_2$ in aqueous solution was used in computing the effect of total pressure.

Item 63 lists the mole fraction of $CO_2$ in the gaseous mixture, $x(CO_2)$.

(63)  $x(CO_2) = n^f(CO_2 \text{ gas})/n^f(\text{gas.})$                    0.1198

Washburn gives an equation for $\mu$ in the equation of state, $PV = nRT(1 - \mu P)$, for $O_2 - CO_2$ mixtures as a function of $x(CO_2)$ [Equation 28 of reference (1)]. The equation applies strictly at 20 °C, but may be used at 25° and 30 °C without significant loss of accuracy.

(64)  $\mu^f(\text{gas.}) = \mu(O_2)\{1 + 3.21x(CO_2)[1 + 1.33x(CO_2)]\}$

in which

$$\mu(O_2) = (890 - 11.3t_h)10^{-6}. \qquad 0.00088 \text{ atm}^{-1}$$

The pressure of the final gaseous mixture is calculated from the equation of state.

(65)  $P^f(\text{gas.}) = \dfrac{1}{[V^f(\text{gas.})/0.082054(t_h + 273.2)n^f(\text{gas.})] + \mu^f(\text{gas.})}$

                    27.66 atm

The ratio, $g$, of the vapor pressure of water over the solution of $H_2SO_4$ and $HNO_3 + HNO_2$ to that over pure $H_2O$ is obtained by interpolation from a large scale plot. Such a plot may be constructed from the values of $g$ in the table given below, which is based on data from a number of sources (14,9b). For the range of concentration and temperature of interest here, $g$ is not a function of temperature (14b).

| wt.% $HNO_3$ | wt.%($H_2SO_4$) | | | | | | | | |
| + $HNO_2$) | 0 | 2 | 4 | 6 | 8 | 10 | 12 | 14 | 16 | 18 |
|---|---|---|---|---|---|---|---|---|---|---|
| 0.0 | 1.0000 | .9905 | .9812 | .9720 | .9618 | .9522 | .9416 | .9290 | .9147 | .8983 |
| 0.4 | | .9973 | .9878 | .9785 | .9693 | .9591 | .9495 | .9389 | .9263 | .9120 | .8956 |
| 0.8 | | .9947 | .9852 | .9759 | .9662 | .9565 | .9469 | .9363 | .9237 | .9094 | .8930 |
| 1.2 | | .9920 | .9825 | .9732 | .9640 | .9538 | .9442 | .9336 | .9210 | .9067 | .8903 |

(66)  $g$                    0.961

In connection with calculating the number of moles of water in the gaseous phase in the initial state of the isothermal bomb process, values of $C_O$ and $\alpha$ for $O_2$ in the equation $C_W = C_O + \alpha P$ have been given. The data of Wiebe and Gaddy (15) for the concentration of saturated water vapor in $CO_2$ at 25 atm lead to the following values of $\alpha$ for $CO_2$: 0.00040, 0.00048, and 0.00056 g liter$^{-1}$ atm$^{-1}$ for 20°, 25°, and 30°C. Assuming that $\alpha$ for $O_2$-$CO_2$ mixtures varies linearly with the mole fraction of $CO_2$, one may write:

$$C_W = C_0 + \{\alpha(O_2) + [\alpha(CO_2) - \alpha(O_2)]x(CO_2)\}P \qquad \text{g. liter}^{-1}$$

This relationship is used to calculate the number of moles of $H_2O$ vapor in the gaseous phase.

(67)  $n^J(H_2O \text{ vap.})$

$$= \frac{g[C_0 + \{\alpha(O_2) + [\alpha(CO_2) - \alpha(O_2)]x(CO_2)\}P^J(\text{gas.})]V^J(\text{gas.})}{18.016}$$

0.000477 mole

(c) *Energy Factors and Calorimetric Data.* The description of the initial and final states of the isothermal bomb process is complete with item 67. Before the calculation of the actual corrections, it is convenient to tabulate values of certain quantities that are unique for the particular experiment or the particular substance and, therefore, cannot be expressed in a general form. These quantities are tabulated in items 68–80.

The first of these are values of $(\partial E/\partial P)_T$ for the materials that constitute the substance. As discussed by Washburn [reference (1), pp. 542–43], it is a satisfactory approximation to take $(\partial E/\partial P)_T$ equal to $-T(\partial V/\partial T)_P$. In the numerical example, the values of $(\partial V/\partial T)_P$ are $1.013 \times 10^{-6}$, $8.50 \times 10^{-7}$, and ca. $10^{-6}$ liter g$^{-1}$ deg$^{-1}$ for 3-methylthiophene, the auxiliary oil, and the fuse respectively.

(68*)  $(\partial E/\partial P)_T{}' = -24.22(t_h + 273.2)(\partial V/\partial T)_P{}'$    $-0.00731$ cal g$^{-1}$ atm$^{-1}$

$(\partial E/\partial P)_T{}'' = -24.22(t_h + 273.2)(\partial V/\partial T)_P{}''$    $-0.00614$ cal g$^{-1}$ atm$^{-1}$

$(\partial E/\partial P)_T{}''' = -24.22(t_h + 273.2)(\partial V/\partial T)_P{}'''$    $-0.007$   cal g$^{-1}$ atm$^{-1}$

The value of $(\partial E/\partial P)_T$ for the final solution is also required. It is read from a large scale plot of this quantity as a function of wt.% ($H_2SO_4$). Such a plot may be made from the following table, which is based on density data for $H_2SO_4$ solutions (9a) and the approximate equality of $(\partial E/\partial P)_T$ and $-T(\partial V/\partial T)_P$.

$(\partial E/\partial P)_T{}^f$(soln.) $\times 10^5$, cal g$^{-1}$ atm$^{-1}$

wt. % $H_2SO_4$

|  | 0 | 2 | 4 | 6 | 8 | 10 | 12 | 14 | 16 | 18 |
|---|---|---|---|---|---|---|---|---|---|---|
| 20° | −147 | −174 | −199 | −210 | −238 | −256 | −273 | −288 | −302 | −315 |
| 25° | −186 | −219 | −235 | −255 | −268 | −281 | −292 | −303 | −314 | −324 |
| 30° | −222 | −244 | −260 | −274 | −286 | −297 | −308 | −317 | −326 | −334 |

(69)  $(\partial E/\partial P)_T{}^f$(soln.)           −0.00266 cal g$^{-1}$ atm$^{-1}$

Values are also required for the change in internal energy for diluting (or concentrating) the $HNO_3$ + $HNO_2$ to a concentration of $0.1N$ and the $H_2SO_4$ to an even concentration close to that obtained in the actual experiment. In the numerical example, the even concentration is selected to be $H_2SO_4 \cdot 70H_2O$. The quantity $\Delta E_{diln.}(HNO_3 + HNO_2)$ is read directly from a plot, and the quantity $\Delta E_{diln.}(H_2SO_4)$ is obtained as the difference between $\Delta Hf°$ of the formation of $H_2SO_4$ at the even concentration and that at the concentration of the final solution. The required values of $\Delta Hf°$ for $H_2SO_4$ are read from a large scale plot of that quantity as a function of $n(H_2O)/n(H_2SO_4)$. Numerical values from which the two plots may be constructed are given below. These are based on data from the tables of selected values (16a). The temperature coefficients were obtained from heat capacity data (18,19).

$\Delta E_{diln.}(HNO_3 + HNO_2)$, cal mole$^{-1}$        $\Delta Hf°(H_2SO_4)$, cal mole$^{-1}$

| wt. % $(HNO_3 + HNO_2)$ | 20° | 25° | 30° | $\dfrac{n(H_2O)}{n(H_2SO_4)}$ | 20° | 25° | 30° |
|---|---|---|---|---|---|---|---|
| 0.0 | +84 | +102 | +120 | 25 | −211159 | −211190 | −211221 |
| 0.1 | +35 | +46 | +57 | 30 | −211244 | −211280 | −211316 |
| 0.2 | +23 | +31 | +39 | 40 | −211335 | −211380 | −211425 |
| 0.3 | +15 | +21 | +27 | 50 | −211388 | −211440 | −211492 |
| 0.4 | +9 | +13 | +17 | 60 | −211418 | −211475 | −211532 |
| 0.5 | +5 | +7 | +9 | 70 | −211445 | −211506 | −211567 |
| 0.6 | +2 | +2 | +2 | 80 | −211470 | −211534 | −211598 |
| 0.8 | −4 | −6 | −8 | 90 | −211496 | −211562 | −211628 |
| 1.0 | −7 | −12 | −17 | 100 | −211522 | −211590 | −211658 |
| 1.5 | −13 | −23 | −33 | 115 | −211558 | −211629 | −211700 |
| 2.0 | −15 | −29 | −43 | 130 | −211592 | −211665 | −211738 |
| 2.5 | −16 | −34 | −52 | 150 | −211636 | −211711 | −211786 |
| 3.0 | −15 | −37 | −59 | 200 | −211742 | −211820 | −211898 |
| 3.5 | −14 | −39 | −64 | 300 | −211917 | −212000 | −212083 |

(70)   $\Delta E_{\text{diln.}}(\text{HNO}_3 + \text{HNO}_2)$          $+14$ cal mole$^{-1}$

(71)   $\Delta E_{\text{diln.}}(\text{H}_2\text{SO}_4)$          $-12$ cal mole$^{-1}$

The next two items list the energy of the idealized combustion reaction $\Delta E c^{\circ}$ for the auxiliary material and for the fuse. These quantities must have been determined in previous series of experiments.

(72*)   $\Delta E c^{\circ}$ (Auxiliary material)          $-152850$ cal mole$^{-1}$

(73*)   $\Delta E c^{\circ}$ (Fuse)          $-106710$ cal mole$^{-1}$

The next three items deal with the energy equivalent of the calorimetric system. This is conveniently divided into two parts, one the energy equivalent of the whole system minus the contents of the bomb, $\mathcal{E}(\text{Calor.})$,* which is the same in the initial and final states, and the other the energy equivalent of the contents of the bomb, $\mathcal{E}(\text{Cont.})$, which is different in the initial and final states. The value of $\mathcal{E}(\text{Calor.})$ must have been determined experimentally, either by electrical calibration or by combustion of a standard substance such as benzoic acid.

(74*)   $\mathcal{E}$ (Calor.)          3909.44 cal deg$^{-1}$

The values of $\mathcal{E}(\text{Cont.})$ are obtained by summing the heat capacity of all the contents of the bomb. The gaseous phase may be considered to be at constant volume, as the total change in volume from thermal expansion of the bomb and of the condensed phases and from vaporization of $\text{H}_2\text{O}$ is negligible. Similarly, the condensed phases may be considered to be at constant pressure, as the change of pressure with temperature is too small to be significant. The effective heat capacity of the two-phase system, liquid $\text{H}_2\text{O}$ or aqueous solution plus $\text{H}_2\text{O}$ vapor, may be represented by two terms, one proportional to the total mass, and the second a "vaporization correction" proportional to the amount of $\text{H}_2\text{O}$ vapor (17). Thus for the initial state

---

* By definition, the energy equivalent of a bomb calorimetric system is the amount of energy that must be added to it, *under the conditions of the combustion experiment*, to raise its temperature from $t$ to $t'$, divided by $(t' - t)$. In a combustion experiment, the pressure in the bomb changes in going from the initial to the final state, and therefore the elastic strain on the bomb proper and the compression of the crucible and other internal parts also changes. The provision "under the conditions of the combustion experiment" means that any energy effects associated with these changes in the bomb and internal parts are included in the definition of the energy equivalent.

$$\varepsilon(\text{H}_2\text{O tot.}) = Am^i(\text{H}_2\text{O tot.}) + Bn^i(\text{H}_2\text{O vap.})$$

and for the final state

$$\varepsilon(\text{soln.} + \text{H}_2\text{O vap.}) = A[m^j(\text{soln.}) + 18n^j(\text{H}_2\text{O vap.})] + Bn^j(\text{H}_2\text{O vap.}).$$

The following values of $A$ as a function of the concentration of the solution are based on heat capacity data for $\text{H}_2\text{SO}_4$ (18) and $\text{HNO}_3$ (19) solutions. As $\text{HNO}_3$, on a wt.% basis, lowers the heat capacity about 1.3 times as much as $\text{H}_2\text{SO}_4$, the independent variable is selected to be wt.%$(\text{H}_2\text{SO}_4)$ + 1.3 wt.%$(\text{HNO}_3 + \text{HNO}_2)$. The variation of $B$ with the concentration of the solution is not significant.

wt. % $(\text{H}_2\text{SO}_4)$ + 1.3 wt. % $(\text{HNO}_3 + \text{HNO}_2)$

| | 0 | 2 | 4 | 6 | 8 | 10 | 12 | 14 | 16 | 18 |
|---|---|---|---|---|---|---|---|---|---|---|
| | | | | | $A$, cal g$^{-1}$ deg$^{-1}$ | | | | | |
| 20° | 0.997 | 0.979 | 0.961 | 0.946 | 0.928 | 0.913 | 0.896 | 0.881 | 0.867 | 0.852 |
| 25° | .997 | .979 | .961 | .945 | .929 | .914 | .898 | .883 | .869 | .854 |
| 30° | .997 | .979 | .961 | .944 | .930 | .915 | .900 | .885 | .871 | .856 |

In the numerical example, the crucible and other parts made of platinum weighed 30.05 g, and the glass ampoule to contain the 3-methylthiophene sample weighed 0.047 g. The applicable heat capacity values are: for 3-methylthiophene, 0.367; for the auxiliary oil, 0.53; and for the fuse, ca. 0.4 cal deg$^{-1}$ g$^{-1}$.

(75) $\varepsilon^i(\text{Cont.}) = C_V(\text{O}_2)n^i[(\text{O}_2 + \text{N}_2)\text{tot.}] + 0.997m^i(\text{H}_2\text{O tot.})$
$+ Bn^i(\text{H}_2\text{O vap.}) + m'C_P' + m''C_P'' + m'''C_P'''$
$+ 0.0325m(\text{Pt}) + 0.17m(\text{glass}) + \ldots$     13.68 cal deg$^{-1}$

(76) $\varepsilon^j(\text{Cont.}) = C_V(\text{O}_2)n^j[(\text{O}_2 + \text{N}_2)\text{tot.}] + C_V(\text{CO}_2)n^j(\text{CO}_2\text{ tot.})$
$+ A[m^j(\text{soln.}) + 18n^j(\text{H}_2\text{O vap.})] + Bn^j(\text{H}_2\text{O vap.})$
$+ 0.0325\,m(\text{Pt}) + 0.17\,m(\text{glass}) + \ldots$     13.78 cal deg$^{-1}$

Values of the heat capacity of $\text{O}_2$, $C_V(\text{O}_2)$, and $\text{CO}_2$, $C_V(\text{CO}_2)$, and $B$ are given below.

| | $C_V(\text{O}_2)$ | $C_V(\text{CO}_2)$ | $B$ |
|---|---|---|---|
| 20° | 5.052 | 7.228 | 575 |
| 25° | 5.056 | 7.251 | 550 |
| 30° | 5.062 | 7.277 | 525 |

The foregoing equations apply strictly to 30 atm, and approximately at any pressure in the usual range of bomb-calorimetric practice. Since the expression for $\mathcal{E}^i$ (Cont.) is somewhat more reliable than that for $\mathcal{E}'$(Cont.), it is advantageous to have the final temperature, $t_f$, close to $t_h$.

The electrical energy supplied to ignite the sample, $\Delta E_{ign.}$, is listed next.

(77*)    $\Delta E_{ign.}$                                            1.35 cal

The next three items list the initial and final temperatures of the actual bomb process, $t_i$ and $t_f$, and the quantity, $\Delta t_{corr.}$, which is the correction that must be applied to the change in temperature of the calorimeter to correct for the heat of stirring and the heat exchanged between the calorimeter and its environment.*

(78*)    $t_i$                                               23.00239 °C
(79*)    $t_f$                                               25.00842 °C
(80*)    $\Delta t_{corr.}$                                       0.00631 deg

* The term, $\Delta t_{corr.}$, is best understood in relation to the calorimetric experiment In the calorimetric experiment, the time of experimental observations is divided into three periods. In the "fore period," the temperature of the calorimeter, $t$, is observed as a function of time, $T$. (In this footnote, $T$ is used to denote time and not Kelvin temperature.) At the end of the fore period, $T = T_i$ and $t = t_i$. The "reaction period" begins at $T_i$. During the reaction period, the sample is ignited, the rapid increase of temperature is observed, and enough time is allowed to elapse so that the rate of change of temperature is again uniform. The "after period" begins at $T_f$, at which time the temperature is $t_f$. In the after period, the observation of the temperature as a function of time is continued. From the observations in the fore and after periods, the rates of change of temperature at $T_i$ and $T_f$, $(dt/dT)_i$ and $(dt/dT)_f$, are determined.

The changes of internal energy equivalent to the heat of stirring and the heat exchanged between the calorimeter and its environment are designated by $\Delta E_{stir.}$ and $\Delta E_{ex.}$. By definition

$$\Delta t_{corr.} = [\Delta E_{stir.} + \Delta E_{ex.}]/[\mathcal{E}(Calor.) + \mathcal{E}'(Cont.)]. \tag{I}$$

For the determination of the small correction term, $\Delta t_{corr.}$, the difference in $\mathcal{E}$ (Cont.) in the initial and final states is not significant, and $\mathcal{E}^i$ (Cont.) could have been used in Equation I instead of $\mathcal{E}'$ (Cont.).

If the rate at which heat of stirring is supplied to the calorimeter is constant, and if the rate of heat exchange between the calorimeter and environment is proportional to the temperature difference (Newton's law), then at $T_i$ and $T_f$

$$(dt/dT)_i = z + \alpha(t_{env.} - t_i) \tag{II}$$

and

$$(dt/dT)_f = z + \alpha(t_{env.} - t_f). \tag{III}$$

In Equations II and III, $t_{env.}$ is the temperature of the environment. The first

(*Footnote continued on page 95*)

term on the right is the constant rate of temperature change from stirring, and the second is the rate of temperature change from heat exchange.

There are at least three methods in common use for calculating $\Delta t_{\text{corr.}}$. In the first, $t_{\text{env.}}$ is measured, and $z$ and $\alpha$ are evaluated by simultaneous solution of Equations II and III. The values of $z$ and $\alpha$ are then substituted into the relation

$$\Delta t_{\text{corr.}} = \int_{T_i}^{T_f} [z + \alpha(t_{\text{env.}} - t)] dT. \tag{IV}$$

The second method does not require the determination of $t_{\text{env.}}$. A "convergence temperature," $t_c$, is defined by $t_c = z/\alpha + t_{\text{env.}}$. Physically, $t_c$ is the limiting value the calorimeter temperature would approach after an indefinitely long period of time. Equations II, III, and IV may be rewritten as

$$(dt/dT)_i = \alpha(t_c - t_i), \tag{V}$$

$$(dt/dT)_f = \alpha(t_c - t_f), \tag{VI}$$

and

$$\Delta t_{\text{corr.}} = \alpha \int_{T_i}^{T_f} (t_c - t) dT. \tag{VII}$$

The values of $\alpha$ and $t_c$ are obtained by simultaneous solution of Equations V and VI and are then substituted into Equation VII.

In the third method, which is probably the most convenient one, a "mid-time," $T_m$, is defined by the relationship

$$\int_{T_i}^{T_m} (t_i - t) dT = - \int_{T_m}^{T_f} (t_f - t) dT. \tag{VIII}$$

Separation of the integral of Equation IV into two parts, the addition and subtraction of $t_i$ in the first integrand and the addition and subtraction of $t_f$ in the second yields

$$\Delta t_{\text{corr.}} = \int_{T_i}^{T_m} [z + \alpha(t_{\text{env.}} - t_i + t_i - t)] dT$$

$$+ \int_{T_m}^{T_f} [z + \alpha(t_{\text{env.}} - t_f + t_f - t)] dT. \tag{IX}$$

By use of Equation VIII, this may be reduced to

$$\Delta t_{\text{corr.}} = [z + \alpha(t_{\text{env.}} - t_i)](T_m - T_i) + [z + \alpha(t_{\text{env.}} - t_f)](T_f - T_m)$$

$$= (dt/dT)_i(T_m - T_i) + (dt/dT)_f(T_f - T_m). \tag{X}$$

The value of $T_m$ is obtained from the relationship derivable from Equation VIII

$$T_m = T_f - [1/(t_f - t_i)] \int_{T_i}^{T_f} (t - t_i) dT. \tag{XI}$$

Substitution into Equation X then yields the value of $\Delta t_{\text{corr.}}$.

*(Footnote concluded)*

(d) *Changes in Internal Energy.* In this subsection, the idealized combustion reaction is considered as occurring in a series of steps, and the change of internal energy of each is calculated. The symbol, $\Delta E_{operation}$ (Material), is used to denote the change of internal energy when the indicated *operation* is performed on the indicated *material*. The operations are abbreviated as follows: vaporization, vap.: dilution, dil.; solution, sol.; mixing, mix.; and decomposition, decomp. The symbol, $\Delta E(\text{Material})]_{P'}^{P''}$ is used to denote the change in internal energy of the indicated material when the pressure changes from $P'$ to $P''$. When used without a superscript, $\Delta E$ applies either to a mole or to a gram of material as convenience dictates. (The units of $\Delta E$ are always evident from the necessity that the equations be dimensionally consistent.) When used with a superscript $i$ or $f$, $\Delta E$ applies to the actual amount of material involved in the combustion experiment.

*Step 1.* $n^i(\text{H}_2\text{O vap.})$ moles of liquid $\text{H}_2\text{O}$ in its standard state at $t_h$ is decompressed from 1 atm to its saturation pressure at $t_h$, $P_{\text{sat.}}(\text{H}_2\text{O})$, vaporized, and then decompressed in the vapor state to a negligibly small pressure. The change in internal energy is

$$n^i(\text{H}_2\text{O vap.})\left\{ \Delta E(\text{H}_2\text{O liq.})]_1^{P_{\text{sat.}}(\text{H}_2\text{O})} \right.$$

$$\left. + \Delta E_{\text{vap.}}(\text{H}_2\text{O}) + \Delta E(\text{H}_2\text{O vap.})]_{P_{\text{sat.}}(\text{H}_2\text{O})}^0 \right\}$$

The two decompression terms are negligibly small,* and only the vaporization term need be considered in the computation form. The data of reference (5) give $\Delta H_{\text{vap.}}(\text{H}_2\text{O})$ = 10565, 10514, and 10463 cal mole$^{-1}$ for 20, 25, and 30°C., from which it follows that $\Delta E_{\text{vap.}}(\text{H}_2\text{O})$ is 9973, 9922, and 9871 cal mole$^{-1}$ for these temperatures.

(81)    $\Delta E_{\text{vap.}}^i (\text{H}_2\text{O}) = \Delta E_{\text{vap.}}(\text{H}_2\text{O})n^i(\text{H}_2\text{O vap.})$              $+4.71$ cal

*Step 2.* $(a + b/4 - c/2 + 3d/2)n(\text{Sub.})$ moles of $\text{O}_2$ in the ideal gas state at $t_h$ is decompressed from 1 atm to a negligibly small pressure.

*Step 3.* The $\text{O}_2$ gas from step 2 is mixed with $n^i(\text{H}_2\text{O vap.})$ moles of $\text{H}_2\text{O}$ vapor from Step 1 and $n^i[(\text{O}_2 + \text{N}_2) \text{ tot.}] - (a + b/4 - c/2 +$

* In the numerical example, the decompression terms are 0.000016 and 0.0024 cal.

$3d/2)n$(Sub.) moles of excess $O_2$ and $N_2$ gas initially at a negligibly small pressure at $t_h$.

*Step 4.* $n^i(H_2O$ liq.) moles of liquid $H_2O$ and $n$(Sub.) moles of the substance in their respective standard states are placed in the bomb at $t_h$. Steps 2, 3, and 4 do not involve any change in internal energy.

*Step 5.* The liquid water is compressed to a pressure of $P^i$(gas.). For the pressure range involved, $(\partial E/\partial P)_T$ may be assumed to be constant. The change of internal energy is $n^i(H_2O$ liq.)$(\partial E/\partial P)_T$ $(H_2O$ liq.)$[P^i$(gas.) $- 1]$. Values of $(\partial E/\partial P)_T(H_2O$ liq.) are $-0.00147$, $-0.00186$, and $-0.00222$ cal $g^{-1}$ atm$^{-1}$ (see table immediately preceding item 69) or $-0.0265$, $-0.0335$, and $-0.0400$ cal mole$^{-1}$ atm$^{-1}$ for 20°, 25°, and 30°C, respectively.

(82) $\quad \Delta E^i(H_2O$ liq.$)]_1^{P^i(gas.)}$

$\quad = (\partial E/\partial P)_T(H_2O$ liq.$)n^i(H_2O$ liq.$)[P^i$(gas.$) - 1]$ $\qquad -0.54$ cal

*Step 6.* The substance is similarly compressed.

(83) $\quad \Delta E^i($sub.$)]_1^{P^i(gas.)} = [m'(\partial E/\partial P)_T' + m''(\partial E/\partial P)_T''$

$\quad + m'''(\partial E/\partial P)_T'''][P^i$(gas.$) - 1]$ $\qquad -0.19$ cal

If the compound is enclosed in a sealed ampoule which it does not fill, the energy of compression of the compound must be replaced by the energy of compression of the ampoule in item 83. As the latter is difficult to estimate, it is desirable to enclose a volatile compound in a completely filled, thin-walled ampoule so that the pressure in the bomb is transmitted to the compound. Such a procedure was followed in the numerical example.

*Step 7.* $n^i[(O_2 + N_2)$ diss.] moles of $O_2$ and $N_2$ gas from the mixture of Step 3 are dissolved in the liquid $H_2O$. The change in internal energy is $\Delta E_{soln.}(O_2 + N_2)n^i[(O_2 + N_2)$ diss.]. The values of $\Delta E_{soln.}(O_2)$ for aqueous $H_2SO_4$ solutions will be discussed under Step 15; the limiting values, $\Delta E_{soln.}^*(O_2)$, for pure $H_2O$ are $-3400$, $-3200$, and $-3000$ cal mole$^{-1}$ for 20°, 25°, and 30°C.

(84) $\quad \Delta E_{soln.}^i(O_2 + N_2) = \Delta E_{soln.}^*(O_2)n^i[(O_2 + N_2)$diss.]$ $\qquad -1.12$ cal

*Step 8.* $n^i$(gas.) moles of mixture of $O_2$ gas, $N_2$ gas, and $H_2O$ vapor is compressed into the remaining space of the bomb to the pressure, $P^i$(gas.). If the effect of the small concentration of $H_2O$ vapor is neglected and the $N_2$ is treated as though it were $O_2$, the change in internal energy may be represented by $(\partial E/\partial P)_T(O_2 \text{ gas})P^i(\text{gas.})$ $n^i(\text{gas.})$. The calorimetric data of Rossini and Frandsen (20) for $O_2$ at 28°, when corrected by use of a temperature coefficient (21) of $-0.4\%$ deg$^{-1}$ for $(\partial E/\partial P)_T$ give $-1.605$, $-1.574$, and $-1.543$ cal atm$^{-1}$ mole$^{-1}$ for values of $(\partial E/\partial P)_T(O_2 \text{ gas})$ at 20°, 25°, and 30°C.

$$(85) \quad \Delta E^i(\text{gas.})\big]_0^{P^i(\text{gas.})} = (\partial E/\partial P)_T(O_2 \text{ gas})P^i(\text{gas.})n^i(\text{gas.}) \qquad -19.83 \text{ cal}$$

*Step 9.* The bomb is placed in the calorimetric system at $t_h$. This step, for which there is no change in internal energy, brings the system to the initial state of the isothermal bomb process.

In the foregoing discussion, it has been assumed that all of the substance is liquid or solid in the initial state and that it does not interact in any way with the other materials in the bomb. This assumption may not be strictly true for relatively nonvolatile materials that are not sealed in ampoules but are exposed directly to the bomb gases. For such materials there are energy effects associated with volatilization of a small amount of the material, with the solution of $O_2$, $N_2$, and $H_2O$ in liquids, and with the adsorption of these on solids. The corrections for these effects are difficult to assess in practice. Therefore in precision calorimetry, the experiments must be designed in such a way that these effects are negligibly small.

*Step 10.* The temperature of the system is changed from $t_h$ to $t_i$. The equivalent change in internal energy is $[\mathcal{E}(\text{Calor.}) + \mathcal{E}^i(\text{Cont.})]$ $(t_i - t_h)$.

*Step 11.* The actual bomb reaction is caused to occur, and the temperature of the system increases from $t_i$ to $t_f$. The equivalent change in internal energy is the sum of the electrical energy supplied to ignite the sample, the stirring energy, and the energy exchanged between the calorimeter and its environment, $\Delta E_{\text{ign.}} + \Delta E_{\text{stir.}} + \Delta E_{\text{ex.}} = \Delta E_{\text{ign.}} + [\mathcal{E}(\text{Calor.}) + \mathcal{E}^f(\text{Cont.})]\Delta t_{\text{corr.}}$.

*Step 12.* The temperature of the system is changed from $t_f$ to $t_h$. This step brings the system to the final state of the isothermal bomb process. The equivalent change in internal energy is $[\mathcal{E}(\text{Calor.}) + \mathcal{E}^f(\text{Cont.})](t_h - t_f)$.

The change of internal energy for the isothermal bomb process, $\Delta E_{\text{I.B.P.}}$, is the sum of the changes of internal energy for Steps 10, 11, and 12.

(86)    $\Delta E_{\text{I.B.P.}} = \varepsilon(\text{Calor.})(t_i - t_f + \Delta t_{\text{corr.}}) + \varepsilon^i(\text{Cont.})(t_i - t_h)$

    $+ \varepsilon^f(\text{Cont.})(t_h - t_f + \Delta t_{\text{corr.}}) + \Delta E_{\text{ign.}}$                      $-7843.79$ cal

*Step 13.* The liquid and gas phases are removed from the bomb and calorimeter at $t_h$ and are confined separately at a pressure of $P^f(\text{gas.})$. No change of internal energy is associated with this step.

*Step 14.* The dissolved $CO_2$ is allowed to escape from the liquid phase and expand to a negligibly small pressure, and is then brought to its standard state at $t_h$. The change in internal energy is $- \Delta E_{\text{soln.}}$ $(CO_2)n^f(CO_2 \text{ diss.})$. For pure $H_2O$ as solvent, the "selected value" for $\Delta H_{\text{soln.}}(CO_2)$ is $-4640$ cal mole$^{-1}$ at 25°C (16b); the corresponding value of $\Delta E_{\text{soln.}}(CO_2)$ is $-4050$ cal mole$^{-1}$. The solubility of $CO_2$ in $H_2SO_4$ solutions has been studied as a function of temperature by Geffcken (12) $(O - 4N)$ and Sunner (13) $(O - 1.2N)$. Values of the heat of solution were computed from these solubility data, reduced to 25°C by use of the temperature coefficient given by Harned and Davis (22), and converted to values of the change of internal energy. The equation, $\Delta E_{\text{soln.}}(CO_2) = \Delta E^*_{\text{soln.}}(CO_2) + 240 \ N(H_2SO_4)$ cal mole$^{-1}$, was selected to represent the values so obtained. If $-4050$ is used for $\Delta E^*_{\text{soln.}}(CO_2)$ at 25°C, this equation is consistent with the "selected value" for pure water as solvent, and fits the values for $H_2SO_4$ solutions with an average deviation of 110 cal mole$^{-1}$. The assumption that the difference between 20° and 25°C or between 25° and 30°C is independent of the $H_2SO_4$ concentration and the use of the temperature coefficient of Harned and Davis (22) give similar equations for 20° and 30°C in which $\Delta E^*_{\text{soln.}}(CO_2)$ is $-4265$ and $-3830$ cal mole$^{-1}$, respectively.

(87)    $\Delta E^f_{\text{soln.}}(CO_2)$

     $= [- \Delta E^*_{\text{soln.}}(CO_2) - 240 \ N(H_2SO_4)]n^f(CO_2 \text{ diss.})$          $+3.47$ cal

*Step 15.* The dissolved $O_2$ and $N_2$ are allowed to escape from the liquid phase and expand to a negligibly small pressure. The change in internal energy is $- \Delta E_{\text{soln.}}(O_2)n^f[(O_2 + N_2) \text{ diss.}]$. The data of Geffcken (12) on the solubility of $O_2$ in $H_2SO_4$ solutions at 15° and 25°C lead to values of $\Delta E_{\text{soln.}}(O_2)$ at 20°C which may be represented by the equation, $\Delta E_{\text{soln.}}(O_2) = \Delta E^*_{\text{soln.}}(O_2) + 280N \ (H_2SO_4)$. The assumption that the difference between 20° and 25°C or between 25° and 30°C is independent of the $H_2SO_4$ concentration gives similar equations for 25° and 30°C. For pure water as solvent, the "selected value" (16c) for $\Delta H_{\text{soln.}}(O_2)$ is $-3800$ cal mole$^{-1}$; the corresponding value for $\Delta E_{\text{soln.}}(O_2)$ is $-3200$ cal mole$^{-1}$. This value is used as $\Delta E^*_{\text{soln.}}(O_2)$ for 25 °C. The use of a temperature coefficient of $+40$ cal mole$^{-1}$ deg$^{-1}$ (estimated from the solubility data) gives values of $-3400$ and $-3000$ cal mole$^{-1}$ for $\Delta E^*_{\text{soln.}}(O_2)$ at 20° and 30 °C.

(88)  $\Delta E^f_{\text{soln.}}(O_2 + N_2)$

$\qquad = [-\Delta E^*_{\text{soln.}}(O_2) - 280\ N(H_2SO_4)]n^f[(O_2 + N_2)\ \text{diss.}]$ $\qquad$ $+0.72$ cal.

*Step 16.* The liquid phase is decompressed to a final pressure of 1 atm.

(89)  $\Delta E^f(\text{soln.})]^1_{P^f(\text{gas.})} = (\partial E/\partial P)_{T^f}(\text{soln.})m^f(\text{soln.})[1 - P^f(\text{gas.})]$ $\ +0.80$ cal.

*Step 17.* The $HNO_3 + HNO_2$ are removed from the solution and dissolved in the amount of $H_2O$ (in its standard state) required to give a $0.1N$ solution.

(90)  $\Delta E^f_{\text{diln.}}(HNO_3 + HNO_2)$

$\qquad = \Delta E_{\text{diln.}}(HNO_3 + HNO_2)[n^f(HNO_3) + n^f(HNO_2)]$ $\qquad$ $+0.01$ cal.

*Step 18.* Water (in its standard state) is added to or removed from the solution to bring the concentration of $H_2SO_4$ to the selected even concentration.

(91)  $\Delta E^f_{\text{diln.}}(H_2SO_4) = n^f(H_2SO_4)\Delta E_{\text{diln.}}(H_2SO_4)$ $\qquad\qquad\qquad$ $-0.10$ cal.

*Step 19.* The $HNO_3$ and $HNO_2$ are decomposed according to the reactions $HNO_3(\text{aq. } 0.1N) = \frac{1}{2}H_2O(\text{liq.}) + \frac{1}{2}N_2(g) + \frac{5}{4}O_2(g)$ and $HNO_2(\text{aq. } 0.1N) = \frac{1}{2}H_2O(\text{liq.}) + \frac{1}{2}N_2(g) + \frac{3}{4}O_2(g)$. The $O_2$ and $N_2$ are allowed to expand to a negligibly small pressure. The water used to make the solution in Step 17 and that formed in the decomposition reactions is brought to its standard state. The values of $\Delta E$ for the reactions are calculated from the "selected values" of the heats of formation of $HNO_3$, $HNO_2$, and $H_2O$ (16d) to be 14074 and $-6600$ cal mole$^{-1}$ at 25 °C. For the calculation of the values of $\Delta E$ for the reactions at 20° and 30 °C the temperature coefficients were estimated to be $+40$ cal mole$^{-1}$ deg$^{-1}$ for each reaction.

(92)  $\Delta E^f_{\text{decomp.}}(HNO_3 + HNO_2)$

$\qquad = \Delta E_{\text{decomp.}}(HNO_3)n^f(HNO_3) + \Delta E_{\text{decomp.}}(HNO_2)n^f(HNO_2)$ $\quad$ $+9.68$ cal.

in which equation $\Delta E_{\text{decomp.}}(HNO_3)$ and $\Delta E_{\text{decomp.}}(HNO_2)$ have the following values.

| | $\Delta E_{\text{decomp.}}(\text{HNO}_3)$ | $\Delta E_{\text{decomp.}}(\text{HNO}_2)$ |
|---|---|---|
| 20° | 13874 | $-6800$ |
| 25° | 14074 | $-6600$ |
| 30° | 14274 | $-6400$ |

*Step 20.* The gaseous phase containing $O_2$, $N_2$, $CO_2$, and $H_2O$ vapor is expanded to a negligibly small pressure. The change in internal energy is $\Delta E(\text{gas.})]_{P'(\text{gas.})}^{0} n^f(\text{gas.})$. The calorimetric data of Rossini and Frandsen (20) for the change of internal energy for the compression of $O_2$–$CO_2$ mixtures, may be presented by

$$\Delta E]_0^P = (\partial E/\partial P)_T(O_2\text{ gas.})\{1 + 1.69x(CO_2)[1 + x(CO_2)]\}P \text{ cal mole}^{-1}.$$

Values of $(\partial E/\partial P)_T(O_2\text{ gas.})$ have been given immediately preceding item 85.

(93) $\quad \Delta E^f(\text{gas.})]_{P'(\text{gas.})}^{0}$

$\quad = (\partial E/\partial P)_T(O_2\text{ gas.})\{1 + 1.69x(CO_2)[1 + x(CO_2)]\}\ P^f(\text{gas.})n^f(\text{gas.})$

$\hspace{10cm} +20.82 \text{ cal}$

*Step 21.* The $O_2$, $N_2$, $CO_2$, and $H_2O$ vapor are separated from each other, and the $CO_2$ is brought to its standard state. There is no change in internal energy in this step.

*Step 22.* The $H_2O$ vapor is compressed to its saturation pressure, $P_{\text{sat.}}(H_2O)$, condensed to liquid, and further compressed to a final pressure of 1 atm. The changes in internal energy are

$n^f(H_2O\text{ vap.})\{\Delta E(H_2O\text{ vap.})]_0^{P_{\text{sat.}}(H_2O)}$

$\hspace{4cm} - \Delta E_{\text{vap.}}(H_2O) + \Delta E(H_2O\text{ liq.})]_{P_{\text{sat.}}(H_2O)}^{1}\}.$

As in Step 1, only the vaporization term is significant.

(94) $\quad \Delta E_{\text{vap.}}^f(H_2O) = -\Delta E_{\text{vap.}}(H_2O)n^f(H_2O\text{ vap.})$ $\hspace{3cm} -4.73 \text{ cal}$

In the foregoing series of 22 steps, the calorimeter, the bomb, the $N_2$, the excess $O_2$, and the excess $H_2O$ are all returned to their original state. The net change is simply the idealized combustion reaction. The energy of the idealized combustion reaction, for the actual amount of substance involved in the combustion experiment, $n\Delta E c^\circ$ (Sub.), is therefore just the sum of the changes in internal energy for all of the steps.

(95) $\quad n\Delta E c^\circ(\text{Sub.})$, sum of items 81–94 incl. $\hspace{3cm} -7830.09 \text{ cal}$

The previous item applies to the total substance. Corrections for the auxiliary material and fuse are applied in the next three items to obtain the value for the compound alone.

(96)  $n''\Delta Ec°$ (Auxiliary material)                                          $-588.08$ cal.

(97)  $n'''\Delta Ec°$ (Fuse)                                                        $-16.09$ cal.

(98)  $n'\Delta Ec°$(Compound) $= n\Delta Ec°$(Sub.)

   $- n''\Delta Ec°$(Auxiliary material) $- n'''\Delta Ec°$(Fuse)          $-7225.92$ cal.

The quantity in item 98 is converted to units of cal g$^{-1}$ and kcal mole$^{-1}$ in the final two items.

(99)  $\dfrac{\Delta Ec°}{M}$ (Compound) $= \dfrac{n'\Delta Ec°\text{(Compound)}}{m'}$

$-8430.2$ cal g$^{-1}$

(100)  $\Delta Ec°$(Compound) $= \dfrac{n'\Delta Ec°\text{(Compound)}}{1000n'}$

$-827.54$ kcal mole$^{-1}$

For a series of experiments in which $t_h$, $P^i$(gas.), $V$(Bomb), and $m^i$(H$_2$O tot.) are held constant, and the composition of the substance varies little from experiment to experiment, certain of the items that constitute $n\Delta Ec°$(Sub.), item 95, are essentially the same for all experiments of the series. When such is the case, it is advantageous to express $\Delta Ec°$(Compound) as the sum of two arbitrarily defined quantities, $\Delta E_B$(Compound) and $\Delta E_\Sigma$.

The quantity $\Delta E_B$(Compound) may be defined as follows.

$\Delta E_B$(Compound) $= 1/n'[\mathcal{E}(\text{Calor.})(t_i - t_f + \Delta t_{corr.}) + \mathcal{E}^i(\text{Cont.})(t_i - t_h)$
$+ \mathcal{E}^f(\text{Cont.})(t_h - t_f + \Delta t_{corr.}) + \Delta E_{ign.} + \Delta E_{decomp.}(\text{HNO}_3)n^f(\text{HNO}_3)$
$+ \Delta E_{decomp.}(\text{HNO}_2)n^f(\text{HNO}_2) - n''\Delta Ec°(\text{Auxiliary material}) - n'''\Delta Ec°(\text{Fuse})]$

or, in terms of item numbers,

$\Delta E_B$(Compound) $= [\text{items } 86 + 92 - 96 - 97]/n'$.

For the limiting case in which no auxiliary material or fuse is used and no HNO$_3$ is produced, $\Delta E_B$(Compound) is simply the change of energy for the isothermal combustion reaction as it occurs under actual bomb conditions. Otherwise, $\Delta E_B$(Compound), as defined above, does not have any simple physical interpretation, but is merely an arbitrarily selected sum of terms, most of which are different for each experiment of the series and must be calculated each time.

The quantity $\Delta E_\Sigma$ is defined as a sum of terms that are essentially constant for all experiments of a series and need to be calculated only once.

$$
\begin{aligned}
\Delta E_\Sigma =\ & \Delta E_{vap.}(H_2O)n^i(H_2O \text{ vap.}) \\
& + (\partial E/\partial P)_T(H_2O \text{ liq.})n^i(H_2O \text{ liq.})[P^i(\text{gas.}) - 1] \\
& + [m'(\partial E/\partial P)_T' + m''(\partial E/\partial P)_T'' + m'''(\partial E/\partial P)_T'''][P^i(\text{gas.}) - 1] \\
& + \Delta E^*_{soln.}(O_2)n^i[(O_2 + N_2) \text{ diss.}] + (\partial E/\partial P)_T(O_2 \text{ gas.})P^i(\text{gas.})n^i(\text{gas.}) \\
& + [-\Delta E^*_{soln.}(CO_2) - 240\ N(H_2SO_4)]n^j(CO_2 \text{ diss.}) \\
& + [-\Delta E^*_{soln.}(O_2) - 280\ N(H_2SO_4)]n^j[(O_2 + N_2) \text{ diss.}] \\
& + (\partial E/\partial P)_T n^j(\text{soln.})m^j(\text{soln.})[1 - P^j(\text{gas.})] \\
& + \Delta E_{diln.}(HNO_3 + HNO_2)[n^j(HNO_3) + n^j(HNO_2)] \\
& + \Delta E_{diln.}(H_2SO_4)n^j(H_2SO_4) \\
& + (\partial E/\partial P)_T(O_2 \text{ gas.})\{1 + 1.69x(CO_2)[1 + x(CO_2)]\}P^j(\text{gas.})n^j(\text{gas.}) \\
& - \Delta E_{vap.}(H_2O)n^j(H_2O \text{ vap.})
\end{aligned}
$$

or, in terms of item numbers,

$$\Delta E_\Sigma = \text{items } 81 + 82 + 83 + 84 + 85 + 87 + 88 + 89 +$$
$$90 + 91 + 93 + 94.$$

Items 99 and 100 then become

(99)  $\Delta Ec^\circ/M(\text{Compound}) = \Delta E_B(\text{Compound})/M' + \Delta E_\Sigma/m'$

(100)  $\Delta Ec^\circ(\text{Compound}) = \Delta E_B(\text{Compound}) + \Delta E_\Sigma/n'$

If the change in the composition of the substance throughout a series is such that the variation in $\Delta E_\Sigma$ is slightly more than desirable, it is still advantageous to use items 99 and 100 as given immediately above. The quantity $\Delta E_\Sigma$ need then be calculated only for the two experiments with the extremes of composition, and interpolated values may be used for the other experiments. If the composition of the substance varies grossly throughout the series, it is necessary to make the entire calculation for each experiment, and no advantage is gained by separation of $\Delta E_\Sigma$ from the other terms.

The calculation of $\Delta Hc^\circ(\text{Compound})$ at 25°C from $\Delta Ec^\circ(\text{Compound})$ at $t_h$ is done in two steps:

(1) $\Delta Hc^\circ(\text{Compound})$ at $t_h$ is calculated from the equation

$$\Delta Hc°(\text{Compound}) = \Delta Ec°(\text{Compound}) + \Delta(PV)°$$

in which $\Delta(PV)°$ is the sum of the product of pressure and volume for each of the products less the sum of the product of pressure and volume of each of the reactants. For $P = 1$ atm, $\Delta(PV)°$ is approximately $1.987(t_h + 273.2)\Delta n$ cal, $\Delta n$ being the difference in the number of moles of gaseous products and gaseous reactants.

(2) $\Delta Hc°(\text{Compound})$ at 25°C is calculated from the equation

$$\Delta Hc°(\text{Compound}, 25°) = \Delta Hc°(\text{Compound}, t_h) + \int_{t_h}^{25} \Delta C_P \mathrm{d}t$$

in which $\Delta C_P$ is the difference of the heat capacity at constant pressure of the products and reactants. For a small temperature range, $\Delta C_P$ may be taken as constant, and the second term on the right become $+\Delta C_P(25 - t_h)$.

(e) *Comments.* In the foregoing presentation, the treatment has been given in a very general form. In its application to particular calorimetric experiments, certain simplifications will always be possible. For example, since it is a customary procedure always to charge the bomb to a certain predetermined pressure, $P^i(\text{gas.})$ will be the same for all experiments and can be introduced as a constant in items 28, 32, 34, 82, 83, and 85 of the computation form. The temperature, $t_h$, to which the isothermal bomb process is referred will be the same for all experiments in any one laboratory. Consequently, it will be a constant and the temperature variation may be taken out of all the equations.

The calibration of bomb calorimeters is usually carried out by the combustion of benzoic acid. The standard samples of benzoic acid issued by the National Bureau of Standards are certified in terms of an energy quantity, $\Delta E_B$. In the notation of this paper, $\Delta E_B$ is $[\Delta E_{\text{I.B.P.}} + \Delta E^f_{\text{decomp.}}(\text{HNO}_3 + \text{HNO}_2) + \Delta E^f_{\text{diln.}}(\text{HNO}_3 + \text{HNO}_2) - n'''\Delta Ec°(\text{Fuse})]$. If the conditions of the calibration experiment meet the specifications of the certificate with respect to the $O_2$ pressure, the ratio of the mass of sample to the volume of the bomb, and the ratio of the mass of $H_2O$ placed in the bomb to the volume of the bomb, then the certified value of $\Delta E_B$ may be used directly to compute $\varepsilon(\text{Calor.})$. If the conditions differ from those specified in the certificate, it is necessary to compute $\Delta Ec°$ for the benzoic acid and then reverse the calculations for the new conditions to obtain $\varepsilon(\text{Calor.})$ from the value of $\Delta Ec°$.

### 3. Organic nitrogen compounds of the general formula, $C_aH_bO_cN_d$.

The previous section discussed the corrections to standard states of bomb calorimetric data for sulfur compounds and gave a computation form of 100 items for use in the application of the corrections. This section treats the modifications in the items of the computation form that are necessary to make them applicable to bomb calorimetric data for nitrogen compounds. It consists of a tabulation of the necessary changes in the various items, interspersed with explanatory text.

The items that deal with the description of the substance are changed only by substitution of the symbol and atomic weight of nitrogen for those of sulfur, and the items that deal with the description of the initial state are unchanged.

Item 1, change S to N.
Items 2–6, inclusive, unchanged.
Item 7, change S to N.
Items 8–12, inclusive, unchanged.
Item 13, change S to N.
Items 14–23, inclusive, unchanged.
Item 24, change 32.066 to 14.008.
Items 25–36, inclusive, unchanged.

In the final state, the substance has reacted with $O_2$ according to the net equation,

$$C_aH_bO_cN_d + (a + b/4 - c/2)O_2 = aCO_2 + b/2H_2O + d/2N_2,$$

and the same side reactions may have occurred as in the case of sulfur compounds. As $N_2$ is a product of the combustion reaction, more is present in the final than in the initial state, and it is necessary to treat the extra $N_2$ in the final state separately from the $O_2$. (However, the approximation is retained of treating any $N_2$ initially present in the bomb as though it were $O_2$.) In the equations to follow, the extra $N_2$ in the final state is designated $N_2^*$. The final solution contains no $H_2SO_4$, but it may have a higher concentration of $HNO_3 + HNO_2$ than in the case of combustion experiments with sulfur compounds. The items that deal with the final state must be changed by (a) appropriate modification of terms that involve stoichiometry, (b) inclusion of terms to treat the $N_2^*$ separately from the $O_2 + N_2$, (c) deletion of terms that depend only on the amount or concentration of $H_2SO_4$, and (d) provision for higher concentrations of $HNO_3 + HNO_2$.

Items 37 and 38, unchanged.

Item 39, change to:  $n^J(N_2{}^*) = d/2n(\text{Sub.}) - {}^1/_2 n^J(HNO_3) - {}^1/_2 n^J(HNO_2)$.

Item 40, change second term on the right to $+b/2n(\text{Sub.})$.

Item 41, delete second term on the right.

Item 42, delete.

Item 43, unchanged.

Item 44, delete second term on the right.

Item 45, unchanged.

Item 46, delete.

Item 47, unchanged.

Item 48, delete.

Items 49, 50, and 51, unchanged.

The value of $K(CO_2)$ in item 51 for higher concentrations of $HNO_3$ + $HNO_2$ may be obtained from a plot of the following values (12)

$N(HNO_3 + HNO_2)$

| | 0.0 | 1.0 | 2.0 | 3.0 | 4.0 | 5.0 |
|---|---|---|---|---|---|---|

$K(CO_2) \times 10^4$

| | 0.0 | 1.0 | 2.0 | 3.0 | 4.0 | 5.0 |
|---|---|---|---|---|---|---|
| 20° | 390.2 | 400 | 410 | 410 | 420 | 430 |
| 25° | 340.5 | 350 | 360 | 370 | 380 | 390 |
| 30° | 296.0 | 310 | 320 | 330 | 340 | 350 |

Items 52–55, inclusive, unchanged.

Item 56, change to:  $n^J[(O_2 + N_2)\text{ tot.}] = n^i[(O_2 + N_2)\text{ tot.}] - (a + b/4 - c/2)n(\text{Sub.}) - {}^5/_4 n^J(HNO_3) - {}^3/_4 n^J(HNO_3)$.

Items 57, 58, and 59, unchanged.

Item 60, substitute $\{n^J[(O_2 + N_2)\text{ tot.}] + n^J(N_2{}^*)\}$ for $n^J[(O_2 + N_2)\text{ tot.}]$ on the right side of the equation.

Item 61, unchanged.

Item 62, add to the right side of the equation the term, $+n^J(N_2{}^*)$.

Item 63, unchanged.

Two new items are required to list the mole fractions of $O_2 + N_2$ and $N_2{}^*$ in the gaseous mixture.

(63a)   $x(O_2 + N_2) = n^J[(O_2 + N_2)\text{gas}]/n^J(\text{gas.})$

(63b)   $x(N_2{}^*) = n^J(N_2{}^*)/n^J(\text{gas.})$

Items 64–70, inclusive, unchanged.

The values of $g$ in item 66, of $(\partial E/\partial P)_T{}^J(\text{soln.})$ in item 69, and of $\Delta E_{\text{diln.}}(HNO_3 + HNO_2)$ in item 70 for higher concentrations of $HNO_3$ and $HNO_2$ may be obtained from plots of the following values (9a, 9b, 16a).

| wt. % ($HNO_3 + HNO_2$) | | | | | |
|---|---|---|---|---|---|
| 0 | 5 | 10 | 15 | 20 | 25 |

g

| | | | | | |
|---|---|---|---|---|---|
| 1.000 | 0.972 | 0.944 | 0.910 | 0.867 | 0.808 |

$(\partial E/\partial P)_T{}^f$(soln.) $\times 10^5$, cal g$^{-1}$ atm$^{-1}$

| | 0 | 5 | 10 | 15 | 20 | 25 |
|---|---|---|---|---|---|---|
| 20° | $-147$ | $-198$ | $-242$ | $-280$ | $-316$ | $-350$ |
| 25° | $-186$ | $-230$ | $-268$ | $-303$ | $-336$ | $-368$ |
| 30° | $-222$ | $-261$ | $-293$ | $-325$ | $-356$ | $-387$ |

$\Delta E_{\text{diln.}}$($HNO_3 + HNO_2$), cal mole$^{-1}$

| | 0 | 5 | 10 | 15 | 20 | 25 |
|---|---|---|---|---|---|---|
| 20° | $+84$ | $-7$ | $+22$ | $+19$ | $-30$ | $-118$ |
| 25° | $+102$ | $-41$ | $-36$ | $-59$ | $-126$ | $-232$ |
| 30° | $+120$ | $-75$ | $-94$ | $-137$ | $-222$ | $-346$ |

Item 71, delete.

Items 72–75, inclusive, unchanged.

Item 76, add to the right of the equation the term, $+C_V(N_2)n^f(N_2{}^*)$. Values of $C_V(N_2)$ are 4.998, 4.996, and 4.995 cal deg$^{-1}$ mole$^{-1}$ at 20°, 25°, and 30°C.

Items 77–86, inclusive, unchanged.

Item 87, change the term in brackets on the right to

$$[-\Delta E^*{}_{\text{soln.}}(CO_2) - 200N(HNO_3 + HNO_2)].$$

Item 88, change the term in brackets on the right to

$$[-\Delta E^*{}_{\text{soln.}}(O_2) - 530N(HNO_3 + HNO_2)].$$

The variation of $\Delta E_{\text{soln.}}(CO_2)$ and $\Delta E_{\text{soln.}}(O_2)$ with acid concentration is based on Geffcken's (12) data for the solubility of $CO_2$ and $O_2$ in $HNO_3$ solutions as a function of temperature. The assumption that this variation is independent of temperature is made to obtain the equations given above.

Items 89 and 90, unchanged.

Item 91, delete.

Item 92, unchanged.

Item 93, change to: $\Delta E^f(\text{gas.})\big]{}^{0}_{P^f(\text{gas.})} = (\partial E/\partial P)_T(O_2 \text{ gas})\{x(O_2 + N_2)$

$\qquad + \; 0.908x(N_2{}^*) + 2.691x(CO_2) + 1.69[x(CO_2)]^2\} P^f(\text{gas.})n^f(\text{gas.}).$

Items 94–100 inclusive, unchanged.

## 4. Organic chlorine compounds of the general formula, $C_aH_bO_cCl_d$.

The techniques of combustion bomb calorimetry for chlorine and bromine compounds are similar. In each case, a solution of a reducing agent must be present initially in the bomb to insure the complete reduction of the halogen to the $-1$ oxidation state. The reducing agents that are commonly used for this purpose are hydrazine dihydrochloride and arsenious oxide. This section treats the corrections to standard states of bomb calorimetric data for chlorine compounds when hydrazine dihydrochloride is used as the reducing agent. The next section treats the corresponding corrections for bromine compounds when arsenious oxide is used as the reducing agent. Treatments for the other two cases of interest, namely, chlorine compound with arsenious oxide as the reducing agent and bromine compounds with hydrazine dihydrochloride as the reducing agent, may be obtained readily from the treatments given in this and the next section.

As in the previous section, the presentation here is given as a tabulation, with interspersed explanatory text, of the necessary modifications in the computation form for sulfur compounds. However, a critical selection is not made of all of the numerical quantities that enter into the corrections, as reliable experimental values for some of the quantities are lacking.

The equation of the idealized combustion reaction is

$$C_aH_bO_cCl_d(c \text{ or liq.}) + (a + b/4 - c/2 - d/4)O_2(g)$$

$$+ (nd - b/2 + d/2)H_2O(\text{liq.}) = aCO_2(g) + d(HCl \cdot nH_2O)(\text{liq.}).$$

The standard states for hydrochloric acid solution and hydrazine dihydrochloride solution are the liquids at specified concentrations under a pressure of 1 atm.

The items that deal with the description of the substance are changed only by substitution of the symbol and atomic weight of chlorine for those of sulfur.

Item 1, change S to Cl.
Items 2–6, inclusive, unchanged.
Item 7, change S to Cl.
Items 8–12, inclusive, unchanged.
Item 13, change S to Cl.
Items 14–23, inclusive, unchanged.
Item 24, change 32.066 to 35.457.
Item 25, unchanged.

Some of the items that deal with the initial state are changed because the liquid added to the bomb is $N_2H_4 \cdot 2HCl$ solution and not pure water.

Item 26, unchanged.

Item 27, change to $V^i$(soln.), the volume, in liters, of $N_2H_4 \cdot 2HCl$ solution introduced into the bomb.

Item 28, unchanged.

Item 29 is replaced by five new items that relate to the initial solution.

(29*)  $C^i$(soln.), the concentration of $N_2H_4 \cdot 2HCl$ in the initial solution in moles liter$^{-1}$.

(29a)  $n^i(N_2H_4.2HCl) = C^i$(soln.)$V^i$(soln.), the number of moles of $N_2H_4 \cdot 2HCl$ initially in the bomb.

(29b)  $\rho^i$(soln.), the density of the initial solution in g liter$^{-1}$.

(29c*)  $g^i$, the ratio of the vapor pressure of $H_2O$ over the initial solution to that over pure $H_2O$.

(29d*)  $K^i(O_2)$, the solubility of $O_2$ in the initial bomb solution in moles per liter of solution per atm $O_2$ partial pressure.

Item 30, change to:

$$n^i(H_2O \text{ tot.}) = [V^i(\text{soln.})\rho^i(\text{soln.}) - 104.978 n^i(N_2H_4 \cdot 2HCl)]/18.016.$$

Item 31, change second term on the right to $-V^i$(soln.).

Item 32, change to:  $n^i(H_2O \text{ vap.}) = g^i[C_0 + \alpha P^i(\text{gas.})]V^i(\text{gas.})/18.016.$

The changes in the amount, concentration, and properties of the initial solution from the vaporization of the small amount, $n^i(H_2O$ vap.), of water are neglected.

Item 33, delete.

Item 34, unchanged.

Item 35, change to:  $n^i[(O_2 + N_2) \text{ diss.}] = K^i(O_2)V^i(\text{soln.})[P^i(\text{gas.}) - P^i(H_2O \text{ vap.})].$

Item 36, unchanged.

The stoichiometry of the bomb process is the same as if the substance reacted with $O_2$ according to the equation,

$$C_aH_bO_cCl_d + (a + b/4 - c/2 - d/4)O_2 = aCO_2 + (b/2 - d/2)H_2O + dHCl,$$

and side reactions occurred according to the equations,

$$N_2H_4 \cdot 2HCl + O_2 = N_2 + 2H_2O + 2HCl,$$

$$N_2H_4 \cdot 2HCl + H_2O = 2NH_4Cl + 1/2O_2,$$

and

$$1/2N_2 + 5/4O_2 + 1/2H_2O = HNO_3$$

Nitrous acid is not formed in thermally significant amounts. As $N_2$ is a product of the bomb process, more is present in the final than in the initial state, and it is necessary to treat the extra $N_2$ in the final state separately from the $O_2$. The extra $N_2$ in the final state is designated $N_2^*$. The final solution contains $N_2H_4 \cdot 2HCl$, HCl, $NH_4Cl$, and $HNO_3$ instead of $H_2SO_4$, $HNO_3$, and $HNO_2$. The items that deal with the final state must be changed by (a) appropriate modification of terms that involve stoichiometry, (b) inclusion of terms to treat the $N_2^*$ separately from the $O_2 + N_2$, (c) deletion of terms that depend only on the amounts or concentrations of $H_2SO_4$ and $HNO_2$, and (d) inclusion of the necessary terms that depend on the amounts or concentrations of $N_2H_4 \cdot 2HCl$, HCl, and $NH_4Cl$.

Item 37, unchanged.

Item 38 is replaced by two new items.

(38*)    $n^f(N_2H_4 \cdot 2HCl)$, the number of moles of $N_2H_4 \cdot 2HCl$ in the final solution, as determined by chemical analysis.

(38a*)    $n^f(NH_4Cl)$, the number of moles of $NH_4Cl$ in the final solution, as determined by chemical analysis.

Item 39, change to:   $n^f(HCl) = dn(\text{Sub.}) + 2[n^i(N_2H_4 \cdot 2HCl) - n^f(N_2H_4 \cdot 2HCl)] - n^f(NH_4Cl)$.

Item 40, change to:   $n^f(H_2O \text{ liq.}) = n^i(H_2O \text{ tot.}) + (b/2 - d/2)n(\text{Sub.}) + 2[n^i(N_2H_4 \cdot 2HCl) - n^f(N_2H_4 \cdot 2HCl)] - {}^3/_2 n^f(NH_4Cl) - {}^1/_2 n^f(HNO_3) - n^i(H_2O \text{ vap.})$.

Item 41, change to:   $m^f(\text{soln.}) = 18.016 n^f(H_2O \text{ liq.}) + 36.465 n'(HCl) + 105 n^f (N_2H_4 \cdot 2HCl) + 53.5 n^f(NH_4Cl) + 63 n^f(HNO_3)$.

Item 42 is replaced by three new items.

(42)    wt. % $(N_2H_4 \cdot 2HCl) = 10498 n^f(N_2H_4 \cdot 2HCl)/m^f(\text{soln.})$

(42a)    wt. %(HCl) $= 3646 n^f(HCl)/m^f(\text{soln.})$

(42b)    wt. %($NH_4Cl$) $= 5350 n^f(NH_4Cl)/m^f(\text{soln.})$

Item 43, change to:   wt. %($HNO_3$) $= 6302 n^f(HNO_3)/m^f(\text{soln.})$.

Item 44, change to:   $\rho^f(\text{soln.})$, the density of the final solution in g liter$^{-1}$.

There are density data from the I.C.T. (9c) which, though incomplete, will aid in estimating $\rho^i(\text{soln.})$ of item 29b and $\rho^f(\text{soln.})$ of the preceding item.

Item 45, unchanged.

Item 46, change to:   $n^f(N_2^*) = n^i(N_2H_4 \cdot 2HCl) - n^f(N_2H_4 \cdot 2HCl) - {}^1/_2 n^f(NH_4Cl) - {}^1/_2 n^f(HNO_3)$.

Item 47, change to:   $N(HNO_3) = n^f(HNO_3)/V^f(\text{soln.})$

Item 48 is replaced by a tabulation of the mole ratios of solutes to $H_2O$ in the following solutions: Soln. I, the solution remaining after removal of $O_2 + N_2$, $CO_2$, and $HNO_3$ from the final bomb solution; Soln. II, the solution remaining after $dn$(Sub.) moles of HCl is removed from Soln. I; Soln. III, the solution remaining after the $NH_4Cl$ in Soln. II is oxidized with $O_2$ gas to $N_2H_4 \cdot 2HCl$ and $H_2O$; and Soln. IV, the solution remaining after $n^J(N_2{}^*) + \frac{1}{2} n^J(HNO_3)$ moles of $N_2$ gas react with HCl and $H_2O$ in Soln. III to produce $N_2H_4 \cdot 2HCl$ and liberate $O_2$ gas.

(48)

| Soln. | $N_2H_4 \cdot 2HCl$ | HCl | $NH_4Cl$ |
|---|---|---|---|
| I | $\dfrac{n^J(N_2H_4 \cdot 2HCl)}{n^J(H_2O\ \text{liq.})}$ | $\dfrac{n^J(HCl)}{n^J(H_2O\ \text{liq.})}$ | $\dfrac{n^J(NH_4Cl)}{n^J(H_2O\ \text{liq.})}$ |
| II | $\dfrac{n^J(N_2H_4 \cdot 2HCl)}{n^J(H_2O\ \text{liq.})}$ | $\dfrac{n^J(HCl) - dn(\text{Sub.})}{n^J(H_2O\ \text{liq.})}$ | $\dfrac{n^J(NH_4Cl)}{n^J(H_2O\ \text{liq.})}$ |
| III | $\dfrac{n^J(N_2H_4 \cdot 2HCl) + \frac{1}{2}n^J(NH_4Cl)}{n^J(H_2O\ \text{liq.}) + \frac{1}{2}n^J(NH_4Cl)}$ | $\dfrac{n^J(HCl) - dn(\text{Sub.})}{n^J(H_2O\ \text{liq.}) + \frac{1}{2}n^J(NH_4Cl)}$ | $0$ |
| IV | $\dfrac{n^i(N_2H_4 \cdot 2HCl)}{n^J(H_2O\ \text{liq.}) + \frac{1}{2}n^J(NH_4Cl) - 2n^J(N_2{}^*) - n^J(HNO_3)}$ | $0$ | $0$ |

Items 49 and 50, unchanged.

Item 51, change to: $K(CO_2)$, the solubility of $CO_2$ in the final solution in moles per liter of solution at unit fugacity (in atm) of $CO_2$ gas.

Items 52–55, inclusive, unchanged.

Item 56, change to: $n^J[(O_2 + N_2)\text{tot.}] = n^i([O_2 + N_2)\text{tot.}] - \frac{5}{4}n^J(HNO_3) - (a + b/4 - c/2 - d/4)n(\text{Sub.}) - n^i(N_2H_4 \cdot 2HCl) + n^J(N_2H_4 \cdot 2HCl) + \frac{3}{4}n^J(NH_4Cl)$

Item 57, change to: $K^J(O_2)$, the solubility of $O_2$ in the final bomb solution in moles per liter of solution at unit fugacity (in atm) of $O_2$ gas.

Items 58 and 59, unchanged.

Item 60, substitute $\{n^J[(O_2 + N_2)\text{tot.}] + n^J(N_2{}^*)\}$ for $n^J[(O_2 + N_2)\text{tot.}]$ on the right side of the equation.

Item 61, unchanged.

Item 62, add to the right side of the equation the term, $+n^J(N_2{}^*)$.

Item 63, unchanged.

Two new items are required to list the mole fractions of $O_2 + N_2$ and $N_2{}^*$ in the gaseous mixture.

(63a)  $x(O_2 + N_2) = n^J[(O_2 + N_2)\ \text{gas}]/n^J(\text{gas.})$

(63b)  $x(N_2{}^*) = n^J(N_2{}^*)/n^J(\text{gas.})$

Items 64 and 65, unchanged.

Item 66, change to: $g'$, the ratio of the vapor pressure of $H_2O$ over the final solution to that over pure $H_2O$.

Item 67, substitute $g'$ for $g$ on the right side of the equation.

The concentration of HCl in the gaseous mixture is thermally negligible if the concentration in the solution is less than 18 wt.%.

Item 68, unchanged.

The values of $(\partial E/\partial P)_T$ in cal g$^{-1}$ atm$^{-1}$ must be listed for both the initial and final bomb solutions in item 69.

(69)  $(\partial E/\partial P)_T{}^i(\text{soln.}) = -24.22(t_h + 273.2)(\partial V/\partial T)_P{}^i(\text{soln.})$
      $(\partial E/\partial P)_T{}^f(\text{soln.}) = -24.22(t_h + 273.2)(\partial V/\partial T)_P{}^f(\text{soln.})$

Item 70, change to $\Delta E_{\text{diln.}}(\text{HNO}_3)$.

Item 71 is replaced by seven new items.

(71)    $\Delta E'_{\text{soln.}}(O_2 + N_2)$, the change of internal energy in cal mole$^{-1}$ at $t_h$ for the solution of $O_2 + N_2$ in the initial bomb solution.

(71a)   $\Delta E''_{\text{soln.}}(O_2 + N_2)$, the change of internal energy in cal mole$^{-1}$ at $t_h$ for the solution of $O_2 + N_2$ in the final bomb solution.

(71b)   $\Delta E''_{\text{soln.}}(CO_2)$, the change of internal energy in cal mole$^{-1}$ at $t_h$ for the solution of $CO_2$ in the final bomb solution.

(71c)   $\Delta E_{\text{diln.}}(\text{HCl})$, the change of internal energy in cal mole$^{-1}$ at $t_h$ for the transfer of HCl from Soln. I to pure $H_2O$ to produce Soln. II and HCl$\cdot$ $nH_2O$ when all four liquids are under a pressure of 1 atm.

(71d)   $\Delta E_{\text{oxid.}}(\text{NH}_4\text{Cl})$, the change of internal energy in cal mole$^{-1}$ at $t_h$ for the reaction of $NH_4Cl$ in Soln. II with $O_2$ gas in its standard state according to the equation, $NH_4Cl + {}^1/_4O_2 = {}^1/_2N_2H_4\cdot2HCl + {}^1/_2H_2O$, to produce $N_2H_4\cdot2HCl$ and $H_2O$ in Soln. III when both Soln. II and III are under a pressure of 1 atm.

(71e)   $\Delta E_{\text{red.}}(\text{N}_2{}^*)$, the change of internal energy in cal mole$^{-1}$ at $t_h$ for the reaction of $N_2$ gas in its standard state with $H_2O$ and HCl in Soln. III according to the equation, $N_2 + 2H_2O + 2HCl = N_2H_4\cdot2HCl + O_2$, to produce $N_2H_4\cdot2HCl$ in Soln. IV and $O_2$ gas in its standard state when both Soln. III and IV are under a pressure of 1 atm.

(71f)   $\Delta E_{\text{diln.}}(\text{N}_2\text{H}_4\cdot2\text{HCl})$, the change of internal energy in cal per mole of $N_2H_4\cdot2HCl$ at $t_h$ for the removal of liquid $H_2O$ in its standard state from Soln. IV to bring its concentration to $C^i(\text{soln.})$ when the solution is under a pressure of 1 atm.

Items 72, 73, and 74, unchanged.

Item 75, replace the second term on the right with $+A^i[V^i(\text{soln.})\rho^i(\text{soln.})]$ in which $A^i$ is the heat capacity, $C_P$, in cal g$^{-1}$ deg$^{-1}$, of the initial bomb solution under a pressure of 30 atm.

Item 76, replace the third term on the right with $+A^f[m^f(\text{soln.}) + 18n^f(\text{H}_2\text{O vap.})]$ $+ C_V(N_2)n^f(N_2{}^*)$, in which $A^f$ is the heat capacity, $C_P$, in cal g$^{-1}$ deg$^{-1}$, of the final bomb solution under a pressure of 30 atm, and $C_V(N_2)$ has values given for item 76, section 3.

Items 77–81, unchanged.

Item 82, change to:

$$\Delta E^i(\text{soln.})\Big]_1^{P^i(\text{gas.})} = (\partial E/\partial P)_T{}^i(\text{soln.})V^i(\text{soln.})\rho^i(\text{soln.})[P^i(\text{gas.}) - 1].$$

Item 83, unchanged.

Item 84, change to: $\Delta E^i_{\text{soln.}}(O_2 + N_2) = \Delta E'_{\text{soln.}}(O_2 + N_2)n^i[(O_2 + N_2) \text{ diss.}].$

Items 85 and 86, unchanged.

Item 87, change to: $\Delta E_{\text{soln.}}(CO_2) = -\Delta E''_{\text{soln.}}(CO_2)n^f(CO_2 \text{ diss.}).$

Item 88, change to: $\Delta E'_{\text{soln.}}(O_2 + N_2) = -E''_{\text{soln.}}(O_2 + N_2)n^f[(O_2 + N_2) \text{ diss.}].$

Item 89, unchanged.

Item 90, change to: $\Delta E^f_{\text{diln.}}(HNO_3) = \Delta E_{\text{diln.}}(HNO_3)n^f(HNO_3).$

## Item 91 is replaced by four new items.

(91) $\quad \Delta E^f_{\text{diln.}}(HCl) = \Delta E_{\text{diln.}}(HCl)dn(\text{sub.})$

(91a) $\quad \Delta E^f_{\text{oxid.}}(NH_4Cl) = \Delta E_{\text{oxid.}}(NH_4Cl)n^f(NH_4Cl)$

(91b) $\quad \Delta E_{\text{red.}}(N_2*) = \Delta E_{\text{red.}}(N_2*)[n^f(N_2*) + \frac{1}{2}n^f(HNO_3)]$

(91c) $\quad \Delta E^f_{\text{diln.}}(N_2H_4 \cdot 2HCl) = \Delta E_{\text{diln.}}(N_2H_4 \cdot 2HCl)n^i(N_2H_4 \cdot 2HCl)$

Item 92, change to: $\Delta E^f_{\text{decomp.}}(HNO_3) = \Delta E_{\text{decomp.}}(HNO_3)n^f(HNO_3).$

Item 93, change to: $\Delta E^f(\text{gas.})\big]_{P^f(\text{gas.})}^0 = (\partial E/\partial P)_T(O_2 \text{ gas})\{x(O_2 + N_2) + 0.908x(N_2*) + 2.691x(CO_2) + 1.69[x(CO_2)]^2\}P^f(\text{gas.})n^f(\text{gas.}).$

Items 94–100, inclusive, unchanged.

If it is desired to express the idealized combustion reaction with elemental chlorine and water as products instead of $HCl \cdot nH_2O$, i.e.,

$C_aH_bO_cCl_d(\text{c or liq.}) + (a + b/4 - c/2)O_2(g) = aCO_2(g) + b/2H_2O$ (liq.) $+ d/2Cl_2(g)$, then it is necessary to add to $\Delta Ec^\circ$ in item 100 the quantity $d\Delta E^\circ_{\text{oxid.}}(HCl)$, the value of $\Delta E^\circ$ for the reaction.

$$d(HCl \cdot nH_2O)(\text{liq.}) + d/4O_2(g) = d(n + \frac{1}{2})H_2O(\text{liq.}) + d/2Cl_2(g).$$

Values of $\Delta E^\circ_{\text{oxid.}}(HCl)$ are tabulated below as a function of $n(16f)$.

$\Delta E^\circ_{\text{oxid.}}(HCl)$, kcal mole$^{-1}$

| $n$ | 20° | 25° | 30° |
|-----|-----|-----|-----|
| 20 | +4.754 | +4.911 | +5.068 |
| 30 | 4.938 | 5.106 | 5.274 |
| 40 | 5.035 | 5.209 | 5.383 |
| 50 | 5.091 | 5.270 | 5.449 |
| 75 | 5.172 | 5.358 | 5.544 |
| 100 | 5.216 | 5.406 | 5.596 |
| 200 | 5.293 | 5.491 | 5.689 |
| 300 | 5.329 | 5.530 | 5.731 |
| 400 | 5.349 | 5.552 | 5.755 |
| 500 | 5.362 | 5.567 | 5.772 |
| 700 | 5.381 | 5.588 | 5.795 |

In the foregoing, no reference has been made to corrections for corrosion of the bomb or fittings by the combustion gases, because such corrections are specific for the particular materials of construction that are used. However, if corrosion of platinum occurs, $Pt + 6HCl + O_2 = H_2PtCl_6 + 2H_2O$, and the chloroplatinic acid is subsequently mixed with the bomb solution, as in the moving bomb method, so that it is reduced, $H_2PtCl_6 + N_2H_4 \cdot 2HCl = Pt + N_2 + 8HCl$, then the net change is merely the oxidation of more of the reducing agent, $N_2H_4 \cdot 2HCl + O_2 = N_2 + 2H_2O + 2HCl$, and no special correction is required.

**5. Organic bromine compounds of the general formula, $C_aH_bO_cBr_d$.** This section treats the corrections to standard states of bomb calorimetric data for bromine compounds when arsenious acid is used as the reducing agent in the bomb solution. The presentation, as in the two previous sections, is given as a tabulation, with interspersed explanatory text, of the necessary modifications in the computation form for sulfur compounds. A critical selection is not made of all of the numerical quantities that enter into the corrections, as reliable experimental values for some of the quantities are lacking.

The equation of the idealized combustion reaction is

$$C_aH_bO_cBr_d(c \text{ or liq.}) + (a + b/4 - c/2 - d/4)O_2(g)$$
$$+ (nd - b/2 + d/2)H_2O \text{ (liq.)} = aCO_2(g) + d(HBr \cdot nH_2O)(\text{liq.}).$$

The standard states for hydrobromic acid solution and arsenious acid solution are the liquids at specified concentrations under a pressure of 1 atm.

The items that deal with the description of the substance are changed only by substitution of the symbol and atomic weight of bromine for those of sulfur.

Item 1, change S to Br.
Items 2–6, inclusive, unchanged.
Item 7, change S to Br.
Items 8–12, inclusive, unchanged.
Item 13, change S to Br.
Items 14–23, inclusive, unchanged.
Item 24, change 32.066 to 79.916.
Item 25, unchanged.

Some of the items that deal with the initial state are changed because the liquid added to the bomb is $As_2O_3$ solution and not pure water.

Item 26, unchanged.

Item 27, change to $V^i$(soln.), the volume, in liters, of $As_2O_3$ solution introduced into the bomb.

Item 28, unchanged.

Item 29 is replaced by five new items that relate to the initial solution.

(29*) $C^i$(soln.), the concentration of $As_2O_3$ in the initial solution in moles liter$^{-1}$.

(29a) $n^i(As_2O_3) = C^i$(soln.)$V^i$(soln.), the number of moles of $As_2O_3$ initially in the bomb.

(29b) $\rho^i$(soln.), the density of the initial solution in g liter$^{-1}$

(29c*) $g^i$, the ratio of the vapor pressure of $H_2O$ over the initial solution to that over pure water.

(29d*) $K^i(O_2)$, the solubility of $O_2$ in the initial bomb solution in moles per liter$^{-1}$ of solution per atm $O_2$ partial pressure.

Item 30, change to: $n^i(H_2O$ tot.) $=$
$[V^i$(soln.)$\rho^i$(soln.) $-$ 197.82$n^i(As_2O_3)]/18.016$.

Item 31, change second term on the right to $- V^i$(soln.).

Item 32, change to:

$$n^i(H_2O \text{ vap.}) = g^i[C_0 + \alpha P^i(\text{gas.})] V^i(\text{gas.})/18.016.$$

The changes in the amount, concentration, and properties of the initial solution from the vaporization of the small amount, $n^i(H_2O$ vap.), of water are neglected.

Item 33, delete.

Item 34, unchanged.

Item 35, change to:

$$n^i[(O_2 + N_2) \text{ diss.}] = K^i(O_2)V^i(\text{soln.})[P^i(\text{gas.}) - P^i(H_2O \text{ vap.})].$$

Item 36, unchanged.

The stoichiometry of the bomb process is the same as if the substance reacted with $O_2$ according to the equation,

$$C_aH_bO_cBr_d + (a + b/4 - c/2 - d/4)O_2 = aCO_2 + (b/2 - d/2)H_2O + dHBr,$$

and side reactions occurred according to the equations,

$$As_2O_3 + O_2 = As_2O_5$$

and

$$^1/_2N_2 + {}^5/_4O_2 + {}^1/_2H_2O = HNO_3.$$

Nitrous acid is not formed in thermally significant amounts. The final solution contains $As_2O_3$, $As_2O_5$, HBr, and $HNO_3$ instead of $H_2SO_4$,

$HNO_3$, and $HNO_2$. The items that deal with the final state must be changed by (a) appropriate modifications of terms that involve stoichiometry, (b) deletion of terms that depend only on the amounts or concentrations of $H_2SO_4$ and $HNO_2$, and (c) inclusion of the necessary terms that depend on the amounts or concentrations of $As_2O_3$, $As_2O_5$, and HBr.

Item 37, unchanged.

## Item 38 is replaced by two new items.

(38*)  $n^f(As_2O_3)$, the number of moles of $As_2O_3$ in the final solution, as determined by chemical analysis.

(38a)  $n^f(As_2O_5) = n^i(As_2O_3) - n^f(As_2O_3)$, the number of moles of $As_2O_5$ in the final solution.

Item 39, change to:  $n^f(HBr) = dn(Sub.)$
Item 40, change to:  $n^f(H_2O \text{ liq.}) = n^i(H_2O \text{ tot.}) + (b/2 - d/2)n(Sub.)$
 $- \frac{1}{2} n^f(HNO_3) - n^i(H_2O \text{ vap.})$.
Item 41, change to:  $m^f(\text{soln.}) = 18.016n^f(H_2O \text{ liq.}) + 80.924n^f(HBr)$
 $+ 197.82 n^f(As_2O_3) + 229.82n^f(As_2O_5) + 63n^f(HNO_3)$.

## Item 42 is replaced by three new items.

(42)  wt. %(HBr) $= 8092n^f(HBr)/m^f(\text{soln.})$
(42a)  wt.%($As_2O_3$) $= 19782n^f(As_2O_3)/m^f(\text{soln.})$
(42b)  wt.%($As_2O_5$) $= 22982n^f(As_2O_5)/m^f(\text{soln.})$

Item 43, change to:  wt.%($HNO_3$) $= 6302n^f(HNO_3)/m^f(\text{soln.})$.
Item 44, change to:  $\rho^f(\text{soln.})$, the density of the final solution in g liter$^{-1}$

There are density data in the I.C.T. (9d) which, though incomplete, will aid in estimating $\rho^i(\text{soln.})$ of item 29b and $\rho^f(\text{soln.})$ of the preceding item.

Item 45, unchanged.
Item 46, delete.
Item 47, change to:  $N(HNO_3) = n^f(HNO_3)/V^f(\text{soln.})$.

Item 48 is replaced by a tabulation of the mole ratios of solutes to $H_2O$ in the following solutions:  Soln. I, the solution remaining after removal of $O_2 + N_2$, $CO_2$, and $HNO_3$ from the final bomb solution; Soln. II, the solution remaining after the HBr is removed from Soln. I; and Soln. III, the solution remaining after the $As_2O_5$ in Soln. II is decomposed to $As_2O_3$ with the liberation of $O_2$ gas.

(48)

| Soln. | $As_2O_3$ | $As_2O_5$ | HBr |
|---|---|---|---|
| I | $\dfrac{n^f(As_2O_3)}{n^f(H_2O\ liq.)}$ | $\dfrac{n^f(As_2O_5)}{n^f(H_2O\ liq.)}$ | $\dfrac{n^f(HBr)}{n^f(H_2O\ liq.)}$ |
| II | $\dfrac{n^f(As_2O_3)}{n^f(H_2O\ liq.)}$ | $\dfrac{n^f(As_2O_5)}{n^f(H_2O\ liq.)}$ | 0 |
| III | $\dfrac{n^i(As_2O_3)}{n^f(H_2O\ liq.)}$ | 0 | 0 |

Items 49 and 50, unchanged.

Item 51, change to: $K(CO_2)$, the solubility of $CO_2$ in the final bomb solution in moles per liter of solution at unit fugacity (in atmospheres) of $CO_2$ gas.

Items 52–55, inclusive, unchanged.

Item 56, change to: $n^f[(O_2 + N_2)\ tot.] = n^i[(O_2 + N_2)\ tot.] - \frac{7}{4}n^f(HNO_3) - (a + b/4 - c/2 - d/4)n(Sub.) - n^f(As_2O_5)$.

Item 57, change to: $K^f(O_2)$, the solubility of $O_2$ in the final bomb solution in moles per liter of solution at unit fugacity (in atm.) of $O_2$ gas.

Items 58–65, inclusive, unchanged.

Item 66, change to: $g^f$, the ratio of the vapor pressure of $H_2O$ over the final solution to that over pure $H_2O$.

Item 67, substitute $g^f$ for $g$ on the right side of the equation.

Item 68, unchanged.

The values of $(\partial E/\partial P)_T$, in cal g$^{-1}$ atm$^{-1}$ must be listed for both the initial and final bomb solutions in item 69.

(69)  $(\partial E/\partial P)_T{}^i(soln.) = -24.22(t_h + 273.2)(\partial V/\partial T)_P{}^i(soln.)$
$(\partial E/\partial P)_T{}^f(soln.) = -24.22(t_h + 273.2)(\partial V/\partial T)_P{}^f(soln.)$

Item 70, change to $\Delta E_{diln.}(HNO_3)$.

Item 71, is replaced by six new items.

(71)  $\Delta E'_{soln.}(O_2 + N_2)$, the change of internal energy in cal mole$^{-1}$ at $t_h$ for the solution of $O_2 + N_2$ in the initial bomb solution.

(71a)  $\Delta E_{soln.}(O_2 + N_2)$, the change of internal energy in cal mole$^{-1}$ at $t_h$ for the solution of $O_2 + N_2$ in the final bomb solution.

(71b)  $\Delta E''_{soln.}(CO_2)$, the change of internal energy in cal mole$^{-1}$ at $t_h$ for the solution of $CO_2$ in the final bomb solution.

(71c)  $\Delta E_{diln.}(HBr)$, the change of internal energy in cal mole$^{-1}$ at $t_h$ for the transfer of HBr from Soln. I to pure $H_2O$ to produce Soln. II and HBr·$n$·$H_2O$ when all four liquids are under a pressure of 1 atm.

(71d)  $\Delta E_{decomp.}(As_2O_5)$, the change of internal energy in cal mole$^{-1}$ at $t_h$ for the decomposition of $As_2O_5$ in Soln. II to $As_2O_3$ in Soln. III and $O_2$ gas in its standard state when both solutions are under a pressure of 1 atm.

(71e)  $\Delta E_{diln.}(As_2O_3)$, the change of internal energy in cal per mole of $As_2O_3$ at $t_h$ for the removal of liquid $H_2O$ in its standard state from Soln. III to bring its concentration to $C^i$(soln.), when the solution is under a pressure of 1 atm.

Items 72, 73, and 74, unchanged.

Item 75, replace the second term on the right with $+A^i[V^i(\text{soln.})\rho^i(\text{soln.})]$ in which $A^i$ is the heat capacity, $C_P$, in cal g$^{-1}$ deg$^{-1}$, of the initial bomb solution under a pressure of 30 atm.

Item 76, replace $A$ with $A^f$ in the third term on the right. $A^f$ is the heat capacity, $C_P$, in cal g$^{-1}$ deg$^{-1}$, of the final bomb solution under a pressure of 30 atm.

Items 77–81, unchanged.

Item 82, change to: $\Delta E^i(\text{soln.})\Big]_1^{P^i(\text{gas.})} =$
$(\partial E/\partial P)_T{}^i(\text{soln.})V^i(\text{soln.})\rho^i(\text{soln.})[P^i\,(\text{gas.}) - 1]$.

Item 83, unchanged.

Item 84, change to: $\Delta E^i_{\text{soln.}}(O_2 + N_2) = \Delta E'_{\text{soln.}}(O_2 + N_2)n^i[(O_2 + N_2)\,\text{diss.}]$.

Items 85 and 86, unchanged.

Item 87, change to: $\Delta E^f_{\text{soln.}}(CO_2) = -\Delta E''_{\text{soln.}}(CO_2)n^f(CO_2\,\text{diss.})$

Item 88, change to: $\Delta E^f_{\text{soln.}}(O_2 + N_2) = -\Delta E''_{\text{soln.}}(O_2 + N_2)n^f[(O_2 + N_2)\,\text{diss.}]$

Item 89, unchanged.

Item 90, change to: $\Delta E^f_{\text{diln.}}(HNO_3) = \Delta E_{\text{diln.}}(HNO_3)n^f(HNO_3)$

Item 91 is replaced by three new items.

(91)   $\Delta E^f_{\text{diln.}}(HBr) = \Delta E_{\text{diln.}}(HBr)n^f(HBr)$
(91a)  $\Delta E^f_{\text{decomp.}}(As_2O_5) = \Delta E_{\text{decomp.}}(As_2O_5)n^f(As_2O_5)$
(91b)  $\Delta E^f_{\text{diln.}}(As_2O_5) = \Delta E_{\text{diln.}}(As_2O_3)n^i(As_2O_3)$

Item 92, change to: $\Delta E^f_{\text{decomp.}}(HNO_3) = \Delta E_{\text{decomp.}}(HNO_3)n^f(HNO_3)$.
Items 93–100, inclusive, unchanged.

If it is desired to express the idealized combustion reaction with elemental bromine and water as products instead of HBr·$n$H$_2$O, i.e., $C_aH_bO_cBr_d$(c or liq.) $+ (a + b/4 - c/2)O_2(g) = aCO_2(g) + b/2H_2O$ (liq.) $+ d/2Br_2$(liq.), then it is necessary to add to $\Delta Ec°$ in item 100 the quantity $d\Delta E°_{\text{oxid.}}(HBr)$, the value of $\Delta E°$ for the reaction,

$$d(HBr·nH_2O)(\text{liq.}) + d/4O_2(g) = d(n + \tfrac{1}{2})H_2O(\text{liq.}) + d/2Br_2(\text{liq.}).$$

Values of $\Delta E°_{\text{oxid.}}(HBr)$ are tabulated (see page 119) as a function of $n$(16g).

As in the previous section, no reference has been made to corrections for corrosion of the bomb or fittings by the combustion gases, because such corrections are specific for the particular materials of construction that are used.

$$\Delta E^{\circ}_{\text{oxid.}}(\text{HBr}), \text{ kcal. mole}^{-1}$$

| $n$ | 20° | 25° | 30° |
|-----|-----|-----|-----|
| 20 | −5.88 | −5.76 | −5.64 |
| 30 | −5.74 | −5.60 | −5.46 |
| 40 | −5.68 | −5.53 | −5.38 |
| 50 | −5.63 | −5.47 | −5.31 |
| 75 | −5.57 | −5.40 | −5.23 |
| 100 | −5.54 | −5.36 | −5.18 |
| 200 | −5.49 | −5.30 | −5.11 |
| 300 | −5.47 | −5.27 | −5.07 |
| 400 | −5.45 | −5.25 | −5.05 |
| 500 | −5.44 | −5.24 | −5.04 |
| 700 | −5.44 | −5.23 | −5.02 |

**6. Organic iodine compounds of the general formula, $C_aH_bO_cI_d$.**
This section treats the corrections to standard states of bomb calorimetric data for iodine compounds.    When the combustion of an
iodine compound occurs in a calorimetric bomb, the iodine is converted substantially to elemental iodine.    The calorimetric techniques
are simpler than those for chlorine or bromine compounds in that no
solution need be added to the bomb initially to direct the course of the
reaction, and the corrections to standard states are simpler for the
same reason.    The presentation here, as in the three previous sections, is given as a tabulation, with interspersed explanatory text,
of the necessary modifications in the computation form for sulfur
compounds.

The equation of the idealized combustion reaction is

$$C_aH_bO_cI_d(\text{c or liq.}) + (a + b/4 - c/2)O_2(g) = aCO_2(g) + b/2H_2O(\text{liq.}) + d/2I_2(c)$$

The standard state for elemental iodine is the solid under a pressure of
1 atm.

The items that deal with the description of the substance are
changed only by substitution of the symbol and atomic weight of
iodine for those of sulfur, and the items that deal with the description
of the initial state are unchanged.

Item 1, change S to I.
Items 2–6, inclusive, unchanged.
Item 7, change S to I.
Items 8–12 inclusive, unchanged.
Item 13, change S to I.
Items 14–23, inclusive, unchanged.
Item 24, change 32.066 to 126.91.
Items 25–36, inclusive, unchanged.

In the final state, the substance has reacted with $O_2$ according to the net equation,

$$C_aH_bO_cI_d + (a + b/4 - c/2)O_2 = aCO_2 + b/2H_2O + d/2I_2,$$

and the same side reactions may have occurred as in the case of sulfur compounds, although the amount of nitrous acid formed is probably negligibly small. The iodine produced in the combustion reaction exists mostly as the solid in the final state, but part of it is dissolved in the bomb solution and part of it is in the vapor state. The items that deal with the final state must be changed by ($a$) appropriate modification of terms that involve stoichiometry, ($b$) deletion of terms that depend only on the amount or concentration of $H_2SO_4$, and ($c$) inclusion of terms to treat the $I_2$ in the solid, solution, and vapor states.

Items 37 and 38, unchanged.
Item 39, change to:  $n^f(I_2 \text{ tot.}) = d/2n(\text{sub.})$.
Item 40, change second term on the right to $+b/2n(\text{sub.})$.

A new item is required to list the number of moles of dissolved $I_2$, $n^f(I_2 \text{ diss.})$. The solubility of $I_2$, $K(I_2)$, (23) may be expressed as 0.0000203, 0.0000238, and 0.0000274 moles per mole of $H_2O$ at 20°, 25°, and 30°C.

(40a) $n^f(I_2 \text{ diss.}) = K(I_2)n^f(H_2O \text{ liq.})$

Item 41, change the second term on the right to $+254n^f(I_2 \text{ diss.})$.
Item 42, delete.
Item 43, unchanged.
Item 44, delete second term on the right.

The effect of the small amount of dissolved $I_2$ on the density of the solution is neglected in item 44.

Item 45, unchanged.
Item 46, delete.
Item 57, unchanged.
Item 48, delete.
Item 49, add to the right side of the equation the term, $-0.0515n^f(I_2 \text{ tot.})$.
Items 50–55, inclusive, unchanged.

The effect of the small amount of dissolved $I_2$ on the solubility of gases in the solution is neglected in item 51 (and also in item 57).

Item 56, change second term on the right to:  $-(a + b/4 - c/2)n(\text{Sub.})$.
Items 57–61, unchanged.

Two new items are required to list the number of moles of $I_2$ in the vapor state, $n^f(I_2$ gas$)$, and in the solid state, $n^f(I_2$ sol.$)$. The concentration of saturated iodine vapor, $C(I_2)$, is calculated from vapor pressure data (24) to be 0.000011, 0.000017, and 0.000025 mole liter$^{-1}$ at 20°, 25°, and 30°C.

(61a)  $n^f(I_2$ gas$) = C(I_2)V^f($gas.$)$

(61b)  $n^f(I_2$ sol.$) = n^f(I_2$ tot.$) - n^f(I_2$ gas.$) - n^f(I_2$ diss.$)$

Item 62, add to the right side of the equation the term, $+n^f(I_2$ gas$)$.

Items 63–70, inclusive, unchanged.

Item 71, delete.

Items 72–75, unchanged.

Item 76, add to the right side of the equation the term, $+C_P(I_2)n^f(I_2$ tot.$)$. The selected value (16e) for $C_P(I_2)$ is 13.14 cal deg$^{-1}$ mole$^{-1}$ at 25°C. A temperature coefficient of 0.008 cal mole$^{-1}$ deg$^{-2}$ may be calculated from data of the I.C.T. (9f). This coefficient combined with the selected value gives 13.10 and 13.18 cal deg$^{-1}$ mole$^{-1}$ for $C_P(I_2)$ at 20° and 30°C.

Items 77–90, inclusive, unchanged.

Item 91 is replaced by two new items that list the changes of internal energy for the removal of dissolved iodine from solution and for the decompression of the solid iodine. The "selected value" of the heat of solution (16e) and density data from the I.C.T. (9e) were used to obtain the numerical coefficients:

(91)   $\Delta E^f_{\text{soln.}}(I_2) = -\Delta E_{\text{soln.}}(I_2)n^f(I_2$ diss.$)$, in which equation $\Delta E_{\text{soln.}}(I_2)$ is 5900, 5000, and 4100 cal mole$^{-1}$ at 20°, 25°, and 30°C.

(91a)  $\Delta E^f(I_2$ sol.$)\big]^1_{P^f(\text{gas.})} = -(\partial E/\partial P)_T(I_2$ sol.$)n^f(I_2$ sol.$)[P^f($gas.$) - 1]$, in which equation $(\partial E/\partial P)_T(I_2$ sol.$)$ is $-0.118$, $-0.120$, and $-0.123$ cal mole$^{-1}$ atm$^{-1}$ at 20°, 25°, and 30°C.

Items 92, 93, and 94, unchanged.

A new item is required to list the change of internal energy for condensation of the iodine vapor. The heat of sublimation of $I_2$ at 25°C. (16e) and the heat capacities of solid and gaseous $I_2$ were used to calculate values of $\Delta E_{\text{subl.}}(I_2)$, which are 14271, 14284, and 14296 cal mole$^{-1}$ at 20°, 25°, and 30°C.

(94a)  $\Delta E^f_{\text{subl.}}(I_2) = -\Delta E_{\text{subl.}}(I_2)n^f(I_2$ gas$)$

Items 95–100, inclusive, unchanged.

## 7. Simplification of the computation for specified conditions.

The foregoing discussion of the reduction of bomb calorimetric data to standard states has been as general and rigorous as it was practical to make it. A computation form may be made by arranging the numbered items in order. The computation is then made with the use of the equations of each item.

For certain uses, some advantage might be gained by combination of terms into one equation.  Such an equation would read as item 95,

$$n\Delta Ec^\circ(\text{Sub.}) = \text{sum of items 81–94 inclusive,}$$

in which each item would be written as a function of only input data and of $a$, $b$, $c$, and $d$, the subscripts of C, H, O, and the symbol of the fourth element in the empirical formula of the substance (items 19–22).  Such an equation on a completely general and rigorous basis would be extremely complex.  However, it is easy for each investigator to derive such an equation for the conditions that are maintained constant in his laboratory, or to derive several equations, each for a different set of conditions.

As an illustration of the derivation of a simplified and yet rigorous equation, an example is given here.  This example is for the combustion of compounds that contain only carbon, hydrogen, and oxygen, i.e., that have the empirical formula $C_aH_bO_c$.  The temperature, $t_h$, to which the combustion reaction is referred is 25°C.  The bomb is always charged, after removal of air, with an amount of oxygen such that the initial pressure, $P^i(\text{gas.})$, is 30 atm.  The bomb has an internal volume, $V(\text{bomb})$, of 0.3471 liter.  The amount of water added to the bomb, $m^i(H_2O \text{ tot.})$, is 1.00 g.  The above quantities, $t_h$, $P^i(\text{gas.})$, $V(\text{bomb})$, and $m^i(H_2O \text{ tot.})$ have been fixed in this example to show the maximum amount of simplification.  Similar equations can be derived for any fixed set of conditions.

It is necessary to select an arbitrary limit on the accuracy to which each item must be calculated to serve the purpose of the particular investigation.  In this example, the energy equivalent of the calorimetric system plus the contents of the bomb is about 4000 cal deg$^{-1}$, and the mass of substance is always such that the rise in temperature, $t_f - t_i$, is approximately 2°.  Therefore, approximately 8000 cal is evolved in each experiment.  If the over-all correction to standard states is to be accurate to $\pm 0.005$ per cent of the total energy or $\pm 0.4$ cal, a reasonable limit to which the calculation of each item should be accurate is one tenth of that or $\pm 0.04$ cal.  This limit is taken for the example.

In Steps 17 and 19 of the rigorous treatment in Section 2, the nitric acid, after removal from the bomb at 1 atm. pressure, is decomposed to $N_2$, $O_2$, and $H_2O$ in their standard states because the energy change of the reaction is better established for standard conditions than for actual bomb conditions. However, if the amount of nitric acid formed is small enough, decomposition of the nitric acid under bomb conditions immediately after Step 12 eliminates the terms involving $n^f(HNO_3)$ from items 40, 41, 44, 47, and 56 and subsequent items based on these. Such a procedure leads to simplification of the corrections without significant loss of accuracy. In the example, in which the air is removed from the bomb before charging with oxygen, the correction for the amount of nitric acid formed can be expected to be about 1 cal. The energy change for the decomposition of the nitric acid then must be known to about ±4 per cent of itself. Since the energy change for the decomposition reaction as it occurs under bomb conditions, 13,820 cal mole$^{-1}$ (see Chapter 3), differs only 2 per cent from 14,074 cal mole$^{-1}$, the energy change for the reaction under standard conditions, it is apparent that for this example the nitric acid may be decomposed under bomb conditions. A quantity, $n(\Delta E_B(\text{Sub.})$ may be defined as $\Delta E_{\text{I.B.P.}} + 13820n^f(HNO_3)$.

In the example, the fixing of $t_h$, $P^i(\text{gas.})$, $V(\text{bomb})$, and $m^i(H_2O)$ automatically makes certain other items constant. Variation of the volume of substance, $V' + V'' + V'''$, over the possible range of values has an insignificant effect on $V^i(\text{gas.})$ in item 31, and $V' + V'' + V'''$ may be assigned a constant intermediate value of 0.0008 liter. The value of $V^i(\text{gas.})$ is then fixed as 0.3453 liter. Other items, the values of which are now constant, are listed below with their constant values.

(27)  $V^i(H_2O \text{ tot.}) = 0.0010$ liter
(30)  $n^i(H_2O \text{ tot.}) = 0.0555$ mole
(32)  $n^i(H_2O \text{ vap.}) = 0.000488$ mole
(33)  $n^i(H_2O \text{ liq.}) = 0.0550$ mole
(34)  $n^i(\text{gas.}) = 0.4313$ mole
(35)  $n^i[(O_2 + N_2) \text{ diss.}] = 0.000035$ mole
(36)  $n^i[(O_2 + N_2) \text{ tot.}] = 0.4308$ mole
(81)  $\Delta E^i_{\text{vap.}}(H_2O) = +4.84$ cal
(82)  $\Delta E^i(H_2O \text{ liq.})]_1^{P^i(\text{gas.})} = -0.05$ cal
(84)  $\Delta E^i_{\text{soln.}}(O_2 + N_2) = -0.11$ cal
(85)  $\Delta E^i(\text{gas.})]_0^{P^i(\text{gas.})} = -20.37$ cal

Since $HNO_3$ is decomposed under bomb conditions and no $HNO_2$ or $H_2SO_4$ are formed, the values for the following items are zero and/or can be omitted: 38, 39, 42, 43, 46, 47, 48, 70, 71, 90, and 91. Certain other items assume constant values because the final bomb solution is pure water.

(44)  $\rho^f$(soln.) = 0.9970 g ml$^{-1}$
(51)  $K(CO_2)$ = 0.03405 mole liter$^{-1}$ atm$^{-1}$
(57)  $K(O_2)$ = 0.00126 mole liter$^{-1}$ atm$^{-1}$
(66)  g = 1.000
(69)  $(\partial E/\partial P)_T^f$(soln.) = $-0.00186$ cal g$^{-1}$ atm$^{-1}$

In the calculation of $n^f$(CO$_2$ diss.) and subsequently of $\Delta E_{soln.}^f$(CO$_2$), which is approximately 0.8 cal, if $D(CO_2)$ is known to 5 per cent of itself, the arbitrary accuracy requirement of $\pm 0.04$ cal per item is met. For the ranges, $x(CO_2)$ = 0.08 $-$ 0.18 and $P^f$(gas.) = 25–30 atm, $D(CO_2)$ has values of 0.86 $\pm$ 0.02. Consequently, it may be taken here as a constant.

(52)  $D(CO_2)$ = 0.86
(53)  $K^*(CO_2)$ = 0.02928 mole liter$^{-1}$ atm$^{-1}$

In the calculation of $n^f[(O_2 + N_2)$ diss.] and subsequently of $\Delta E_{soln.}^f$(O$_2$ + N$_2$), which is approximately 0.2 cal, $D(O_2)$ need be known to only 20 per cent of itself. For the same ranges of $x(CO_2)$ and $P^f$(gas.) taken above, $D(O_2)$ is 0.93 $\pm$ 0.01, and may be taken as a constant.

(58)  $D(O_2)$ = 0.93
(59)  $K^*(O_2)$ = 0.00117 mole liter$^{-1}$ atm$^{-1}$

The remaining items may be expressed in terms of constants and $a$, $b$, and $c$. In a few instances, to avoid overly cumbersome equations, the expression given uses an item previously given in terms of constants and $a$, $b$, and $c$.

(40)  $n^f$(H$_2$O liq.) = 0.0550 + $b/2$ mole.
(41)  $m^f$(soln.) = 0.991 + 9.008$b$ g.
(45)  $V^f$(soln.) = 0.000994 + 0.00904 $b$ liter.
(49)  $V^f$(gas.) = 0.3461 $-$ 0.009$b$ liter.
(50)  $n^f$(CO$_2$ tot.) = $a$ mole.
(56)  $n^f[(O_2 + N_2)$ tot.] = 0.4308 $-$ $a$ $-$ $b/4$ + $c/2$ mole.

As mentioned before, $n^f$(CO$_2$ diss.) needs to be known to only 5 per cent of itself. Consequently, a reasonable value of $b$, 0.10 (extremes considered were 0 and 0.15), may be taken to obtain a value of $V^f$(gas.), 0.3452 liter, that may be considered constant in the calculation of $n^f$(CO$_2$ diss.). The quantity, 1 + 0.082054($t_h$ + 273.2) $K^*(CO_2)V^f$(soln.)/$V^f$(gas.), may also be taken as a constant, equal to 1.004, for this calculation. For $V^f$(soln.) in the numerator in item 54, the expression of item 45 above is used.

(54)  $n^f(CO_2 \text{ diss.}) = a(0.00205 + 0.0187b)$ mole.
(55)  $n^f(CO_2 \text{ gas.}) = a(0.9979 - 0.0187b)$ mole.

The calculation of $n^f[(O_2 + N_2 \text{ diss.}]$ is handled in a manner similar to that for $n^f(CO_2 \text{ diss.})$. The denominator in item 60 is taken as 1.0016 and $V^f(\text{gas.})$ is again taken as 0.3452 liter.

(60)  $n^f[(O_2 + N_2) \text{ diss.}] = (0.0000823 + 0.00075b)(0.4308 - a - b/4 + c/2)$ mole
(61)  $n^f[(O_2 + N_2) \text{ gas}] = (0.9999 - 0.00075b)(0.4308 - a - b/4 + c/2)$  mole
(62)  $n^f(\text{gas.}) = (0.9999 - 0.00075b)(0.4308 - a - b/4 + c/2) + a(0.9979 - 0.0187b) + 0.0005$  mole.

Because of the inconvenience of carrying the right-hand side of the above equation through the remaining items $n^f(\text{gas.})$ is used instead. The same procedure is followed in the use of $x(CO_2)$, $\mu^f(CO_2)$, $P^f(\text{gas.})$, and $n^f(H_2O \text{ vap.})$.

(63)  $x(CO_2) = a(0.9979 - 0.0187b)/n^f(\text{gas.})$.
(64)  $\mu^f(\text{gas.}) = 0.00061 + 0.00196x(CO_2)[1 + 1.33x(CO_2)]$ atm$^{-1}$.

(65)  $P^f(\text{gas.}) = \dfrac{1}{(0.014147 - 0.00037b)/n^f(\text{gas.}) + \mu^f(\text{gas.})}$ atm.

(67)  $n^f(H_2O \text{ vap.}) = \{0.001279 + [0.00000444 + 0.000022x(CO_2)]P^f(\text{gas.})\}$ $(0.3461 - 0.009b)$  mole.

The total correction can now be computed with only constants along with $a$, $b$, and $c$ and the five items immediately above which themselves are computed from constants and $a$, $b$, and $c$.

The total energy of the idealized combustion reaction, for the actual amount of material involved in the combustion experiment, is item 95, $n\Delta Ec°(\text{Sub.})$, which is equal to the sum of items 81 to 94, inclusive. In this example, items 81, 82, 84, and 85 have constant values, the sum of which is $-15.69$ cal. The quantity $n\Delta E_B$ (Sub.) has been taken equal to $\Delta E_{I.B.P.} + 13820n^f(HNO_3)$ and consequently replaces, in effect, items 86, 90, and 92. Item 91 is zero. Therefore,

$n\Delta Ec°(\text{Sub.}) = n\Delta E_B(\text{Sub.}) - 15.69 +$ items 83, 87, 88, 89, 93 and 94.

This entire calculation then can be made by use of the following equation,

$$n\Delta Ec^\circ(\text{Sub.}) = n\Delta E_\text{B}(\text{Sub.}) - 15.69 + 29[m'(\partial E/\partial P)_T'$$
$$+ m''(\partial E/\partial P)_T'' + m'''(\partial E/\partial P)_T'''] + a(8.34 + 75.7b)$$
$$+ (0.264 + 2.4b)(0.4308 - a - b/4 + c/2)$$
$$+ (0.00184 + 0.0168b)[P^f(\text{gas.}) - 1]$$
$$+ \{1.574 + 2.66x(\text{CO}_2)[1 + x(\text{CO}_2)]\}P^f(\text{gas.})n^f(\text{gas.})$$
$$- 9922n^f(\text{H}_2\text{O vap.})$$

in which equation the values of $(\partial E/\partial P)_T$ must be taken as appropriate for the compound, auxiliary material, and fuse. It should be reemphasized that the above equation applies only to the fixed set of conditions for this example. A similar equation can be easily derived from the complete treatment for any other fixed values of $t_h$, $P^i$(gas.), $V$(bomb), and $m^i$(H$_2$O tot.). It is also possible to derive similar but somewhat more complex equations for cases in which not as many conditions are fixed.

**8. Summary and discussion.** Bomb calorimetric data for sulfur compounds may be corrected to standard states by use of the computation form of 100 items given in Section 2. The revisions of the items of the computation form that are tabulated in Sections 3, 4, 5, and 6 make it applicable to nitrogen and halogen compounds as well as sulfur compounds. The corrections for hydrocarbons and for compounds of carbon, hydrogen, and oxygen are limiting cases of the corrections for the other classes of compounds. Simplification of the computation for these limiting cases is illustrated in Section 7. Thus all classes of organic compounds are considered for which the techniques of combustion calorimetry have been refined to the point that the application of Washburn corrections is necessary. As techniques of combustion calorimetry are developed for other classes of compounds, it will be possible for investigators to make the necessary revisions in the computation form for sulfur compounds to make it applicable to those other classes of compounds as well. The revisions, in general, will be along the same lines as those illustrated here for nitrogen and halogen compounds.

In the cases of sulfur, nitrogen, and iodine compounds, a critical selection has been made of all of the numerical values that enter into the corrections. However, in the cases of chlorine and bromine compounds, the lack of certain required data has made it impossible to make a critical selection of all of the numerical values. As progress in combustion calorimetry depends as much on the availability of necessary auxiliary data as on the development of improved methods and techniques, it is to be hoped that combustion calorimetrists interested in chlorine and bromine compounds will soon obtain the necessary auxiliary data.   The determinations that need to be made include those of the heat capacity and $(\partial V/\partial T)_P$ of aqueous solutions over the concentration ranges likely to be encountered in the initial and final states of the combustion experiments, the solubility and heat of solution of $O_2$ and $CO_2$ in these solutions, the lowering of the vapor pressure of water over these solutions, certain integral heats of dilution, and certain heats of reaction that involve integral heats of dilution.   The numerical quantities for which definitive values are lacking can still be estimated closely enough that the corrections to standard states can be applied with at least moderate accuracy.   The heat capacity, $(\partial V/\partial T)_P$, and vapor pressure of the solutions, and the solubilities and heats of solution of gases in the solutions, will not differ greatly from these properties for pure water.   Heats of dilution may be neglected, and standard heats of reaction used in place of heats of reaction for the actual concentrations, without serious loss of accuracy.   It is recommended that investigators who report heat of combustion data for chlorine and bromine compounds state what provisional values they used for the computation of the corrections to standard states and give enough experimental details that revision of the corrections may be made, if necessary, when definitive values are obtained for the numerical quantities that enter into the Washburn corrections for chlorine and bromine compounds.

## References

1. E. W. Washburn, *J. Research Natl. Bur. Standards* **10**, 525 (1933).
2. E. J. Prosen, National Bureau of Standards Report No. 1119.
3. W. N. Hubbard, D. W. Scott, and G. Waddington, *J. Phys. Chem.* **58**, 152 (1954).
4. J. P. McCullough, S. Sunner, H. L. Finke, W. N. Hubbard, M. E. Gross, R. E. Pennington, J. F. Messerly, W. D. Good, and G. Waddington, *J. Am. Chem. Soc.* **75**, 5075 (1953).
5. N. S. Osborne, H. F. Stimson, and D. C. Ginnings, *J. Research Natl. Bur. Standards* **23**, 261 (1939).
6. (a) E. P. Bartlett, *J. Am. Chem. Soc.* **49**, 65 (1927);  (b) F. Pollitzer and E. Strebel, *Z. physik. Chem.* **110**, 768 (1924).
7. (a) A. W. Saddington and N. W. Krase, *J. Am. Chem. Soc.* **56**, 353 (1934); (b) W. M. Deaton and E. M. Frost, Jr., *Am. Gas Assoc., Proc. Natural Gas Sect.* **1941**, 143.

8.  J. A. Beattie and O. C. Bridgeman, *Proc. Am. Acad. Arts Sci.* **63**, 229 (1928).
9.  (a) "International Critical Tables," Vol. III, pp. 56–59, McGraw-Hill Book Company, Inc., New York, N. Y., 1928; (b) *ibid.*, Vol. III, p. 304; (c) *ibid.*, Vol. III, pp. 54, 58, and 60; (d) *ibid.*, Vol. III, pp. 55, 58, and 61, Vol. VII, p. 66; (e) *ibid.*, Vol. III, p. 21; (f) *ibid.*, Vol. V, pp. 85 and 88.
10. A. E. Markham and K. A. Kobe, *J. Am. Chem. Soc.* **63**, 1165 (1941).
11. K. A. Kobe and J. S. Williams, *Ind. Eng. Chem., Anal. Ed.* **7**, 37 (1935).
12. G. Geffcken, *Z. physik. Chem.* **49**, 257 (1904).
13. S. Sunner, Thesis, University of Lund, Carl Bloms Boktryckerie, Lund, Sweden, 1949.
14. (a) C. H. Greenewalt, *Ind. Eng. Chem.* **17**, 522 (1925); (b) E. M. Collins, *J. Phys. Chem.* **37**, 1191 (1933); (c) S. Shankman and A. R. Gordon, *J. Am. Chem. Soc.* **61**, 2370 (1939).
15. R. Wiebe and V. L. Gaddy, *J. Am. Chem. Soc.* **63**, 475 (1941).
16. (a) "Selected Values of Chemical Thermodynamic Properties," Series I, Tables 14-7 and 18-6, *Nat. Bur. Standards Circ. 500*, Washington, D. C., 1952; (b) *ibid.*, Table 23-3; (c) *ibid.*, Table 1-1; (d) *ibid.*, Tables 18-5, 18-6, and 2a-1; (e) *ibid.*, Tables 12-1; (f) *ibid.*, Tables 2-1 and 10-4; (g) *ibid.*, Tables 2-1 and 11-2.
17. H. J. Hoge, *J. Research Natl. Bur. Standards* **36**, 111 (1946).
18. M. Randall and M. D. Taylor, *J. Phys. Chem.* **45**, 959 (1941). Note that the values of $c_p$ listed in Tables 2 and 3 of reference (18) are per gram of $H_2O$ and not per gram of solution.
19. F. D. Rossini, *J. Research Natl. Bur. Standards* **7**, 47 (1931).
20. F. D. Rossini and M. Frandsen, *J. Research Natl. Bur. Standards* **9**, 733 (1932).
21. E. W. Washburn, *J. Research Natl. Bur. Standards* **9**, 521 (1932).
22. H. S. Harned and R. Davis, *J. Am. Chem. Soc.* **65**, 2030 (1943).
23. A. Seidell, *Solubilities of Inorganic and Metal Organic Compounds*, 3d ed. D. Van Nostrand Company, Inc., New York, N. Y., 1940.
24. (a) W. F. Giauque, *J. Am. Chem. Soc.* **53**, 507 (1931); (b) L. J. Gillespie and L. H. D. Fraser, *J. Am. Chem. Soc.* **58**, 2260 (1936).

# CHAPTER 6

# Combustion in a Bomb of Compounds Containing Carbon, Hydrogen, Oxygen, and Nitrogen

EDWARD J. PROSEN

**1. Introduction.** This chapter describes a method of determining heats of combustion of organic compounds containing carbon, hydrogen, and oxygen and organic compounds containing nitrogen, from the data obtained with a bomb calorimeter.

The bomb process is defined and the method of evaluating the quantity of heat liberated in the process is described. The calculation of the temperature of the equivalent isothermal process to which the heat may be assigned is also described. The heat of combustion in the bomb process is calculated and the process to which it refers is defined.

The reduction to the thermodynamically useful standard decrement in internal energy for the reaction of combustion, with all the reactants and products in their standard states, is described. The reduction described is an improved one which follows essentially that given by Washburn (21).

**2. General method.** As discussed in Chapter 1, the determination of a heat of any reaction or process may be considered to consist of two parts, a calorimetric part and a chemical part. The calorimetric part involves the determination of the quantity of heat evolved by some reaction or process taking place in a certain portion of the apparatus. The chemical part of the determination involves the assignment of the quantity of heat to a definite amount of a reproducible reaction or process. As the energy evolved in any reaction or process depends only on the initial and final states of the system, it is only these states which need to be described.

129

In the determination of heats of reaction using a bomb calorimeter, the quantity of heat $Q$ is that heat which is given to the calorimeter system by whatever process takes place in the bomb. This quantity $Q$ can be determined with high accuracy (approximately 1 part in 10,000) by the use of modern apparatus and procedures. The chemical part of the determination of heats of reaction using a bomb calorimeter involves the quantitative description of the initial and final states of the system inside the bomb. The quantity of heat $Q$ is then assigned to the process of transforming the initial state into the final state (including all energy introduced into the bomb, for example, in the ignition process).

If this process takes place over a range of temperatures (i.e., if the temperature of the initial state is different from the temperature of the final state, as in a constant-temperature-jacket calorimeter), the quantity $Q$ can be assigned to the isothermal process at the final temperature, without any assumptions whatsoever, if one considers the reactants to be a part of the calorimeter system which is calibrated. The temperature to which the reaction is to be referred has been discussed in Chapters 1 and 3 and will also be discussed later in this chapter.

After one has made the determinations necessary to define sufficiently the initial and final states, it has been the practice to evaluate the quantity $-\Delta E_B$, called the "heat of combustion in the bomb process."* This quantity is evaluated by subtracting from $Q$ a standard correction for the energies of certain side reactions and ignition energy and dividing by the grams of substance burned (or grams of carbon dioxide formed or other measure of the amount of reaction). In the combustion of carbon-hydrogen-oxygen-nitrogen compounds these corrections are for the nitric acid formed and the ignition energy. The standard correction for nitric acid $q_n$ is made by assuming a standard value of 57.8 kj/mole for the energy of formation and the standard correction for the ignition energy $q_i$ is determined in separate experiments or by calculation from the energy of combustion of the fuse wire plus the electrical energy used in firing. Since there are other effects of the nitric acid formation and the ignition process which are not taken into account in these standard corrections (such as the effects of the con-

---

* In a few places in this chapter $-\Delta E_B$ refers to a gram of reaction rather than to a mole of reaction as it properly should. However, it was felt better to do this than to use additional symbols, as long as the units are given.

sumption of some oxygen by these processes which are subsequently taken into account in the reduction to $-\Delta E^\circ$), $-\Delta E_B$ is not precisely the heat of combustion in the bomb process had there been no nitric acid formed or ignition energy added; rather it is only a defined quantity equal to $(Q - q_n - q_i)$/grams reaction. However, it has its utility in that it is usually approximately equal to the heat of combustion in the bomb process, assuming no nitric acid had been formed and no ignition energy added; hence, in a series of experiments on one substance, all performed under approximately the same conditions, the values of $-\Delta E_B$ may be averaged, and the further, somewhat more complicated reduction to $-\Delta E^\circ$ may then be applied to this average value of $-\Delta E_B$ (applying to the average conditions) rather than to the value for each individual experiment. In cases of large variations in conditions or in amounts of side reactions (such as in cases involving combustion of compounds containing other elements than CHON or inorganic materials) it may be necessary to perform the reduction to $-\Delta E^\circ$ on each individual experiment and the quantity $-\Delta E_B$ may lose its usefulness entirely.

**3. Determination of the heat of the bomb process.** (*a*) *Method and Principles*. Most laboratories making precise measurements of heats of combustion in an oxygen bomb use a constant-temperature-jacket calorimeter. As most of the principles involved apply to other types of calorimeters as well, the calorimeter and methods used will be described briefly.

The calorimeter assembly consists essentially of a nickel-plated calorimeter can surrounded on all sides by a nickel-plated constant-temperature jacket. The standard calorimeter system is considered to consist of the calorimeter can with cover, containing a standard mass of water, platinum resistance thermometer, stirrer, heater with leads, and bomb with firing leads. The bomb includes all the permanent internal and external parts and contains oxygen at a pressure of 30 atm at 28 °C and the fuse wire but no sample.

The quantity of energy required to raise the temperature of this standard calorimeter system through approximately 3°, divided by the temperature rise (expressed in degrees or other suitable temperature unit, such as ohms when a platinum resistance thermometer is used) is called the energy equivalent $\varepsilon$. Assuming that no changes are made in the system between calibration and combustion experiments, the only correction that needs to be applied to the energy equivalent of the standard calorimeter system $\varepsilon$ is the heat capacity of the substance to be burned.

Determination of the heat $Q$ evolved in an experiment is accomplished by producing the standard temperature rise in the calorimeter system by combustion of the proper amount of standard sample benzoic acid in one series of experiments (calibration experiments) and reproducing the temperature rise, as closely as possible, by combustion of the substance under investigation in another series of experiments (combustion experiments). Since the heat of combustion of benzoic acid is accurately known, and the combustion of the substance produced the same temperature rise in the calorimeter, one thus knows the energy produced in the combustion experiments. In practice, one cannot reproduce the temperature rise and other conditions exactly, hence the energy equivalent is calculated from the corrected temperature rise and the mass of benzoic acid burned in the calibration experiments and expressed in joules/degree (or other temperature unit). Then from the corrected temperature rise in a combustion experiment, one computes the heat $Q$ evolved in that experiment at the actual final temperature of the experiment.

(b) *Computation of the Energy Equivalent of the Calorimeter.* The results of a series of representative calibration experiments using standard benzoic acid are given in Table 1. There are tabulated the experiment number, the mass of benzoic acid burned (corrected to vacuum), the deviation $\Delta e_1$ of the energy equivalent from that of the standard calorimeter system, the corrected temperature rise $\Delta R_c$, the ignition

TABLE 1

Data from Calibrating Experiments with Benzoic Acid

| Expt. No. | Mass of benzoic acid, g | $\Delta e_1$, j/ohm | $\Delta R_c$ ohms | $q_i$, j | $q_n$, j | $\varepsilon_s$, j/ohm | Deviation from mean, j/ohm |
|-----------|------------------------|---------------------|-------------------|----------|----------|------------------------|----------------------------|
| 1 | 1.51107 | 18.1 | 0.292263 | 36.7 | 8.8 | 136796.9 | + 2.5 |
| 2 | 1.51352 | 18.2 | .292770 | 34.9 | 9.2 | 136776.2 | −18.2 |
| 3 | 1.51149 | 18.1 | .292366 | 35.0 | 8.3 | 136779.1 | −15.3 |
| 4 | 1.51302 | 18.9 | .292601 | 34.7 | 9.4 | 136809.4 | +15.0 |
| 5 | 1.49983 | 18.9 | .290099 | 35.6 | 9.7 | 136791.8 | − 2.6 |
| 6 | 1.50962 | 18.8 | .291939 | 34.9 | 8.1 | 136808.2 | +13.8 |
| 7 | 1.51083 | 20.7 | .292194 | 35.0 | 8.8 | 136799.0 | + 4.6 |

| | | | | | | | |
|---|---|---|---|---|---|---|---|
| Mean | | | | | | 136794.4 | |
| Standard deviation of the mean | | | | | | ±4 9 | |

energy correction $q_i$, the standard nitric acid correction $q_n$, the energy equivalent $\mathcal{E}_s$, and the deviation from the mean.

The values of $q_n$ were computed from the amount of nitric acid formed using the value 57.8 kj/mole for the standard heat of formation of nitric acid from nitrogen, oxygen, and liquid water. The values of $q_i$ were obtained from separate ignition experiments in which a standard mass of 4.60 mg of iron was burned (standard $q_i$ = 34.6j) but are corrected to the actual mass of iron burned in each experiment using 7.5 j/mg for the heat of combustion of iron. The value of $\Delta e_1$ for each experiment was computed from the heat capacity of benzoic acid taken as 1.21 j/g°C at 26.5°C (minus the heat capacity 0.03 j/°C ml of that amount of oxygen at 30 atm and 28°C which is displaced by the benzoic acid) converted to j/ohm on the resistance thermometer used. As the standard calorimeter system is considered to include everything in the bomb except the sample, the heat capacity of the sample at the average temperature of the experiment is the only deviation which needs to be applied. (For completeness corrections may also be applied for deviations of the average temperature of the experiment from the standard average temperature, computed from the calculated change of heat capacity of the calorimeter system with temperature, or other small variations from standard conditions. These corrections are almost always negligible.) Changes in calorimeter parts are, of course, also included in $\Delta e_1$.

From the data in Table 1, the energy equivalent of the standard calorimeter system $\mathcal{E}_s$ is computed as follows:

$$\mathcal{E}_s = \left\{ \left[ -\Delta E_B(28°C)m_s + q_i + q_n \right] / (\Delta R_c \right\} - \Delta e_1 \qquad \text{joules/ohm}$$

$$(1)$$

where $-\Delta E_B$ (28°C) is the heat of combustion of standard benzoic acid under the actual bomb conditions computed from the value 26433.8 ± 2.6 j/g for the standard conditions at 25°C, and $m_s$ is the mass of benzoic acid burned. The value of $-\Delta E_B$ (28°C) for the conditions used here is 26431.8 j/g.

(c) *Computation of the Heat of the Bomb Process.* The results of a series of representative combustion experiments on naphthalene recently performed in this laboratory (1) are given in Table 2. These experiments were performed soon after the calibration experiments described above. The amount of reaction was determined from the mass of carbon dioxide formed. There are tabulated the experiment number, the mass of carbon dioxide produced in the combustion, the deviation $\Delta e_2$ from the standard calorimeter system, the corrected temperature rise $\Delta R_c$, the heat evolved $Q$ (28 °C), the ignition energy $q_i$, the nitric acid correction $q_n$, the heat of combustion in the bomb process, $-\Delta E_B$, and the deviation from the mean. The value of $\Delta e_2$ for each experiment was computed from the heat capacity of naphthalene taken as 1.30 j/g °C at 26.5 °C (minus the heat capacity of oxygen displaced) and from the heat capacity of any parts of the calorimeter which were changed. The values of $q_n$ and $q_i$ were obtained in the same manner as for the calibration experiments.

From the data in Table 2, the heat evolved in each combustion experiment was computed as follows:

$$Q(28\,°C) = (\mathcal{E}_s + \Delta e_2)\Delta R_c \text{ joules} \qquad (2)$$

and the heat of combustion in the bomb process was

$$-\Delta E_B(28\,°C) = (Q - q_i - q_n)/g \text{ carbon dioxide.} \qquad (3)$$

This value of $-\Delta E_B$ (28 °C) thus obtained is in joules/gram carbon dioxide. It may be converted to kj/mole naphthalene, using the factor $10(44.011)/1000$ where 10 is the number of moles of carbon dioxide per mole of naphthalene and 44.011 is the molecular weight of carbon dioxide.

TABLE 2

Data from Combustion Experiments with Naphthalene

| Expt. No. | Mass of carbon dioxide, g | $\Delta e_2$, j/ohm | $\Delta R_c$, ohm | $Q$ (28°C), j | $q_i$, j | $q_n$, j | $-\Delta E_B$ (28°C), j/(gCO₂) | Deviation from mean, j/(gCO₂) |
|---|---|---|---|---|---|---|---|---|
| 1 | 3.41712 | 17.3 | 0.292686 | 40042.9 | 33.6 | 9.4 | 11705.7 | +3.2 |
| 2 | 3.42010 | 17.3 | .292887 | 40070.4 | 34.6 | 10.0 | 11703.1 | +0.6 |
| 3 | 3.42162 | 17.3 | .292897 | 40071.7 | 35.3 | 10.0 | 11698.1 | −4.4 |
| 4 | 3.41699 | 17.3 | .292547 | 40023.9 | 34.3 | 10.5 | 11700.1 | −2.4 |
| 5 | 3.41532 | 17.8 | .292552 | 40024.7 | 35.3 | 10.1 | 11705.9 | +3.4 |
| 6 | 3.41620 | 17.8 | .292537 | 40022.6 | 35.8 | 10.0 | 11702.1 | −0.4 |
| Mean | | | | | | | 11702.5 | |
| Standard deviation of the mean | | | | | | | ±1.3 | |

(d) *Procedure for the Calibration and Combustion Experiments.* To illustrate the method, a brief description of the procedure used in both the calibration and combustion experiments follows.

A pellet of benzoic acid is made (or the sample of composition $C_aH_bO_cN_d$ is prepared) and weighed in the crucible in which it is to be burned. The weights are corrected to vacuum [density of benzoic acid = 1.320 g/cm³ at 25 °C (2)]. One milliliter of water is placed in the bottom of the bomb, the iron wire fuse (or other ignition system) is fixed in position, and the crucible with sample is placed in its holder. The bomb is assembled, flushed with purified oxygen, and filled to a pressure of 30 atm at 28 °C. The standard mass of water is weighed into the calorimeter can (temperature of water approximately 24 °C), the bomb lowered into the water, and the calorimeter assembled. The temperature of the calorimeter jacket is maintained constant (throughout the experiment) to ±0.002 °C at about 28.02 °C. Energy is supplied to the calorimeter heater to bring the calorimeter to its standard starting temperature slightly below 25 °C. After equilibrium is established, the calorimetric observations begin. These are divided into three parts: (a) a "fore" period of 20 min, in which observations of the temperature of the calorimeter system are made every 2 min; (b) a "reaction" period of 16 min, in which ignition and combustion occur, followed by reestablishment of thermal equilibrium in the calorimeter; and (c) an "after" period of 20 min, in which observations of the temperature of the calorimeter system are made every 2 min. During the first 5 min of the reaction period, when the temperature of the calorimeter system is rising rapidly, temperature measurements are made at frequent and fixed intervals of temperature (or resistance of the platinum resistance thermometer). This is done by preselecting values of resistance and recording on a chronograph the time at which these values of resistance are reached. During the remaining 11 min of the "reaction" period, when the rate of rise of temperature is small, observations of the temperature are made every minute.

After the calorimetric measurements are completed, the analyses of the products of combustion are made. In the benzoic acid experiments it is found that, with the proper crucible and pelleting, complete combustion occurs in all but a very few experiments. It is thus only necessary to titrate the bomb washings with standard $0.1N$ sodium hydroxide solution, using methyl orange as an indicator, to determine the amount of nitric acid formed. The ignition energy is determined in separate experiments in which the ignition process alone occurs.

The heat of combustion of NBS standard sample benzoic acid

under certain specified standard conditions and referred to 25 °C is certified to be 26433.8 ± 2.6 j/gram (3–5). It is necessary to convert this value to apply to the conditions actually used in the calibration experiments and to 28 °C (the temperature to which the present experiments are referred). If there is not a large departure from the specified standard conditions, the formula given by Jessup (3) can be used for this purpose. If the bomb conditions used vary considerably from the standard conditions specified, it is necessary to calculate $-\Delta E_B$ as described in Chapter 5 and in Section 6 of this chapter. It must of course be shown that large deviations from the specified bomb conditions do not lead to nonequilibrium conditions in the final state of the reaction or to other errors.

As described in Chapter 3, electrical energy may also be used for calibration. However, this requires additional apparatus and is much more difficult and time-consuming. It would be well to determine the heat of combustion of standard benzoic acid as a check in any case.

(e) *Computation of the Corrected Temperature Rise.* The corrected temperature rise, $\Delta R_c$, is computed essentially as described in Chapters 3 and 4. A plot is made of the resistance thermometer readings taken during the "fore" period (on a sliding scale to obtain sufficient sensitivity in the plot) and the "after" period, versus time. The resistances at 0, the tenth, and the twentieth minutes ($R_0$, $R_{10}$, and $R_{20}$) are read from the smooth curve drawn through the points for the fore period and $R_{36}$, $R_{46}$, and $R_{56}$ obtained from the smooth curve for the after period. $R_{20}$ is the initial temperature of the system and $R_{36}$ the final temperature; thus $R_{36} - R_{20}$ is the observed temperature rise. The slope of the time-temperature curve at the tenth minute is taken as $S_{10} = (R_{20} - R_0)/20$, and at the forty-sixth minute as $S_{46} = (R_{56} - R_{36})/20$.

The average temperature of the calorimeter during the reaction period (twentieth to thirty-sixth minutes) is obtained graphically or by use of the trapezoidal rule. From this average temperature $R_{\text{ave.}}$ and the constant temperature of the jacket $R_j$, the area A bounded by the time-temperature curves of the calorimeter system and jacket is obtained: $A = 16(R_j - R_{\text{ave.}})$. One can show that, to within the precision of the measurements, the rate of temperature rise during periods of equilibrium, due to heat of stirring and heat transfer, can be described according to the equation

$$dR/dt = u + k(R_j - R), \tag{4}$$

where $R$ is the temperature of the calorimeter system, $R_j$ is the constant jacket temperature, and $u$ and $k$ are constants for the experiment. This equation expresses Newton's law of cooling. Thus for the fore and after periods we have

$$S_{10} = u + k(R_j - R_{10}) \tag{5}$$

$$S_{46} = u + k(R_j - R_{46}). \tag{6}$$

Solving these equations for $u$ and $k$, we obtain

$$k = (S_{10} - S_{46})/(R_{46} - R_{10}) \tag{7}$$

$$u = S_{46} - k(R_j - R_{46}). \tag{8}$$

Assuming that this same law applies to the heat of stirring and heat transfer during the reaction period when heat is also produced in the bomb, one can calculate the corrected temperature rise $\Delta R_c$:

$$\Delta R_c = R_{36} - R_{20} - 16u - kA. \tag{9}$$

As the correction to the observed temperature rise may not be exact, due to nonequilibrium during the reaction period, convection in the annular space between the calorimeter system and jacket, etc., it is important that all calorimetric experiments be carried out in as much the same manner as possible.

It should be noted in the above that the value of the temperature of the jacket $R_j$ is not required since it cancels out in the calculations:

$$\begin{aligned}\Delta R_c &= R_{36} - R_{20} - 16(S_{46} - k(R_j - R_{46})) - 16k(R_j - R_{\mathrm{ave.}}) \\ &= R_{36} - R_{20} - 16S_{46} - 16k(R_{46} - R_{\mathrm{ave.}}). \end{aligned} \tag{10}$$

It is only required that the jacket remain at constant temperature throughout the experiment. However, it is convenient to use the actual $R_j$ and calculate $u$ and $k$. Then appreciably different values of $u$ and $k$ obtained in different experiments may indicate that the calorimeter is not functioning properly.

**4. Chemical considerations.** (a) *Purity of the Substance.* The accuracy with which the heat of combustion can be determined depends, of course, on how well the chemical composition of the substance is known. For measurements of high accuracy, an accurate measure of the amount and nature of the impurity is required. Precise measurement of the variation of the freezing point with the fraction of substance frozen is often a reliable method of determining the degree of purity.  The nature of the impurity is important; isomeric or other impurities with heats of combustion not greatly different from that of the pure substance can be tolerated in appreciable amounts.

The degree of purity of the substance is often the major factor to be considered in deciding the limits of error to be assigned to the final value.

(b) *Purification of the Oxygen Used for Combustion.*  Although it is possible to use commercial oxygen for combustion, this oxygen must be purified by removal of all combustible impurities.  This may be done by passage of the oxygen (slowly) through a high-temperature furnace (approximately 600 °C) filled with copper oxide, then through an absorption tube containing Ascarite to remove carbon dioxide. This procedure removes combustible impurities but not nitrogen. Since correction is made for nitric acid formed in the combustion, large amounts of nitrogen impurity in the oxygen can be tolerated.  With this procedure for purification of the oxygen, no differences in the heats of combustion have been observed which could be attributed to the oxygen used, although different cylinders of oxygen, different cylinder pressures, and different amounts of nitrogen impurity have been used.

(c) *Methods of Holding or Inclosing the Sample.*  With solids or liquids of very low vapor pressure the material may be placed directly in the crucible in which it is to be burned.  Pelleting of solid materials usually aids in obtaining complete combustion.  Volatile liquids or solids with an appreciable volatility, such as 2,2,3,3-tetramethylbutane (10), must be properly inclosed in an ampoule.  Glass ampoules are most frequently used (7,11,12) and are almost ideal for this purpose.  These glass ampoules are thin-walled and have flexible flat sides.  When filled with liquid the flat sides yield sufficiently so that the pressure is supported by the inclosed liquid.*  Coops and his

---

* Aston *et al.* (16) have had difficulties using thin flat-walled bulbs and doubt whether they ever operate properly.  There is considerable evidence, however, that such bulbs do not break until the fuse wire is fired.  We have frequently re-opened the bomb after filling to 30 atm pressure and found the filled bulbs intact. We have also measured the decrease in volume before breakage upon subjecting the open bulbs to excess external pressure and find values at least ten times as large as these authors found.  Also, the heat of combustion of *n*-pentane, for example, has been determined both in the bomb as a liquid (17) and as a vapor in a flame at constant pressure (18).  The agreement, after correcting the value for the liquid to the vapor state, is within 0.03 per cent (19); whereas, if the bulb had broken when filling the bomb with oxygen, there would have been enough

co-workers (9) describe spherical thin glass bulbs without flattened sides which withstand the pressure of 30 atm in the bomb. We have also recently used such bulbs with satisfactory results and they do have advantages for certain compounds. However, they do require an auxiliary substance besides the iron wire fuse to fire them (where the flattened bulbs do not) and we have had more trouble with splashing upon ignition than with the flattened bulbs. Many other methods of inclosure have been used, but it will suffice to say that the inclosing substance should be such that it does not participate in the bomb process or its effect on the bomb process must be determined.

Inclosure is necessary also with substances which may react with the water or oxygen in the bomb before the time of ignition.

(d) *Determination of the Amount of Reaction.* The mass of substance placed in the bomb has been the classical method of determining the amount of reaction. Inert impurities, such as water, will directly affect the result obtained. Since with many substances, such as the alcohols, it is very difficult to remove all water and weigh the substance in the dry state, it is desirable to eliminate the error due to inert impurities. This can be done by using some other method of determining the amount of reaction. The mass of carbon dioxide formed is a reliable method in most cases (6,17,22). Convenient tubes for absorbing the carbon dioxide have been described (8). Details regarding the accurate determination of the mass of carbon dioxide are given in Chapter 4. Usually the energy of solution of a small quantity of water in the sample is negligible, but its mass may be appreciable.

In some cases it is desirable to distill the material directly into the ampoule in which it is to be burned (9) to eliminate any possible reaction with water or air. This method also eliminates any error due to the effect of water on the measure of the amount of reaction, if water is removed by the distillation.

Evaporation is undesirable for several reasons: accurate determination of the mass of sample is difficult; the amount of material in the vapor state is difficult to determine exactly enough to make proper correction for the energy of evaporation; and vapors usually do not

---

vapor in the bomb to necessitate a correction of approximately 0.7 per cent in the heat of combustion for the heat of vaporization of that amount of vapor. The difficulties of these authors must have been due to too small an area of the flattened sides or perhaps were somewhat dependent on the type of glass used. The procedure for making satisfactory bulbs is described in reference (7).

burn completely in the bomb. In recent measurements on naphthalene in this laboratory (1) it was shown that enough naphthalene vaporized before the sample was sealed in the bomb to have caused an error of about 0.06 per cent had the amount of reaction been determined by the mass-of-sample method. However, as the amount of reaction was determined from the mass of carbon dioxide formed, this error was eliminated without the necessity of inclosing the sample.

(e) *Ignition of the Sample.* Several methods of ignition of the sample are in use. One method is the iron-fuse method. An electric current is passed through an iron wire fuse (approximately 0.012 cm diameter and 2–5 cm long, weighing approximately 2–5 mg) which ignites, burns, and drops on the sample and ignites it. By using a potential drop of about 10 to 24 volts across this fuse, the iron ignites very rapidly and thus breaks the electric circuit after only a small amount of electric energy has been given to the system. The electric energy used is so small that it can be assumed constant in each experiment and the ignition energy may be determined from experiments in which only the iron wire is burned. It is of course necessary to weigh or measure the amount of iron actually burned. Deviation from the standard mass of iron burned may be determined by experiments using different lengths of wire or by use of the value 7.5 kj/g for the energy of combustion of iron. There is no appreciable amount of solution of iron oxide in dilute nitric acid formed in the combustion (3).

In another method of ignition a platinum wire is electrically heated. This ignites a weighed piece of filter paper (13) or cotton string which in turn ignites the sample. It is necessary to measure the amount of electric energy supplied or keep the amount constant in each experiment by passing the current through the wire a fixed length of time. It is necessary to correct for the amount of carbon dioxide produced if the amount of carbon dioxide is used as a measure of the amount of reaction.

A method of ignition for easily ignitable substances has been developed recently (14) in this laboratory. A piece of platinum wire (0.08 mm in diameter and 2 cm long) was put in contact with the sample at one point. When a potential of 24 volts was put across this wire, it was heated to the melting point so rapidly that the electric circuit was broken before a measurable amount of energy was introduced. No ignition energy correction needed to be applied in these experiments. Benzoic acid can be ignited by this method as can many other solids. Materials inclosed in a glass ampoule cannot be ignited in this manner without use of an auxiliary substance, such as a small amount of benzoic acid. The platinum can be recovered.

(*f*) *Determination of the Completeness of Combustion.* It is always necessary to prove that complete combustion has occurred in the bomb. The absence of soot or foul odor upon opening of the bomb is not sufficient evidence of complete combustion. The ratio of mass of carbon dioxide formed to the amount of carbon dioxide calculated stoichiometrically from the mass of sample (4) is strong evidence of complete combustion. As carbon monoxide is a likely product of incomplete combustion, a sensitive test for carbon monoxide in the gaseous products of combustion also presents evidence of complete or incomplete combustion. The test described by Shepherd (15) is a very convenient one to use. In another method, the gaseous products of combustion, after removal of carbon dioxide and water, are passed through a furnace packed with copper oxide (7) and kept at 600 °C to burn any products which had not burned in the bomb and which passed through the absorbents. Any carbon dioxide produced in this way will be evidence of incomplete combustion.

Although proper correction may sometimes be applied for a very small amount of incomplete combustion, the products of incomplete combustion are usually so complex that it is better to strive for complete combustion.

(*g*) *Correction for the Formation of Nitric Acid.* The nitric acid formed in the bomb may be determined by titration of the bomb water after combustion, using standard sodium hydroxide solution and an indicator such as methyl orange which is not sensitive to dissolved carbon dioxide. Large amounts of nitric acid can be formed before significant errors are introduced with this procedure. It has been shown that as long as about 1 ml. of water remains in the bomb no appreciable amount of nitric acid will be lost by slowly releasing the gas from the bomb or flushing the bomb with pure oxygen. The nitric acid will be lost, however, if the bomb is flushed so long as to dry it completely.

The energy evolved in the production of nitric acid in the bomb according to the reaction:

$$\tfrac{1}{2}N_2(gas) + \tfrac{5}{4}O_2(gas) + \tfrac{1}{2}H_2O(liq.) = HNO_3(aq.) \qquad (11)$$

may be taken as 57.8 kj/mole at any temperature near room temperature. This value should be used in the calibration and combustion experiments until a better value of this quantity is available.

Since the heat of dilution of nitric acid between concentrations found in different experiments and in different parts of the bomb is small, this value may be taken to apply to any condition normally encountered in the combustion of carbon-hydrogen-oxygen compounds, where the only source of nitric acid is from the nitrogen impurity in the oxygen used (for nitrogen compounds, see Section 5).

**5. Special considerations for nitrogen compounds.** In the combustion of organic compounds containing no nitrogen, nitric acid is formed by the oxidation of some of the nitrogen remaining as an impurity in the oxygen. In the combustion of organic nitrogen compounds, more nitric acid is formed. However, most of the nitrogen in these compounds is released as nitrogen gas. Usually 10 per cent or less of the nitrogen in the compound appears as nitric acid.

The concentrations of nitric acid obtained may be $3N$ or higher and the nitric acid correction may be 0.3 per cent or more. These conditions point to a need for a more reliable value for the energy of formation of nitric acid. At present it is recommended that the value 57.8 kj/mole be considered to apply to the energy of formation of $0.1N$ nitric acid. The value used should be explicitly stated in each report. Correction for the effect of concentration on the energy of formation of nitric acid may then be taken into account as part of the reduction to standard states.

The effect of a reduction in the amount of water vapor in the final system due to the presence of nitric acid should be calculated and a correction applied if it is appreciable.

Other effects of large amounts of nitric acid should be taken into account, but sufficient information on these effects are not available. Such effects are the solubility and the heat of solution of carbon dioxide in nitric acid solutions. At present the values for the amount and energy of solution of carbon dioxide in water are used in the reduction to standard states and are estimated to be not greatly different from the values for these quantities in dilute nitric acid.

The probable formation of nitrous acid should be considered. In this laboratory it has been found that the mole ratio of nitrous acid to nitric acid was usually about 0.004; this amount can usually be ignored. However, this ratio may differ under different conditions and with different compounds and it is best to check the amount by analysis.

With nitrogen compounds, if large and varying amounts of nitric acid are formed, it is advisable to determine the value of the reduction to the standard states for each experiment rather than to operate on the average value of the heat of the bomb process.

**6. Reduction to the standard heat of combustion.** The evaluation of the Washburn correction (21) to reduce the heat of combustion in the bomb process to the standard heat of combustion, with each substance in its thermodynamic standard state, has been discussed in considerable detail in Chapter 5. In this chapter is given also a brief description of the evaluation of the Washburn correction for combustions of compounds containing carbon, hydrogen, oxygen, and nitrogen. This reduction follows that of Washburn (21) with some alterations for the following reasons: (a) to make it apply to the defined thermodynamic standard state for the gases of unit fugacity (heat content that of the real gas at zero pressure) instead of 1 atm; (b) to make it apply also to nitrogen compounds; and (c) to present it in such a form that the various quantities can be calculated separately for ease in calculation and so that the magnitude of each effect can be readily seen.

The heat evolved in the true bomb process but with the reactants and products both at the final temperature is $Q(t_f)$. To this value has been applied a correction for the amount of nitric acid formed and a correction for the ignition energy to obtain $-\Delta E_B(t_f)$, the "heat of combustion in the bomb process." This value of $-\Delta E_B(t_f)$ is usually expressed in joules/gram of reaction (grams of substance burned or grams of carbon dioxide formed, etc.) or joules/mole. In what follows, we deal with the actual amounts of the various substances in the bomb.

The initial states of the substances in the bomb are the following: (all at a temperature of $t_f$, the final temperature of the calorimetric experiment):

(i) $n_1$ moles of substance of formula $C_aH_bO_cN_d$ in the liquid or solid state at pressure $P_1$ atm. The energy of solution of oxygen or water in the sample may not be negligible and must be considered in the individual case. The amount of substance in the vapor state should be made negligible by proper inclosing of the sample if it has an appreciable volatility.

(ii) A gas phase under a pressure of $P_1$ atm consisting of a mixture of oxygen, a small amount (less than 1 per cent in most cases) of nitrogen, and water vapor. This mixture will have the same energy content for our purpose as that of pure oxygen containing no nitrogen, and the water vapor separated from it. Thus the gas phase can be considered to consist of $r_1$ moles of $O_2$ (gas) at pressure $P_1$, and $m_1$ moles of $H_2O$ (gas) at pressure $P_w$.

(iii) A liquid phase consisting of water containing dissolved oxygen (and a small amount of dissolved nitrogen). The amount and energy of solution of oxygen (and nitrogen) in water is negligible and in any event will tend to cancel that which is dissolved in the products of combustion. Hence we can consider the liquid phase to be $m_1'$ moles of $H_2O$ (liq.) at a pressure $P_1$.

The final states of the substances in the bomb are the following, all at a temperature of $t_f$:

(iv) A gas phase consisting of a mixture of oxygen, nitrogen (produced in the combustion of nitrogen compounds), carbon dioxide, and water vapor. We can consider the water vapor separately but we must consider the mixture of oxygen, nitrogen, and carbon dioxide together. Thus we can consider the gas phase to be $m_2H_2O$ (gas) at pressure $P_w' + [r_2O_2 + s_2N_2 + q_2CO_2]$ (gas) at pressure $P_2$.

(v) A liquid phase consisting of an aqueous solution of nitric acid containing dissolved carbon dioxide, oxygen, and nitrogen. We can again ignore the amounts and energies of solution of oxygen and nitrogen in the solution but must consider both the amount and energy of solution of carbon dioxide. We may represent the liquid phase as $(q_2'CO_2 + m_2'H_2O)$ (liq.) at a pressure $P_2$. The nitric acid is left out of this formula because the energy of its formation has been corrected for to a close enough approximation in most cases. However, the quantity of nitric acid must be considered in calculating the amount of nitrogen and oxygen remaining in the gas phase, the energy of solution of carbon dioxide in nitric acid solution, and solubility of carbon dioxide in the nitric acid solution, etc.

Thus the bomb process (to which $-\Delta E_B$ refers) may be represented by the following equation, with all the reactants at a pressure $P_1$ (water vapor at $P_w$) and temperature $t_f$, and all the products at a pressure $P_2$ (water vapor at $P_w'$) and temperature $t_f$:

$$n_1C_aH_bO_cN_d \text{ (liq. or c) } + r_1O_2(\text{gas}) + m_1H_2O(\text{gas})$$
$$+ m_1'H_2O(\text{liq.}) = (r_2O_2 + s_2N_2 + q_2CO_2)(\text{gas})$$
$$+ m_2H_2O(\text{gas}) + (q_2'CO_2 + m_2'H_2O)(\text{liq.}). \quad (12)$$

It is desirable to convert the heat of combustion in the bomb process $-\Delta E_B$ to the decrement in internal energy of combustion in the thermodynamic standard reaction of combustion, $-\Delta E^\circ$.

The thermodynamic standard reaction may be defined by the following equation, with all the reactants and products in their thermodynamic standard states at the temperature $t_f$:

$$n_1\{C_aH_bO_cN_d(\text{liq. or c}) + [a + (b/4) - (c/2)]O_2(\text{gas})$$

$$= aCO_2(\text{gas}) + (b/2)H_2O(\text{liq.}) + (d/2)N_2(\text{gas})\}. \quad (13)$$

To calculate the difference in energy $\Delta E^\circ - \Delta E_B$, which is the Washburn correction, it is necessary to evaluate the following quantities, all at $t_f$:

(i) The change in energy of $r_1$ moles of oxygen from zero pressure to $P_1$ atm:

$$\Delta u_1 = -6.72P_1r_1 \qquad \text{at } 20\,^\circ\text{C} \qquad\qquad (14)$$

$$= -6.51P_1r_1 \qquad \text{at } 28\,^\circ\text{C}. \qquad\qquad (14a)$$

(ii) The change in energy of a mixture of $r_2$ moles of oxygen, $s_2$ moles of nitrogen, and $q_2$ moles of carbon dioxide from $P_2$ to zero pressure:

$$\Delta u_2 = [6.72R_2 + 6.16S_2 + 29.5Q_2 - 11.4Q_2(R_2 + S_2)] \times$$
$$P_2(r_2 + s_2 + q_2) \qquad \text{at } 20\,^\circ\text{C} \quad (15)$$

$$= [6.51R_2 + 5.97S_2 + 28.5Q_2 - 11.0Q_2(R_2 + S_2)] \times$$
$$P_2(r_2 + s_2 + q_2) \qquad \text{at } 28\,^\circ\text{C} \quad (15a)$$

where $R_2 = r_2/(r_2 + s_2 + q_2)$ is the mole fraction of oxygen in the mixture, $S_2$ that of nitrogen, and $Q_2$ that of carbon dioxide.

(iii) The energy of condensation of $(m_2 - m_1)$ moles of water:

$$\Delta u_3 = -41780(m_2 - m_1) \qquad \text{at } 20\,^\circ\text{C} \qquad\qquad (16)$$

$$= -41380(m_2 - m_1) \qquad \text{at } 28\,^\circ\text{C}. \qquad\qquad (16a)$$

(iv) The energy of vaporization of $q_2'$ moles of carbon dioxide from $m_2'$ moles of water:

$$\Delta u_4 = 18100q_2' \qquad \text{at } 20\,^\circ\text{C} \qquad\qquad (17)$$

$$= 16500q_2' \qquad \text{at } 28\,^\circ\text{C}. \qquad\qquad (17a)$$

(v) The change in energy of $n_1$ moles of the substance $C_aH_bO_cN_d$ from 1 atm to $P_1$ atm: $\Delta u_5$ should be estimated for each substance. It is usually a small quantity. Any appreciable energy of solution of oxygen in the substance should be included in this correction, as well as any significant energy of vaporization, if vaporization is not completely prevented.

(vi) The change in energy of $m_1'$ moles of liquid water from $P_1$ to 1; $m_2'$ moles from 1 to $P_2$; $m_1$ moles of gaseous water, $P_w$ to 0; and $m_2$ moles, 0 to $P_w$ atm: $\Delta u_6$ is negligible under normal conditions.

(vii) Effects of nitric acid not already taken into account, including the energy of dilution to $0.1N$ (the concentration to which the value of 57.8 kj/mole, used in calculating the nitric acid correction in obtaining $-\Delta E_B$, is considered to apply), and the effect of nitric acid in solution on the vapor pressure of water (see discussion in preceding section): $\Delta u_7$ can usually be neglected for compounds containing no nitrogen. The energy of dilution may be obtained from the literature (20). The effect of nitric acid on the vapor pressure of water may be taken into account by using a corrected value of $m_2$ obtained as follows: $m_2$ (corr.) $= 0.03Nm_2$ where $N$ is the normality of the nitric acid solution in the bomb.

The quantities of each substance taking part in the bomb process (Equation 12) may be calculated by the following relations:

$V$ = internal volume of bomb (containing no water or sample) in liters.

$T$ = temperature to which $-\Delta E_B$ was referred (the actual final temperature $t_f$ of the experiment) in °K.

$n_1$ = $m_s/M$, where $m_s$ is the mass of substance and $M$ its gram-formula weight.

$P_1$ = initial oxygen pressure at temperature $T$, in atm.

$m_1'$ = moles of water placed in the bomb minus amount swept out in flushing.

$r_1$ = $P_1V_1/[RT(1 - \mu_1P_1)]$, where $V_1 = V - 0.018m_1' - m_s/(1000d_s)$, $d_s$ = density of substance in g/ml, $\mu_1 = [7.32 - 0.0226P_1]10^{-4}$ at 20°C = $[6.39 - 0.0213P_1]10^{-4}$ at 28°C.

$r_2$ = $r_1 - n_1[a + (b/4) - (c/2)] - (5/4)$(moles $HNO_3$) minus any other appreciable amount of oxygen used to form nongaseous products. For compounds containing no nitrogen use $(7/4)$ in place of $(5/4)$ (moles $HNO_3$).

$m_2' = m_1' + (b/2)n_1.$

$s_2 = n_1(d/2) - \frac{1}{2}(\text{moles } HNO_3).$

$P_2{}^a = [(r_2 + s_2 + an_1)RT(1 - \mu_2 P_1)]/V_2,$ where $P_2{}^a$ is the approximate final pressure and $\mu_2 = \mu_1[1 + 3.21x(1 + 1.33x)]$, $x = an_1/(r_2 + s_2 + an_1) = $ (an approximate value of $Q_2$), $V_2 = V - 0.018m_2'.$

$$m_1 = (9.6 + 0.030P_1)10^{-4}V_1 \qquad \text{at } 20°C$$
$$= (15.1 + 0.048P_1)10^{-4}V_1 \qquad \text{at } 28°C$$
$$m_2 = [9.6 + (0.030 + 0.16x)P_2{}^a]10^{-4}V_2 \qquad \text{at } 20°C$$
$$= [15.1 + (0.048 + 0.25x)P_2{}^a]10^{-4}V_2 \qquad \text{at } 28°C$$
$$q_2' = 6.88(m_2')(10)^{-4}P_2{}^a x \qquad \text{at } 20°C$$
$$= 4.72(m_2')(10)^{-4}P_2{}^a x \qquad \text{at } 28°C$$
$$q_2 = an_1 - q_2'.$$
$$P_2 = [(r_2 + s_2 + q_2)RT(1 - \mu_2 P_2{}^a)]/V_2.$$

In evaluating the reduction of $-\Delta E_B$ to $-\Delta E°$, the quantities of material are evaluated in the order given above. Then these values are used to compute the corrections ($\Delta u_1$ to $\Delta u_7$). It must be remembered that these corrections are in joules and apply to the actual amounts of materials in an experiment (not per g substance or per mole of substance). They can be applied as corrections directly in joules.

The values of the various quantities which change with temperature are given both for 20°C and 28°C. Values at any other temperature may be obtained by interpolation or extrapolation. The values of properties used in the calculations are taken from Washburn (21) or are otherwise estimated.

## References

1. E. J. Prosen and M. Colomina, Unpublished data, National Bureau of Standards.
2. R. S. Jessup, *J. Research Natl. Bur. Standards* **36**, 421 (1946).
3. R. S. Jessup, *J. Research Natl. Bur. Standards* **29**, 247 (1942).
4. E. J. Prosen and F. D. Rossini, *J. Research Natl. Bur. Standards* **33**, 439 (1944).
5. J. Coops, K. van Ness, and Y. Schaafsma (private communication).
6. R. S. Jessup, *J. Research Natl. Bur. Standards* **20**, 589 (1938).
7. E. J. Prosen and F. D. Rossini, *J. Research Natl. Bur. Standards* **27**, 289 (1941).
8. E. J. Prosen and F. D. Rossini, *J. Research Natl. Bur. Standards* **33**, 255 (1944).

9. J. Coops, D. Mulder, J. W. Dienske, and J. Smittenberg, *Rec. trav. chim.* **66,** 153 (1947).
10. E. J. Prosen and F. D. Rossini, *J. Research Natl. Bur. Standards* **34,** 163 (1945).
11. T. W. Richards and F. Barry, *J. Am. Chem. Soc.* **37,** 993 (1915).
12. R. S. Jessup, *J. Research Natl. Bur. Standards* **18,** 115 (1937).
13. H. M. Huffman and E. L. Ellis, *J. Am. Chem. Soc.* **57,** 41 (1935).
14. E. J. Prosen and M. E. Hill, Unpublished data, National Bureau of Standards.
15. M. Shepherd, *Anal. Chem.* **19,** 77 (1947).
16. J. G. Aston, E. J. Rock, and S. Isserow, *J. Am. Chem. Soc.* **74,** 2484 (1952).
17. E. J. Prosen and F. D. Rossini, *J. Research Natl. Bur. Standards* **33,** 255 (1944).
18. F. D. Rossini, *J. Research Natl. Bur. Standards* **12,** 735 (1934).
19. E. J. Prosen and F. D. Rossini, *J. Research Natl. Bur. Standards* **34,** 263 (1945).
20. F. D. Rossini, D. D. Wagman, W. H. Evans, S. Levine, and I. Jaffe, "Selected Values of Chemical Thermodynamic Properties," *Natl. Bur. Standards Circ.* 500 (1952).
21. E. W. Washburn, *J. Research Natl. Bur. Standards* **10,** 525 (1933).
22. F. D. Rossini, *J. Research Natl. Bur. Standards* **6,** 37 (1931).

# CHAPTER 7

# Combustion in a Bomb of Organic Sulfur Compounds

GUY WADDINGTON, STIG SUNNER, AND W. N. HUBBARD

**1. Introduction.**   The bomb calorimetric method for determination of the heats of combustion of compounds containing carbon, hydrogen, oxygen, and nitrogen is well established and is capable of giving results of high accuracy.   The application of this method to compounds that also contain sulfur involves many specific difficulties which have delayed the development of an accurate method for determination of heats of combustion and formation of organic sulfur compounds.   However, experience in two different laboratories with a new combustion technique using a moving bomb system indicates that the heats of combustion of sulfur-containing compounds can now be determined with excellent reproducibility and that an accuracy comparable to that obtained for hydrocarbons is a realizable objective. The words *static* and *moving* will be used to differentiate between conventional stationary bombs and those in which agitation of the bomb contents is achieved by mechanical rotation or oscillation of the bomb.

*(a) Problems Involved.*   The difficulties introduced into bomb calorimetry when sulfur compounds are studied and the means for overcoming these difficulties may be summarized as follows:

(i) The quantitative conversion of sulfur to sulfate ion.   When a compound that contains sulfur is burned in an atmosphere of pure oxygen, both sulfur dioxide and sulfur trioxide are formed.   The composition of this mixture is variable and may change slowly during the after-period of the combustion experiment.   A method must be employed which will result in a quantitative conversion of sulfur to the hexavalent state during the combustion process. This conversion may be catalyzed by nitrogen oxides as in the lead chamber process for the manufacture of sulfuric acid. In combustions of most sulfur compounds it has been found that if the air in the bomb is not removed, before charging with oxygen, sufficient amounts of nitrogen oxides are produced to oxidize the sulfur quantitatively to sulfur trioxide.

(ii) Homogeneity in bomb liquid. The sulfur trioxide produced by the combustion reaction dissolves in the bomb liquid to form sulfuric acid and, if precautions are not taken, the concentration of the acid will not be identical at different parts of the bomb. The heat of dilution of sulfuric acid is large and is not a linear function of concentration; hence, variations in the concentration of the acid between different parts of the bomb may cause significant errors. A method of overcoming this difficulty is to design a calorimeter in which the bomb contents can be agitated after the combustion and to use in the bomb a quantity of water large enough to make the agitation effective.

(iii) Definition of the bomb process. The combustion process leads to a final state consisting of a gas phase containing oxygen, carbon dioxide, and water vapor, and a liquid phase of dilute sulfuric acid which contains, in addition to dissolved oxygen and carbon dioxide, small amounts of nitric and nitrous acids. It is necessary to know the concentration and amount of each component of the vapor and liquid phases so that the calorimetrically observed energy may be associated with a definable thermodynamic process. This necessitates either a determination by chemical analysis or a computation from available data of the amount and concentration of each substance in each phase. This requires, *inter alia*, a knowledge of the solubility of carbon dioxide and oxygen in sulfuric acid over the concentration range corresponding to experimental conditions.

(iv) Correction of data to standard states. In order to obtain useful thermodynamic quantities (i.e., standard heats of combustion and formation) the observed heat of the bomb process must be corrected in such a way that an energy quantity is obtained that corresponds to a reaction in which each reactant and each product is in its appropriate standard state. In the case of compounds of carbon, hydrogen, and oxygen the Washburn equations (1) are available for carrying out the required corrections. When sulfur is also involved the necessary use of a relatively large volume of water and the presence of dilute sulfuric acid as a product have necessitated a modification of the Washburn equations and a critical examination of some of the pertinent data (e.g., the heat of solution of $CO_2$ in the bomb liquid). A revision of the Washburn corrections, that makes them applicable to sulfur compound combustion results, has been made by Hubbard, Scott, and Waddington (2). Their computation form is given in Chapter 5.

(v) Cancellation of systematic errors. In determinations of the heats of combustion of compounds containing carbon, hydrogen, and oxygen, systematic errors inherent in both the combustion and standard calibration experiments will be minimized because the conditions of the combustion and calibration experiments are similar. When a sulfur compound is studied, the final states of the combustion and calibration experiments are quite dissimilar since the former now involves a relatively large volume (ca. 11 ml) of sulfuric acid and the latter a small volume (ca. 2 ml) of water. Under these conditions cancellation of systematic errors may be incomplete. It will be shown later that experiments may be designed so that systematic errors will tend to be nullified in the determination of the heats of *formation* of sulfur compounds.

(vi) Corrosion. The combustion process forms corrosive gases and liquids which may attack the materials used in the construction of the bomb and fittings. The quantitative determination of the amount of the corrosion products and the estimation of the thermal effects which their formation produces may be difficult or impossible. Therefore, all interior parts of the combustion bomb should be fabricated from materials that are not attacked by the intermediate or final combustion products.

(vii) Determination of the amount of reaction. In the case of compounds containing carbon, hydrogen, and oxygen it is possible to determine the amount of reaction by a stoichiometric calculation based on the quantitative determination of the products of combustion. In the case of sulfur compounds this procedure for the determination of mass is not applicable because the available analytical methods for the determination of sulfate or of carbon dioxide in the presence of sulfuric acid are not sufficiently accurate. The amount of reaction is best determined by direct weighing of the sample. This means that the sample must be of known high purity.*

(b) *Historical Development.* Early investigators who attempted to determine the heats of combustion of organic sulfur compounds were aware of some of the foregoing difficulties but failed to develop a generally satisfactory method. Berthelot and Matignon (3–7) published a number of papers on the determination of the heats of combustion of sulfur compounds. In their early experiments they used 10 ml of water in the bomb and later 25 ml. The concentration of sulfuric acid in the final state varied between $H_2SO_4·4H_2O$ and $H_2SO_4·200H_2O$. In 1906 Thomsen (8) published a comprehensive survey of his work on heats of combustion of sulfur compounds. He used combustion in a flame at constant pressure and obtained a final state in which the sulfur was present as sulfur dioxide. A few determinations of the heat of combustion of sulfur-containing compounds were made by Stohmann and Kleber (9), Emery and Benedict (10), Pässler (11), and Lorenz and Sternitzke (12). The foregoing references are now primarily of historical interest. The accuracy of the results is, in general, far from satisfactory; thermodynamic conditions of the combustions are not precisely known, and, in some cases, the description of the experimental method is incomplete. For lack of better data, however, it is still necessary to make use of some of the early values.

In 1934 Becker and Roth (13) studied some sulfur-containing compounds in a bomb to which 10 ml of water had been added. After each combustion these investigators attempted to correct for the varying concentrations of sulfuric acid at different parts of the bomb by collecting and weighing portions of liquid from the top, walls, and bottom of the bomb and analyzing each portion for the sulfuric acid content. They did not attempt to apply corrections for the heat of solution of carbon dioxide in the bomb liquid, but even if these corrections had been attempted, it is doubtful that this method would

---

* It cannot be emphasized too strongly that combustion measurements will be reliable only if carried out on compounds of known high purity. In the case of hydrocarbons, the most probable impurities are hydrocarbons, in many instances isomeric, and small amounts of these can be tolerated without significant error because the heats of combustion of the impurity and sample are approximately the same. In the case of compounds containing carbon, hydrogen, and sulfur, non-isomeric impurities are not improbable and these may have heats of combustion differing considerably from those of the compound being studied.

have given reliable results owing to the probability that equilibrium with respect to the solution of the bomb gases in the final solution was not established.

In 1935 Huffman and Ellis (14) developed a new static method [later also used by Roth and Rist-Schumacher (15)] in which no water was added to the bomb. These investigators assumed that the sulfuric acid was formed as a mist which deposited as a homogeneous solution upon the walls and other interior surfaces of the bomb. The assumption, which has been shown to be incorrect (16,17), and the fact that the sulfuric acid is concentrated and forms complexes with the nitrogen acids present, result in some significant errors. However, when used in correctly planned comparative measurements, the Huffman-Ellis (hereafter abbreviated H-E) method is capable of giving fairly reliable values for the heats of formation of sulfur-containing substances. The H-E method is probably the most reliable of the static methods and may be useful when a moving-bomb calorimeter is not available and the requirements of the investigator are not of the highest. The method will, therefore, be described in later pages.

The first combustion calorimeter designed so that motion could be imparted to the bomb during the combustion period was described in 1933 by Popoff and Schirokich (18), who used it to determine the heats of combustion of halogen compounds. A similar calorimeter was built at Lund (19) for the same purpose and was later rebuilt for the combustion of sulfur compounds (20). An improved moving-bomb calorimeter for sulfur compounds was built at Lund in 1948 (16). Unsuccessful efforts by investigators at Bartlesville to determine accurate heats of combustion for sulfur compounds by the H-E method led them to construct a rotating-bomb calorimeter (17) possessing several unique features.

From the experience of the Lund and Bartlesville laboratories with moving-bomb calorimeters, it seems that the requirements for satisfactory combustion studies of organic sulfur compounds are near fulfillment and that certain small difficulties may soon be resolved. It is also evident that the general methods of moving-bomb calorimetry will be applicable to many types of problems in which the products of combustion exist in the bomb as a vapor phase in contact with a sizable amount of solution or as a vapor–liquid–solid system which must be brought to a state of equilibrium to be thermodynamically definable.  For these reasons it is important that a description and evaluation of the method be presented.

**2. The moving-bomb method.**  The moving-bomb calorimeter differs from conventional calorimeters only in the additional devices necessary for bringing about appropriate agitation of the bomb contents.  Any design of the movable system which fulfills the following requirements may be used: (*a*) The motion imparted to the bomb must be such that the whole inner surface including interior fittings (electrodes, crucibles, etc.) will be adequately rinsed by the bomb liquid.  (*b*) The frictional heat resulting from the motion should be kept to a minimum so that the variations in this energy quantity will be insignificant.  (*c*) The device for producing rotation must not introduce significant heat leaks between the outer and inner vessel of the calorimeter.

In recently designed rotating bombs (16,17,20) the motion imparted is such that the internal walls, top, and bottom of the bomb are washed by the bomb liquid.  The crucible support is so arranged that shortly after rotation begins the crucible falls into the bomb liquid and is rinsed.  The only interior parts of the bomb that escape thorough washing are portions of the electrodes that extend into the bomb.  The magnitude of the total error that could be caused by the incomplete rinsing is insignificant.

The frictional heat effects produced by the motion-producing mechanism are, of course, a function of bomb design.  Experience has shown that the effect can be made small.  Measurement of the force necessary to maintain a constant speed of rotation (16) and calculation of the corresponding frictional heat gave a value of about 0.3 cal per combustion experiment.  A calorimetric determination of the frictional heat in a different calorimeter (17) gave a similar result, i.e., about 0.2 cal per experiment.  Since it is the *variation* in the frictional heat from one experiment to another that is significant, it is evident that friction is not a problem in a well-designed, properly functioning, moving-bomb calorimeter.

The only new heat leaks introduced into a moving-bomb system are associated with the fine copper wire used for imparting motion to the rotating mechanism.  Neither conduction effects nor evaporation through the small orifice provided for the wire have been detected.

In rotating bombs used for sulfur compound studies the materials of construction and the arrangement of the internal fittings of the bomb must be such that the thermal effects of corrosion will be negligible in terms of chemical analysis of the corrosion products. These conditions have been met (16,17) by use of bombs in which the lining, crucible, crucible holder, electrodes, and fittings are fabricated from pure platinum and the gasket is made of fine gold. The corrosion-resistant alloy, illium, used in conventional combustion bombs, is not satisfactory for sulfur compound combustions (21,22).

When the bomb is used in the conventional position (i.e., with the electrodes and crucible support suspended from the top of the bomb) it is advisable to protect the head of the bomb, including gaskets, electrode, and valve inlet fittings, from the combustion blast by placing a platinum shield (16) above the crucible. An alternative arrangement (17,23) for protecting the bomb fittings is to use the bomb in the inverted position and to support the crucible from beneath (see Figure 1). With this arrangement the electrodes and support are removed from the combustion zone and the bomb head with its electrode and valve entries are covered with liquid during the combustion process. Thus the combustion gases can come into contact only with pure platinum and the bomb solution.

A bomb built solely for the determination of heats of combustion of sulfur compounds may be designed with only one valve because the air in the bomb need not be flushed out before filling with oxygen.

(a) *A Typical Apparatus.* To illustrate the design and functioning of a moving-bomb system, a detailed description of the construction and operation of a typical rotating-bomb calorimeter (17) will be presented in the following paragraphs.

The calorimetric system is of the constant-temperature jacket type. Figure 1 shows a diagrammatic sectional view of the apparatus which consists of the conventional parts (i.e., calorimeter A, constant-temperature jacket B and B′, and thermometer C) and a mechanism for rotating the bomb.

The constant-temperature jacket consists of two parts, the tank B, and a lid B′ covering the calorimeter "well" (the air space in which the calorimeter is suspended). The external parts of the jacket are made of brass, nickel-plated and polished. The inner boundary of the jacket (i.e., the walls and top of the well) and the calorimetric can are made from 1-mm copper sheet, chromium-plated and brightly polished to minimize heat transfer by radiation. Water in the jacket is stirred by stirrers D and D′. A centrifugal pump at the base of the stirrer D' circulates water through one side of a hollow-hinge into one side of the double-walled jacket lid, around a partition E in the lid into the other side of the jacket lid, and then back into the jacket tank through the other side of the hinge.

The temperature of the jacket water is controlled to 0.002° by balancing a small constant flow of ice water against an intermittent heat input supplied by a 100-watt tubular heater. The heater is actuated by a vibrating fixed point mercury-in-glass thermoregulator

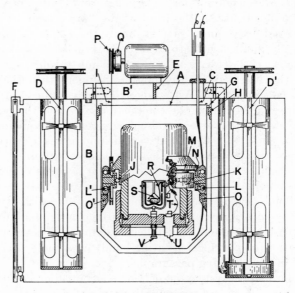

Figure 1. Sectional view of calorimetric system with bomb and rotating mechanism in place in calorimeter.

in conjunction with an electronic-relay. Excess water escapes through the tube F.

The calorimeter A is suspended in the jacket well. Three pegs G near the top of the calorimeter walls rest in V-grooves in corresponding lucite blocks H. The shape of the calorimeter and the walls of the well are such that an air gap 10 mm thick separates them on all sides. The only objects in this space are the three supports H, a part of the thermometer C, the rotating mechanism drive wire I, and four electrical leads which are not shown.

Figure 1 also shows the bomb and rotating mechanism in place in the calorimeter. The bomb is supported by ball bearing J mounted in yoke K, which may rotate in ball bearings L and L'. The yoke is rotated by the withdrawal of copper wire I, wound on a pulley on one axle of the yoke. Rotation of the yoke gives the bomb an end-over-end motion perpendicular to the plane of Figure 1. As the bomb rotates in this manner, gear M fastened to it walks around another gear N, fixed to the stationary outer race of bearing L. These gears cause the bomb to spin about its longitudinal axis. The gear ratio is such that the bomb makes 4 $^3/_8$ end-over-end rotations to 1 spin on its axis, and the path of the liquid in the bomb does not repeat itself until 35 complete end-over-end rotations have occurred.

A few details concerning the use of the rotating mechanism are as follows: The mechanism (including bearings L and L' which in construction are pressed upon the yoke axles) is assembled on the bomb outside the calorimeter. A fine copper wire (No. 28 B & S gage) is fastened to the yoke pulley (by a knot inserted in a keyhole slot) at such a point that tension on the wire when completely unwound will leave the bomb in a predetermined position. The wire is then wound around the pulley 15 times and the bomb and mechanism are lowered into the calorimeter where the bearings L and L' rest in positioning grooves in copper blocks O and O'. Next, the bomb is inverted and two spring clips (one is shown in Figure 3, item 6) which serve as electrical leads and hold the bomb in its stationary position, are connected to the bomb. Then the wire is passed through a sapphire orifice, having a diameter of 0.5 mm (see Figure 3, item 4), in the lid of the calorimeter, through a hole in the jacket lid and to a pulley P driven by a small synchronous motor. Rotation may then be started at the appropriate time by turning on the motor. As motion begins the positioning electrode clips are disconnected and snap out of the way and then a link that connects pulley P directly with a drive plate Q is removed. The pulley P is now being driven only by friction against the plate Q. The direct-drive link is necessary initially, since the starting torque is large because of the positioning springs. When the copper wire has been unwound from the yoke pulley, the drive pulley slips on plate Q, exerting tension on the wire and restoring the bomb to its starting position.

The bomb (internal volume, 0.343 liter) is made of stainless steel and is lined with platinum (0.01 in. thick). The electrodes, gimbal, crucible, and other internal fittings are all fabricated from pure platinum. The sealing gasket, $1/16$ in. thick, is made of fine gold. The crucible is supported in a gimbal-like holder, which permits various preparatory operations, such as adding water to the bomb *while it is in a normal upright position*, after which the bomb may be inverted for the combustion without spilling the crucible contents. When rotation is started, after the combustion, the crucible drops from its support and is washed by the bomb solution.

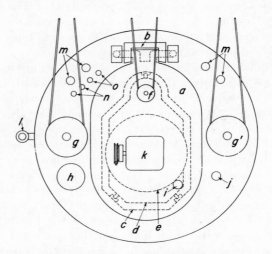

Figure 2. Top view of calorimetric system.

A top view of the calorimetric system is given in Figure 2. This shows the cylindrical form of the outside of the jacket, the shape of the jacket lid $a$, and its hinge $b$. The dotted lines in the hinge show the opening through which jacket water is pumped into and out of the lid. The dotted lines $c$, $d$, and $e$ show the shape and position of the well, calorimeter, and calorimeter lid respectively. Pulley $f$, which is driven by a synchronous motor and a constant-frequency power supply, is the end of a spring collet that drives a stirrer in the calorimeter. Pulleys $g$ and $g'$ drive the jacket stirrers. Ports $h$, $i$, and $j$ are for the jacket thermoregulator, the calorimeter thermometer, and the jacket thermometer, respectively. The sketch also shows the synchronous bomb-rotating motor $k$, the overflow pipe $l$, the jacket heater terminals $m$, the calorimeter heater terminals $n$, and the terminals $o$ for the electrical ignition circuit.

A perspective view of the calorimeter "can" is shown in Figure 3. To accommodate the rotating bomb the calorimeter must be larger for this system than for a static system. The rather unusual shape of this calorimeter is the result of an effort to keep the volume as small as possible. Shown in the drawing are: 1 and 1', the stirrer for circulating water in the calorimeter can and an oil seal through which the

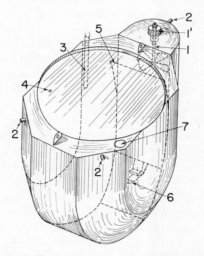

Figure 3. Perspective view of calorimeter can.

stirrer shaft passes; 2, the pegs for suspending the calorimeter in the jacket well; 3, the calorimeter heater that raises the temperature to the desired starting value; 4, a sapphire orifice in the calorimeter lid through which a fine wire passes from the bomb to the winding pulley; 5, a partition that separates the stirrer-well from the body of the calorimeter; 6, a spring-electrode clip and bomb-positioning device; and 7, the opening in which the calorimeter thermometer is placed.

Temperature measurements are made with a 25-ohm calorimetric-type platinum resistance thermometer (bent to fit close to the wall of the calorimeter) in conjunction with a Type G-2 Mueller bridge and a sensitive galvanometer. A rubber bushing on the shaft of the thermometer closes port 7 in the calorimeter when the system is assembled.

(b) *Experimental Procedures.* In general, the calorimetric procedures, when a moving-bomb calorimeter is used, are similar to those employed with the static-bomb calorimeter. However, the necessity of meeting the specific requirements given previously for the combustion of sulfur compounds leads to the following differences of procedure: (a) 10 ml of water is pipetted into the bomb before it is closed; (b) the air is not removed before the bomb is charged with oxygen; (c) a "baffle" of platinum is suspended over the sample; and (d) the bomb is rotated after the combustion reaction has taken place. The reasons for these procedures are discussed in the following four paragraphs.

(i) Volume of water added to the bomb. The choice of the amount of water to be placed in the bomb involves a compromise between two conflicting factors. First, the amount of water must be large enough to rinse the interior of the bomb when it is rotated and to dilute the sulfuric acid formed. Second, in order to avoid large corrections for the heat of solution of gases (particularly carbon dioxide) it is desirable to minimize the volume of water placed in the bomb. Experience has shown that 10 ml of water is a satisfactory compromise.

(ii) Air left in the bomb. The completeness of conversion of sulfur to the hexavalent state during the bomb process is dependent on two factors. First, if no nitrogen oxides are present in the bomb, catalytic oxidation of $SO_2$ to $SO_3$ does not occur and significant amounts of $SO_2$ will be present among the combustion products (16). Combustion of 3 and 5 millimoles of thioformaldehyde ($CH_2S$) in the absence of nitrogen yielded 2.5 and 4 per cent, respectively, of the sulfur as $SO_2$. Second, even with 1 atm of air present, if the atom ratio of sulfur to hydrogen is greater than about 1 : 2, sulfur dioxide may be found among the products of combustion (24). This difficulty is removed if the effective sulfur–to–hydrogen atom ratio is modified by addition to the sample of an appropriate known mass of nonvolatile hydrocarbon oil of known heat of combustion. On the basis of the above information and other experience, the present procedure is to leave 1 atm of air in the bomb (2.6 mole per cent $N_2$ when the total pressure is brought to 30 atm with $O_2$) and, if necessary, to adjust the sulfur–to–hydrogen atom ratio by addition of a suitable hydrocarbon oil. This latter may be the same oil normally used as an "auxiliary material" for initiating combustion.

(iii) Platinum baffle. To obtain complete combustion of some sulfur compounds it has been found necessary (16,17, and discussion page 175) to place a baffle above the sample. Because of the ever-present possibility of the escape of unburned material from the combustion zone, the use of the baffle has become standard practice. The baffle is cone-shaped and may be hung from the edge of the crucible (Figure 1, S) or supported on legs (16). It must be at least 1 mm thick to withstand the temperatures encountered in the combustion zone.

(iv) Rotation of bomb after combustion. The time that elapses between ignition of the substance and the beginning of the rotation must be sufficiently long to insure complete combustion of the sample. Measurements (25) with thermocouples of the temperatures of both shield and crucible during combustion experiments indicate that the maximum temperature was reached within 15 sec. It was, therefore, deemed safe to adopt 45 sec as the interval between ignition of the sample and the onset of rotation and this procedure has proved satisfactory. Another standard procedure (17) is to begin the rotation after a definite temperature rise has occurred rather than at a fixed time interval after the ignition. The reason for this is that errors (in the radiation correction) that might be caused by changes in thermometer lag when rotation starts will tend to cancel if rotation is always started at the same temperature. This selected temperature interval is about 60 per cent of the anticipated total temperature increase. The rotation of the bomb should continue until a state is reached in which errors due to nonequilibration between gaseous and liquid phase and nonhomogeneity of the liquid phase are insignificant.

(c) Chemistry of the Bomb Process. The complexity of the bomb process when sulfur compounds are studied as contrasted with the relative simplicity of the process for a compound containing carbon, hydrogen, and oxygen, is related to the following four factors: (a) the presence of sulfur; (b) the presence of nitrogen in the gas phase; (c) the presence of a relatively large amount of water; and (d) when volatile compounds are investigated, the presence of the ampoule material. The effect of these factors on the chemical part of the combustion experiment is discussed in the following paragraphs.

(i) The presence of sulfur. The amount of sulfur present in the bomb is determined from the mass and composition of the sulfur compound burned. It is desirable that all of the sulfur be converted by the combustion, and subsequent stirring into a sulfuric acid solution of a uniform concentration. Three corollaries of this state-ment follow: (*a*) No significant amount of sulfur dioxide should be present among the products of combustion. The heat of oxidation of $SO_2$ to $H_2SO_4$ (aq.) is about 67 cal per millimole of $SO_2$. Therefore, if the error caused by incomplete oxidation is to be no more than 1 part in 30,000 [see reference (16)], it is necessary to be able to detect 0.001 millimole of $SO_2$. A colorimetric method given by Feigl (26) may be adapted to this purpose. (*b*) All sulfur present should be recoverable as sulfate by gravimetric analysis. However, analytical methods for the determination of sulfate do not give results of an accuracy comparable to the precision of the combustion experiments. Under optimum conditions errors of 1 part in 1000 are probable. Results obtained in two laboratories are in agreement, within the accuracy of the analytical methods, with the hypothesis that the sulfur is converted completely to sulfuric acid. At Lund, extremely careful analyses gave recoveries, of sulfur as sulfate, of $99.9 \pm 0.2$ per cent, whereas at Bartlesville the corresponding value was $100.5 \pm 0.5$ per cent. (*c*) The movement of the bomb has to be effected so that a homogeneous solution of sulfuric acid is obtained. The main sources of inhomogeneity are the small areas of the support and electrode, which, in spite of rotation, are not effectively rinsed by the bomb liquid. An estimation of the cencentration and amount of liquid involved shows that the error from this source is insignificant in the calorimeters used. The addition of 10 ml of water results in a sulfuric acid concentration which is on an almost linear portion of the heat of dilution curve and, hence, differences of concentration, if present, will have only a small effect.

(ii) The presence of nitrogen. The nitrogen oxides formed during the combustion dissolve in the bomb liquid to yield nitrous and nitric acids. The amount of nitrous acid is small and has been found (16,17) to correspond to a correction of approximately 0.1 cal per combustion. It has also been found (17) that the amount of nitrogen oxides in the gas phase after a rotating-bomb experiment is insignificant. The amount of nitric acid is appreciable, and the corresponding thermal correction amounts to 5 to 15 cal per combustion. Analytical procedures used for the determination of nitrous and nitric acids are summarized in the discussion that follows. The total amount of nitrogen acids may be determined by reduction with Devarda's alloy, distillation of the ammonia into standard acid, and determination of the excess acid by titration. The amount of nitrous acid may be determined colorimetrically with Greiss' reagent (27). It is recommended that the amount of nitric acid be obtained by subtraction of the equivalents of nitrous acid found from the total equivalents of nitrogen indicated by the Devarda reduction method. If the postulated chemistry of the bomb process is correct, the total acidity of the bomb solution should equal the sum of the amount of sulfuric acid, predicted by stoichiometric calculation from the initial mass of compound, and the amount of nitrogen acids found. It has been found (17) that the total acid is usually between 99.5 and 100 per cent of the expected value. The discrepancy between the found and calculated values may be greater than the analytical errors. This may indicate that some of the acid is consumed in the combustion process, possibly by corrosive attack on the metal parts of the bomb or by reaction with the glass ampoules.

(iii) The question of equilibrium. The presence of 10 ml of water, necessary for a good definition of states and for proper mixing, may result in nonequilibration of the bomb gases with the bomb solution in both the initial and final states of the combustion process. No direct experimental determination of the absorption rate of carbon dioxide in aqueous solutions under bomb conditions has been made.[*] However, indirect evidence bearing on this question is available. It has been shown (28) that two different calorimeters equipped with moving bombs, and in which 10 and 30 ml of bomb liquid were used respectively, gave the same results for the combustion of paraffin oil when calibrated under the conditions of the combustion experiment. The agreement between the two sets of results was within 7 parts in 100,000. Also several series of combustions of NBS benzoic acid were performed [a typical series is cited in reference (17)] in which alternate experiments had 1 and 10 ml of water present in the bomb. In these cases the deviations between the groups of data ranged between 10 and 15 parts in 100,000. In each case the discrepancy found, although barely significant, was in a direction that could be attributed to nonequilibration of carbon dioxide between the gaseous and liquid phases. Nonequilibration, if present, is either of borderline significance or is compensated for by errors of opposite sign. The experiments cited were not designed to minimize errors caused by nonequilibration of

[*] See, however, the newly published paper of Bjellerup and Sunner (37).

$CO_2$ between the gaseous and liquid phases. Almost complete cancellation of errors resulting from this cause is to be expected when the method of comparative measurements is employed.

(iv) The ampoule material. Soft glass ampoules, used to contain volatile liquids, have been satisfactory in the study of heats of combustion of compounds of carbon, hydrogen, and oxygen. In the case of sulfur compounds, there is evidence that changes of the glass occur, with attendant thermal effects. The glass beads, produced by fusion of the ampoule during the combustion experiment, are frequently observed to be discolored. The color varies from light yellow to dark brown and sometimes dark spots are visible. The fact that ampoules of Pyrex, Vycor, or quartz have not shown discoloration indicates that there may be little or no reaction when these ampoule materials are employed. Additional evidence supporting the hypothesis of chemical attack on soft glass by the combustion products is that evaporation of the bomb liquid may yield as much as several milligrams of solid substance that presumably results in part from action of the hot bomb gases on the glass. To test this hypothesis, samples of ampoule glass and of bomb washings have been analyzed spectrochemically. The bomb washings contained the elements present in the glass. Consistent with these observations is calorimetric evidence that the values of the heat of combustion of sulfur compounds are several calories per combustion higher when the compounds are burned in soft-glass ampoules than when ampoules of Vycor or quartz are used. In studies of the heats of combustion of both thiacyclobutane (17) and 3-methylthiophene (29) combustion experiments were carried out in which soft glass, Pyrex glass, or Vycor glass ampoules were used to contain the sample. The results from the soft-glass experiments were 2.1 and 2.5 cal per combustion higher than those obtained from the experiments in which the more resistant glasses were used.

(d) *Critique of the Chemical Problems.* If a general method is to be developed for the determination of the thermochemical properties of a class of compounds, it is necessary to obtain detailed knowledge of the nature and amounts of the chemical substances produced by the thermochemical process. This may require a meticulous examination of many chemical questions which later prove to be of no consequence in carrying out the thermochemical experiment. When an understanding of the chemical nature of the final state of the bomb process has been obtained, the investigator may reduce the number of analytical operations to the minimum required for definition of the initial and final states of the combustion process.

In the discussion of the chemistry of the combustion process which occurs when sulfur compounds are burned in a bomb, attention was focused on sulfur and nitrogen. In the case of sulfur the primary purpose of the various chemical analyses was to establish the nature and completeness of the combustion reaction. Within the limits of accuracy of the analytical methods available it has been shown that the sulfur compound reacts quantitatively according to the equation

$$C_aH_bO_cS_d(\text{liq. or } c) + (a + b/4 - c/2 + 3d/2)O_2(g)$$
$$+ (nd + d - b/2)H_2O(\text{liq.}) = aCO_2(g) + d(H_2SO_4 \cdot nH_2O)(\text{liq.}) \quad (1)$$

under the conditions of the combustion experiment. The results of the tests performed (sulfate and hydrogen ion determination and tests for the absence of $SO_2$) have not been used in the thermochemical calculations but have been merely corroborative of the assumed course of the reaction. If an analytical method for sulfur were available that had an accuracy equivalent to that of the carbon dioxide determination employed in combustion studies of compounds of carbon, hydrogen, and oxygen, it could be used for an accurate determination of the amount of reaction. In the absence of such a method reliance must be placed on a knowledge of the purity of the sample used. Continuing improvements in the science of purification give increasing confidence in this procedure.

The investigation of the nitrogen compounds formed in the bomb process is for the sole purpose of identifying and determining the amount of each nitrogen compound in the liquid and gaseous phases so that appropriate thermochemical corrections may be applied. Usually, nitrogen oxides do not appear in the gaseous phase. The procedures given for the determination of nitric and nitrous acids in the liquid phase seem to be satisfactory.

In addition to the sulfur and nitrogen problems it has been necessary to consider the effects of hot corrosive gases on the ampoule and on the bomb and bomb parts. There are strong indications that the use of soft-glass ampoules may contribute a thermochemical uncertainty. The use of more resistant ampoule materials may resolve this difficulty.

The over-all aspects of the chemistry of the bomb process for combustions of sulfur compounds are fairly well established. However, confidence in the apparent accuracy of results obtained will increase if further study resolves the present small uncertainties concerning a number of secondary aspects of the chemistry of the bomb process.

**3. Application of the method of comparative measurements.** In bomb calorimetry it is recognized that the combustion experiments and the determination of the energy equivalent of the calorimeter by combustion of standard benzoic acid should be carried out under similar conditions. In this way advantage is taken of "the method of comparative measurements," and systematic errors present in both the calibration and main experiments will tend to cancel. The calorimeter thus becomes an instrument for determining the ratio of the masses of two substances (one the compound of interest and the other benzoic acid) that evolve equivalent amounts of energy in a combustion bomb experiment. The role of benzoic acid when used as the standard reference substance is *to transfer the unit of energy from the standardizing laboratory to the laboratory of the investigator*. At the standardizing laboratory the equivalence between the heat effects produced by combustion of a known mass of benzoic acid and by a measured quantity of electrical energy have been determined, also by the method of comparative measurements.

When compounds containing carbon, hydrogen, and oxygen are studied, full advantage may be taken of the comparative method since differences in conditions between the combustion and calibration experiments are small. Highly accurate final results may be obtained. However, when the compound that is studied contains sulfur (or chlorine or bromine), the conditions of the combustion and calibration must, of necessity, differ from one another and the method of comparative measurements loses some of its value since systematic errors caused primarily by differences in the final states of the systems will not cancel. In the case of sulfur compounds there are two unavoidable differences between the conditions that obtain in the combustion experiments and those that have been recommended by the standardizing laboratory for the calibration experiment with benzoic acid. First, in the combustion experiment the volume of bomb liquid is much greater than in the calibration experiment. Second, the bomb liquid is sulfuric acid in the former experiment and water in the latter. Either or both of these differences may cause systematic errors, and the problem is to design the combustion experiments for the sulfur compound so that the effect of errors arising from these differences will be minimized.

A preliminary consideration is the volume of water to be placed in the bomb in the calibration experiment with benzoic acid. In principle, the use of 1 ml of water in the calibration experiment, as recommended by the standardizing laboratory, is the proper procedure. In practice, if the emphasis is on the determination of the *heat of combustion* of the sulfur compound, the use of 10 ml of water, even though this may result in a slightly less reliable energy equivalent of the calorimeter, is to be preferred. If the heat of *formation* is of importance, an amplification of the simple method of comparative measurements makes 1 ml of water the logical choice for the calibration experiment.

In heat of combustion experiments the reaction of interest is as indicated by Equation 1. To obtain the desired result two experiments must be performed: the calibration of the bomb with benzoic acid and the combustion of the substance of interest. If 1 ml of water is used in the calibration experiments, the presence of 10 ml of water in the initial state and about 11 ml of sulfuric acid in the final state of the main experiment may lead to noncancelling errors traceable to nonequilibration of the bomb gases with the liquid phase, inadequacy of the Washburn equations, and possibly other causes. If 10 ml of water is used in the calibration experiment and in the main experiment, the energy equivalent determined for the system may not be the "true" energy equivalent, but the essential identity of the volumes of bomb liquid in the two cases will tend to equalize solubility and other errors and will lead to fairly complete cancellation of these The solubilities of the bomb gases in dilute sulfuric acid and in water probably do not differ greatly.

A set of experiments has been designed that in principle will yield *heats of formation* (and heats of the reaction indicated by Equation 5) of good accuracy. Three types of experiments are involved: (*a*) the calibration experiments are carried out under precisely the conditions recommended by the standardizing laboratory (*inter alia*, approximately 1 ml of water in the bomb); (*b*) the combustion of the substance of interest (Equation 1) is carried out with 10 ml of water present initially in the bomb; (*c*) the heat of combustion of a mixture of elemental sulfur and hydrocarbon oil (the heat of formation of which has been determined under standard calibration conditions) is

TABLE 1

Heat of Combustion of 1-Pentanethiol[a]

| $m'$, gram | $\Delta T_c$, °C | $q_{oil}$, cal | $q_{fuse}$, cal | $q_{CO}$, cal | $q_N$, cal | $q_{diln}$, cal | $q_{corr}$, cal | Heat of combustion cal g$^{-1}$ |
|---|---|---|---|---|---|---|---|---|
| 0.63892 | 1.67684 | 517.38 | 15.93 | 2.72 | 11.33 | $-0.31$ | $-0.43$ | 9455.2 |
| .62964 | 1.68643 | 640.20 | 15.85 | 2.73 | 10.64 | $-.29$ | $-.42$ | 9459.9 |
| .63193 | 1.67848 | 591.59 | 15.69 | 2.72 | 10.92 | $-.29$ | $-.41$ | 9452.8 |
| .62900 | 1.67633 | 615.00 | 15.93 | 2.73 | 6.50 | $-.28$ | $-.41$ | 9453.1 |
| .61795 | 1.68544 | 745.06 | 16.16 | 2.74 | 11.19 | $-.25$ | $-.38$ | 9461.4 |
| .60463 | 1.68356 | 868.74 | 15.57 | 2.77 | 10.78 | $-.23$ | $-.35$ | 9454.5 |
| .60713 | 1.68432 | 847.20 | 16.05 | 2.76 | 10.78 | $+.01$ | $-.35$ | 9454.8 |
| .52843 | 1.67716 | 1560.71 | 16.01 | 2.88 | 10.64 | $+.01$ | $-.17$ | 9459.5 |
| .56940 | 1.68300 | 1200.54 | 15.65 | 2.82 | 8.98 | $-.10$ | $-.27$ | 9455.4 |
| | | | | | | | Average | 9456.3 ± 1.09[b] |

[a] Mol. wt. = 104.212.    [b] Standard deviation of the mean.

carried out also with 10 ml of water present initially in the bomb. The reaction for the last type of experiment is given by

$$a\mathrm{CH}_2(\text{liq.}) + d\mathrm{S}(\text{c, rhombic}) + (3a/2 + 3d/2)\mathrm{O}_2(\text{g})$$

$$+ (nd + d - a)\mathrm{H}_2\mathrm{O}(\text{liq.}) = a\mathrm{CO}_2(\text{g}) + d(\mathrm{H}_2\mathrm{SO}_4 \cdot n\mathrm{H}_2\mathrm{O})(\text{liq.}) \quad (2)$$

in which the oil is expressed as $\mathrm{CH}_2$ for purposes of illustration. For this reaction the masses of sulfur and oil taken and the volume of water added to the bomb are chosen so that the final state of the system will be nearly identical with that present in the bomb after the combustion of the compound of interest. Systematic errors connected with the final states of reactions represented by Equations 1 and 2 will be almost identical. The difference in the heats of reactions 1 and 2 is the heat of the reaction

$$\mathrm{C}_a\mathrm{H}_b\mathrm{O}_c\mathrm{S}_d(\text{liq. or c}) + (b/4 - a/2 - c/2)\mathrm{O}_2(\text{g}) = d\mathrm{S}(\text{c, rhombic})$$

$$+ a\mathrm{CH}_2(\text{liq.}) + (b/2 - a)\mathrm{H}_2\mathrm{O}(\text{liq.}) \quad (3)$$

and, because the final states of 1 and 2 are the same, systematic errors cancel in taking the difference. Since the heats of formation of the oil and water are known and sulfur and oxygen are elements, the heat of formation of the sulfur compound may readily be obtained from reaction 3.

The energies evolved in reactions 1 and 2 will usually differ. A separate calibration of the bomb for the sulfur and oil experiment may be desirable. It was found (24) that the value for the energy equivalent of the system did not vary greatly (12 parts in 100,000) when the temperature increase varied between 1.7 and 2.5°C. It was also found that the heat of combustion of rhombic sulfur to form sulfuric acid (Equation 4) does not vary significantly when the atom ratio of carbon to sulfur varies between 4 and 6 and that of hydrogen and sulfur varies between 4 and 10. Therefore, in practice the determination of reaction 2 need not be repeated for each compound.

The heats of reactions 4 and 5 are derivable from the results of the foregoing experiments.

$$\mathrm{S}(\text{c, rhombic}) + {}^3\!/_2\mathrm{O}_2(\text{g}) + (n + 1)\mathrm{H}_2\mathrm{O} = \mathrm{H}_2\mathrm{SO}_4 \cdot n\mathrm{H}_2\mathrm{O} \quad (4)$$

$$\mathrm{C}_a\mathrm{H}_b\mathrm{O}_c\mathrm{S}_d(\text{liq. or c}) + (a + b/4 - c/2)\mathrm{O}_2(\text{g}) = a\mathrm{CO}_2 +$$

$$d\mathrm{S}(\text{c, rhombic}) + b/2\mathrm{H}_2\mathrm{O}(\text{liq.}). \quad (5)$$

The heat of reaction 4 is an important fundamental quantity and both reactions 4 and 5 will be referred to in subsequent discussion. The latter, by simple thermochemical computation, leads directly to the standard heat of formation of the compound of interest since the heats of formation of water and carbon dioxide are known accurately.

**4. Thermodynamic states and appropriate thermal corrections.** In 1933 Washburn treated in detail the corrections that must be applied to bomb-calorimetric data for compounds of carbon, hydrogen, and oxygen in order that investigators may obtain values, for the reaction of interest, of the standard change of internal energy. The Washburn corrections have recently been extended by Hubbard, Scott, and Waddington (2) to include sulfur compounds. The treatment of Hubbard *et al.* is given in complete form in Chapter 5.

**5. Results obtained with moving bombs.** It is difficult to assess the accuracy of calorimetric results obtained by use of a complex apparatus. It is doubly difficult when the basic experimental data must be converted to useful thermodynamic quantities by application of complex corrections. It is only when investigators everywhere have agreed on a rigorous method of treating the data of interest that comparisons and estimates of accuracy become meaningful.

In the present instance, heat of combustion and formation data for sulfur compounds have been obtained in two laboratories. The moving-bomb method has been used in each. In a number of cases the same compounds have been studied and in a few instances identical samples have been investigated. It is therefore informative to examine these data.

To illustrate the reproducibility obtainable and the magnitude of some of the thermal corrections, data for a series of combustions of 1-pentanethiol (17) (*n*-amylmercaptan) are given in Table 1. The standard deviation from the mean is about 0.01 per cent. This compares favorably with modern combustion data for hydrocarbons. Sunner (30) has studied a portion of the *same sample* in a moving-bomb calorimeter and has obtained a value of $9455.05 \pm 0.45$ cal $g^{-1}$ from four experiments. The good agreement (within the combined uncertainties of the two sets of data) with the results of Hubbard *et al.*, in spite of numerous small differences of procedure and in the application of the Washburn reduction, supports the view that the moving-bomb method is approaching the status of a precision method.

A number of other compounds have been studied both by Sunner and by Hubbard *et al.* The results from the two laboratories are compared in Table 2. Sunner's data (16) for thiacyclopentane, thiacyclobutane, and sulfur (one series) were reported for 20°C. These data and others (30–32) from the work of the same investigators have been corrected in Table 2 to refer to the reactions at 25°C. The required values of the heat capacity of $H_2SO_4 \cdot 115H_2O$ were taken from the compilation of Craig and Vinal (33).

TABLE 2

Comparison of Lund and Bartlesville Results

| Substance | Laboratory | Sample | Purity, mole per cent | $-\Delta Ec°$ reaction 1 $(n = 115)$, kcal/mole | $-\Delta Ec°$ reaction 5, kcal/mole |
|---|---|---|---|---|---|
| 1-Pentane- | USBM | NBS-906 | 99.92 | $985.05 \pm 0.35^a$ | 842.24 |
| thiol | Lund | NBS-906 | 99.92 | $985.33 \pm .15$ | 842.15 |
| Thiacyclo- | USBM | API-USBM-9 | 99.95 | $773.80 \pm .31$ | 630.99 |
| pentane | Lund | SS$^d$ | ... | $775.25 \pm .10$ | 632.07 |
| Thiacyclo- | USBM | API-USBM-10 | 99.95 | $635.23 \pm .20$ | 492.42 |
| butane | Lund | SS$^d$ | ... | $635.30 \pm .30$ | 492.12 |
| Thianthrene | USBM | SS$^d$ | 99.8 | $1730.01 \pm .38$ | 1444.39 |
| | " | " | 99.8 | $1729.92 \pm .26$ | 1444.30 |
| | Lund | " | 99.8 | $1729.30 \pm .30$ | 1443.32 |
| Sulfur$^b$ | USBM | USBM-P1 | ... | $142.83 \pm .12$ ⎱ | |
| | " | " | | $142.84 \pm .25$ ⎰$^c$ | |
| | " | " | | $142.75 \pm .09$ | |
| | Lund | " | | $143.28 \pm .20$ ⎱ | |
| | " | SS$^d$ | ... | $143.13 \pm .10$ ⎰$_c$ | |
| | " | " | | $143.13 \pm .10$ | |
| | " | " | | $143.18 \pm .20$ | |

$^a$ The uncertainties expressed are twice the "over-all" standard deviations.
$^b$ Reaction 4, in which $n = 115$.
$^c$ USBM and University of Lund are tentatively using 142.81 and 143.18 kcal/mole as weighted means for this datum.
$^d$ Prepared at the University of Lund by Sunner.

As in the case of 1-pentanethiol, portions of the same sample of thianthrene and of sulfur have been studied by the two investigators. For both thianthrene and thiacyclobutane the differences (reaction 1) are within the assigned uncertainty intervals. The poor agreement between the two sets of thiacyclopentane results is probably due to differences in sample purity. The excellent agreement in the 1-pentanethiol values has been mentioned. The generally good agreement in the heats of combustion (reaction 1) suggests that serious errors, caused by differences in methods of calibration and operation, are absent.

The accuracy of the determination of the heat of combustion of elemental sulfur (obtained from reaction 2) affects directly the accuracy of values of the heat of formation obtained by procedures outlined earlier.  Unfortunately, the accuracy with which the heat of combustion of sulfur can be determined by the moving-bomb method suffers from the fact that of the 5000 to 8000 cal evolved during a combustion only about 1000 cal are produced by the sulfur, and the remainder is evolved by combustion of the necessary auxiliary oil. The influence of random errors is increased by a factor of 5 to 8 in comparison with combustions in which the total heat evolved is produced by combustion of the substance of interest.  However, the discrepancy between the two sets of tabulated values for the heat of combustion of sulfur is believed to indicate the presence of a systematic error which may be specific for sulfur.  Certain irregularities found in combustions of sulfur and oil mixtures give support to this belief. In some of these combustions carried out at Lund (25), progressively lower results were obtained from successive experiments.  Concomitantly, a thin grayish film formed on parts of the inner surface of the crucible and the weight of the crucible increased.  The film, which contained sulfur in detectable quantities, was resistant towards ignition.  A "corroded crucible" usually gave low values of the heat of combustion of sulfur (in two cases below 142 kcal per gram atom). After the inner surface was polished with emery cloth, normal values were again obtained.  At Bartlesville (24) the absence of the "platinum effect" was demonstrated by lining the crucible with a thin Vycor shell.

It is unfortunate that more data from different laboratories are not available for comparison.  Some of the small discrepancies between the available heat of combustion and formation values could be removed by adjustments of some of the terms of the Washburn reduction as used by the respective investigators and by agreement on a value for the heat of formation of aqueous sulfuric acid from sulfur, oxygen and water.  These matters are being investigated.

**6. The Huffman-Ellis method.**  When the requirements of the investigator are not of the highest, the bomb calorimetric method described by Huffman and Ellis (14) may be used.  Although the method is subject to small inherent uncertainties, it is relatively simple and merits a brief description and discussion of its good and bad points.

The principal advantage of the H-E method is that any conventional bomb calorimetric system may be used without modification. Huffman and Ellis employed a Dickinson type (34) calorimeter and a Parr Instrument Company bomb made of Illium. Experimental procedures used in the H-E method differ from those of moving-bomb calorimetry in the following respects: (a) water is not added to the bomb; (b) the humidity and temperature of the air initially present in the bomb must be known; and (c) the bomb is not rotated. The analytical requirements and procedures used are the same in both methods. The same methods of correcting the results to standard states are employed. However, the magnitude of the individual correction terms may differ. It is to be noted that the concentration of water vapor at the conclusion of the experiment is much less than at the beginning, and that the corrections for vaporization of water (computation form, items 79 and 92) should not be neglected.

The H-E method has a number of uncertainties which are caused primarily by the small volume of fluid and high concentration of sulfuric acid which obtain in the final state of the combustion experiment. The causes of the uncertainties are, in the order in which they will be discussed: (i) the nonhomogeneity of sulfuric acid in the final state; (ii) the corrosion of bomb parts; (iii) the hydrogen ion discrepancy; (iv) the possibility of unaccounted for side reactions; and (v) the presence of nitrogen oxides in the gas phase. Discussion of these follows.

(i) Nonhomogeneity. The H-E method was developed in an attempt to avoid the errors and inconveniences of the Becker-Roth (13) method in which sulfuric acid is present in varying concentrations, at the end of the experiment, in the "sentina" (13), and on the walls and top of the bomb. Huffman and Ellis assumed that the sulfuric acid is formed in the combustion process as a mist and condenses at a uniform concentration on various parts of the bomb. Tests (16,17) have shown that this assumption is not valid and that errors of more than 2 cal per combustion may arise from this source.

(ii) Corrosion. There is evidence that thermochemical errors caused by corrosion will result if the H-E method is used with an illium bomb. Moore (21) states that "Another source of error is the corrosion of parts of the bomb by $H_2SO_4$ resulting in a small but unknown heat effect. This was apparently confined to the electrodes which became white and pitted after a few runs." Waddington *et al.*

(22) obtained results, in an Illium bomb, for the heat of combustion of thiophene that agreed with those of Moore but which were about 4 cal per gram higher than those obtained when a platinum-lined bomb was used.

(iii) Hydrogen ion discrepancy. As stated earlier the total acidity of the bomb solution should correspond to the sum of the stoichiometrically calculated amount of sulfuric acid and the analytically determined quantity of nitrogen acids. When the H-E method is used, the value found (22,24) for total acidity is 1 to 5 per cent less than the predicted amount. This deficit is considerably greater than the analytical errors and the corresponding discrepancy when the rotating bomb is used. Apparently more acid is "lost" in the H-E method because the acid is formed at a higher concentration and hence is more reactive.

(iv) Unaccounted for side reactions. Much larger amounts of nitrous acid are formed by the H-E method than by the moving-bomb method. This in itself should not cause errors, since the amount of nitrous acid could be determined and appropriate thermochemical corrections could be applied. However, there is evidence that the mixture of concentrated sulfuric and nitrogen acids is chemically complex. A blue color results on slight dilution of the acid mixture (17). Since the chemical nature of the solution is not known with certainty, rigorous thermochemical corrections cannot be applied.

(v) Nitrogen oxides in the gas phase. In moving-bomb experiments in which 10 ml of water are present the amount of nitrogen oxides found in the gas phase is very small (17). With the H-E method a relatively large amount of nitrogen oxides is found in the gas phase in addition to the nitric and nitrous acids in the liquid phase. The amounts found are dependent on the hydrogen to sulfur atom ratio of the compound studied. If the ratio is less than 2 : 1, significant amounts of nitrogen oxides will remain in the gas phase (24). Because of the difficulty of analytically determining the distribution of "fixed" nitrogen between the gas and liquid phases as it exists in the bomb, the relevant thermochemical corrections are treated as though the nitrogen oxides were present in solution as nitrous and nitric acids.

In spite of its inherent uncertainties the H-E method may be used to obtain a moderately good value of the heat of combustion of an organic sulfur compound. Also, when used in correctly planned comparative measurements it will yield accurate values of the heat of formation since cancellation of systematic errors may be partly realized by pairing of appropriate experiments. The results obtainable with the H-E method are well illustrated by combustions of pentanethiol and of sulfur-oil mixtures carried out by Hubbard and co-workers (24). Pentanethiol was studied in; (a) a platinum-lined rotating bomb fitted with a "baffle"; (b) an Illium bomb, without baffle, by the H-E method; (c) an Illium bomb, with baffle, by the H-E method; and (d) a platinum bomb, with baffle, by the H-E method. The heat of combustion of sulfur (Equation 6) was also obtained from combustions of sulfur-oil mixtures by techniques (a) and (b) of the preceding sentence. The data from these experiments are given in Table 3. For ready comparison the reaction heat given is, in each case, for a process yielding $H_2SO_4 \cdot 115H_2O$ as the final product. This is approximately the concentration obtained experimentally in rotating bomb experiments. It is illuminating to compare items 1, 2, and 3 with 4, 5, and 6 of Table 3. It is to be noted that the heats of combustion of both pentanethiol (reaction 7) and sulfur (reaction 6) obtained by the more reliable moving-bomb method are greater than corresponding results obtained by the H-E method by like amounts. It follows that the same value of the heat of reaction 8 is obtained by either method. It is reasonable to postulate that reactions 6 and 7, when studied by use of the H-E method are affected by systematic errors of similar magnitude. Inspection of items 7 and

$$S(c, \text{rhombic}) + {}^3/_2O_2(g) + 116H_2O(\text{liq.}) = H_2SO_4 \cdot 115H_2O(\text{liq.}). \tag{6}$$

$$C_5H_{12}S(\text{liq.}) + {}^{19}/_2O_2(g) + 110H_2O(\text{liq.}) = 5CO_2(g) + H_2SO_4 \cdot 115H_2O(\text{liq.}). \tag{7}$$

$$C_5H_{12}S(\text{liq.}) + 8O_2(g) = 5CO_2(g) + 6H_2O(\text{liq.}) + S(c, \text{rhombic}). \tag{8}$$

8 of Table 3 confirms observations previously reported that higher values are obtained by the H-E method for the heat of combustion in an Illium bomb than in a platinum bomb. Presumably, this is caused by the thermochemical effects of corrosive attack on the Illium by the products of combustion. Information concerning the effect of the platinum baffle is given by comparison of items 4 and 8. When the baffle is used the results obtained are about 0.05 per cent higher and the average deviation is less than when no baffle is used. Use of the baffle is predicated on its increasing the completeness of the combustion reaction and the results obtained are in accord with this idea.

TABLE 3

Comparison of Rotating Bomb and Huffman-Ellis Methods[a]

| Type of experiment | Item no. | Equation number | Number of experiments | Heat of combustion, kcal/mole | Av. dev., kcal/mole |
|---|---|---|---|---|---|
| Rotating Pt bomb | 1 | (7) | 9 | 985.1 | ±0.31 |
| with baffle | 2 | (6) | 14 | 142.8 | ±0.23 |
| | 3 | (8) | | 842.3 | |
| H-E method, Illium | 4 | (7) | 11 | 983.6 | ±0.48 |
| bomb without | 5 | (6) | 7 | 141.4 | ±0.13 |
| baffle | 6 | (8) | | 842.2 | |
| H-E method, Pt | 7 | (7) | 2 | 983.2 | ±0.25 |
| bomb with baffle | | | | | |
| H-E method, Illium | 8 | (7) | 5 | 984.1 | ±0.28 |
| bomb with baffle | | | | | |

[a] For the H-E results Washburn corrections have not been applied. These corrections would tend to lower the values given.

**7. Summary.** Several years hence it may be possible to present the methodology of combustion calorimetry for sulfur compounds without stressing numerous small unresolved difficulties. The efforts of early investigators focused attention on the major problems to be overcome and the development of the moving-bomb method seems to have eliminated or diminished the most serious difficulties. Reference may be made to the following specific advances brought about by use of the moving-bomb technique: (a) the final bomb solution is sufficiently homogeneous; (b) conditions may be adjusted so that the combustion process converts all sulfur to the +6 valence state (insofar as can be determined by available analytical methods); (c) thermochemical uncertainties caused by the presence of nitrogen oxides and acids in concentrated sulfuric acid are eliminated by the dilution used in the moving-bomb method; and (d) the increased dilution also effectively eliminates nitrogen oxides from the gas phase. In addition, thermochemical uncertainties caused by corrosion of bomb parts are reduced to insignificant amounts by use of a properly designed platinum-lined bomb with a gold gasket.

Because of the increased precision obtainable by moving-bomb calorimetry it is now necessary to examine a number of factors producing effects of small magnitude, as follows:

(i) The increased volume of bomb liquid results in a large heat of solution correction for carbon dioxide. It is, therefore, important that the solubility and heat of solution of carbon dioxide in aqueous sulfuric acid be known for the entire range of conditions encountered in the combustion studies on sulfur compounds. New data are needed.

(ii) A related problem is concerned with the nonequilibration of carbon dioxide between the liquid and gas phases. A direct test is desirable, preferably under bomb conditions, of the degree of non-equilibration inherent in present procedures.

(iii) All relevant thermochemical data should be accurately known. Of particular importance is the heat of combustion of rhombic sulfur under conditions which yield aqueous sulfuric acid as a product. Investigators are not yet in agreement on this fundamental datum. Also, because of the relatively large amounts of nitric acid formed in sulfur compound combustions, it is important that the heat of formation of nitric acid from nitrogen, oxygen, and water be known with sufficient accuracy.

(iv) A troublesome problem, which has obtruded itself in sulfur compound studies, is a possibility that a chemical reaction, with attendant thermochemical effects, occurs between hot combustion gases and the soft-glass ampoules used to contain volatile samples. Efforts must be made to find an ampoule material that is nonreactive or that will introduce thermochemical effects for which accurate corrections may be made.

(v) Finally, the over-all chemistry of the bomb process should be subject to continuing examination, by improved analytical methods, until it is certain that the chemical composition of the final state of the bomb process is accurately established.

A thermochemical method will be accepted as capable of giving accurate results only when investigators in different laboratories succeed in duplicating one another's data. An intercomparison of methodology is made easier if a reference substance, possessing the requisite properties, is available. Thioglycolic and sym-diphenyl-thiourea have been proposed as sulfur-containing secondary standards (35). However, these two substances do not meet requirements for secondary standards outlined by Huffman (36). Recently Sunner and Lundin (30) have proposed the use of thianthrene ($C_{12}H_8S_2$) as a suitable secondary standard for combustion studies of sulfur compounds. It is desirable that thianthrene or some other appropriate compound be adopted by thermochemists as a reference substance.

If heats of formation are to be determined, by the method of comparative measurements outlined earlier, it is also desirable that highly purified rhombic sulfur be made available to investigators.

In summary it may be said that the heats of combustion of sulfur compounds may be determined with good precision by the moving-bomb method. Further improvements in the method are possible and will materialize if investigations now in progress are continued. For investigators requiring only moderate accuracy, the Huffman-Ellis method is available.

## References

1. E. W. Washburn, *J. Research Natl. Bur. Standards* **10,** 525 (1933).
2. W. N. Hubbard, D. W. Scott, and G. Waddington, *J. Phys. Chem.* **58,** 152 (1954).
3. M. P. E. Berthelot, *Ann. chim. phys.* [5], **23,** 209 (1881).
4. M. P. E. Berthelot, *Ann. chim. phys.* [6], **28,** 137 (1893).
5. M. P. E. Berthelot, *Ann. chim. phys.* [7], **20,** 197 (1900).
6. M. P. E. Berthelot, *Ann. chim. phys.* [7], **22,** 322 (1901).
7. M. P. E. Berthelot and C. Matignon, *Ann. chim. phys.* [6], **22,** 177 (1891).
8. J. Thomsen, *Z. physik. Chem.* **52,** 348 (1905).
9. F. Stohmann and A. Kleber, *J. prakt. Chem.* [2], **43,** 1 (1891).
10. A. G. Emery and F. G. Benedict, *Am. J. Physiol.* **28,** 301 (1911).
11. W. Pässler, Thesis, Techn. Hochschule, Dresden, 1930.
12. L. Lorenz and H. Sternitzke, *Z. Elektrochem.* **40,** 501 (1934).
13. G. Becker and W. A. Roth, *Z. physik. Chem.* **A169,** 287 (1934).
14. H. M. Huffman and E. L. Ellis, *J. Am. Chem. Soc.* **57,** 41 (1935).
15. W. A. Roth and E. Rist-Schumacher, *Z. Elektrochem.* **50,** 7 (1944).
16. S. Sunner, Thesis, University of Lund, Carl Bloms Boktryckeri, Lund, Sweden, 1949.
17. W. N. Hubbard, C. Katz, and G. Waddington, *J. Phys. Chem.* **58,** 142 (1954).
18. M. M. Popoff and P. K. Schirokich, *Z. physik. Chem.* **A167,** 183 (1933).
19. L. Smith and S. Sunner, *The Svedberg Mem. Ed.*, Uppsala, Sweden, 1944, p. 352.
20. S. Sunner, *Svensk. Kem. Tidskr.* **58,** 71 (1946).
21. G. E. Moore, Thesis, Stanford University, Stanford, California, 1940.
22. G. Waddington, J. W. Knowlton, D. W. Scott, G. D. Oliver, S. S. Todd, W. N. Hubbard, J. C. Smith, and H. M. Huffman, *J. Am. Chem. Soc.* **71,** 797 (1949).
23. W. N. Hubbard, J. W. Knowlton, and H. M. Huffman, *J. Phys. Chem.* **58,** 396 (1954).
24. U. S. Bureau of Mines Thermodynamics Laboratory, Bartlesville, Oklahoma, unpublished measurements.
25. University of Lund Thermochemistry Laboratory, Lund, Sweden, unpublished measurements.

26. F. Feigl, *Qualitative Analyse mit Hilfe von Tüpfelreactionen*, 2d ed., Leipsig, 1935. (Attention is called to an error in the English edition: The malachite green solution should contain 10 mg and not 10 g of dye per 400 ml of solution.)

27. J. H. Yoe, *Photometric Chemical Analysis*, Vol. 1, John Wiley & Sons, Inc., New York, 1928, p. 308.

28. S. Sunner and L. Bjellerup, *Acta Chem. Scand.* **5,** 261 (1951).

29. J. P. McCullough, S. Sunner, H. L. Finke, W. N. Hubbard, M. E. Gross, R. E. Pennington, J. F. Messerly, W. D. Good, and G. Waddington, *J. Am. Chem. Soc.* **75,** 5075 (1953).

30. S. Sunner and B. Lundin, *Acta. Chem. Scand.* **7,** 1112 (1953).

31. S. Sunner, *Acta. Chem. Scand.* **9,** 837 (1955).

32. S. Sunner, *Acta. Chem. Scand.* **9,** 847 (1955).

33. D. N. Craig and G. W. Vinal, *J. Research Natl. Bur. Standards* **24,** 475 (1940).

34. H. C. Dickinson, *Bull. Natl. Bur. Standards* **11,** 189 (1915).

35. Union International de Chimie, Commission Permanente de Thermochimie, *Revue Analytique et Critique de Thermochimie Organique. Appendices au Premier Rapport de la Commission*, Paris, 1936.

36. H. M. Huffman, *J. Am. Chem. Soc.* **60,** 1171 (1938).

37. L. Bjellerup and S. Sunner, *Rec. trav. chim.* **73,** 862 (1954).

# CHAPTER 8

# Combustion in a Bomb of Organic Chlorine Compounds

LENNART SMITH AND W. N. HUBBARD

**1. Introduction and historical development.*** The precise determination by bomb-calorimetric methods of the heats of combustion of organic halogen compounds is accompanied by problems of the same general nature as those encountered in studies of organic sulfur compounds, but the solution of these problems for the former type of compound has been less satisfactory than for the latter. The most serious of the problems associated with studies of halogen compounds is that the halogen may be found in the products of combustion in more than one oxidation state. Consequently, it is difficult to define unambiguously the final state of the combustion process. In Table 1 are shown the relative proportions of free halogen and halogen acid found by various investigators in the products of combustion of halogen compounds. Undoubtedly, different results would be obtained with different experimental methods and with halogen compounds other than those studied, but it is apparent that, in general, the higher the atomic weight of the halogen, the greater is the free halogen content of the products of combustion. Because of the difference in the properties of the products of combustion and their distribution among oxidation states, studies of each type of halogen compound present unique problems.

There are two major problems associated with the determination of heats of combustion of chlorine compounds: (*a*) the precise definition

* The "quartz-spiral" method was developed at the University of Lund and the "glass-cloth" method at the U. S. Bureau of Mines.

181

TABLE 1

Free Halogen, $X_2$, and Halogen Acid, HX, in the Products of Combustion of Organic Halogen Compounds

| Halogen | Free halogen, % | Halogen acid, % |
|---|---|---|
| Fluorine(1) | 0 | 100 |
| Chlorine(2) | 15–20 | 80–85 |
| Bromine(3) | 90–97 | 3–10 |
| Iodine(4) | 100 | 0 |

of the thermodynamic state of the final products, and (b) the corrosive nature of some of the constituents of the combustion gases. Numerous investigators have reported more or less satisfactory solutions to each of these problems. The attempts to direct the combustion process to a definite final state have involved procedures designed to reduce to chloride ion all of the free chlorine formed in the combustion period. The corrosion problem has been attacked by use of bombs lined with (a) corrosion-resistant materials or (b) materials the corrosion products of which may be determined easily by analytical methods. The historical development of solutions to each of these problems will be reviewed separately.

A method for the determination of heats of combustion of chlorine compounds was first proposed by Berthelot and Matignon (5) in 1891. To effect the conversion of chlorine to chloride ion, these investigators added a reducing solution of arsenious oxide to their bomb. For interpreting their data, Berthelot and Matignon assumed that the chlorine was completely reduced after a 10-min reaction period. However, Smith (6,7) later used the same method and found, by analysis of the gas phase for chlorine, that without proper precautions the reduction was not completed in a reasonable length of time. Since the reducing reaction was still in progress at the end of the calorimetric observations, it is apparent that an equilibrium final state of the bomb contents was not obtained by the method of Berthelot and Matignon. Consequently, heat-of-combustion data obtained by that method were not reliable, being always too low.

The use of arsenious oxide as a reducing agent in combustion experiments with chlorine compounds was further developed by Smith and Schjanberg (2). To increase the rate of reduction of chlorine, Smith [reference (2), part I] devised a method to enlarge the surface area of the reducing solution. This method was studied in detail by

Smith and Schjanberg [reference (2), parts II–IV]. Smith's proposal was to support a part of the solution on a bundle of quartz fibers wound in a spiral on the upper part of the inner wall of the combustion bomb. This method, which will be referred to as the "quartz-spiral" method, has been used by Smith and his associates at the University of Lund in determining the heats of combustion of approximately 130 compounds (4,8–11). The data for these combustions were recalculated recently, and the corrected results were published in reference (12).

A modification of the quartz-spiral method was developed (13) at the Thermodynamics Laboratory, U. S. Bureau of Mines, Bartlesville, Okla. In this method, a lining of coarsely woven glass filter cloth was substituted for the quartz spiral, and a reducing solution of hydrazine dihydrochloride was used instead of arsenious oxide.

Although both the quartz-spiral and glass-cloth methods effected complete reduction of the chlorine formed in the combustion process, in neither method was the final bomb solution thoroughly homogeneous in equilibrium with the gas phase. To secure complete reduction of chlorine and thermodynamic equilibrium in the final state of the bomb process, several investigators (3,12,14*) employed moving-bomb calorimeters by means of which thorough agitation and mixing of the bomb solution were obtained. In the first moving-bomb calorimeter described by Popoff and Schirokich (14) in 1933, agitation of the bomb contents was accomplished by oscillation of the bomb about a horizontal axis. A similar calorimeter (3) and a rotating-bomb calorimeter (3,16) were built at the University of Lund. Later (17), the former was improved so that the agitation of the bomb contents was more thorough. Each of these calorimeters was used in about a dozen determinations of the heats of combustion of chlorine compounds (12).

The problem of corrosion of the interior parts of the calorimetric bomb also was studied in the investigations described above. In attempts to prevent corrosion or secure definite corrosion products, investigations were made of the suitability of the following materials for use in fabricating the internal parts of calorimetric bombs: silver chloride (13,14); silver bromide (6,8); platinum (2–5,8,11–13); and

* Roth (15) reported that a calorimeter similar to that of reference (3) had been constructed. However, no description of the apparatus or calorimetric results were given.

tantalum (13). The silver halide type of linings did not prove satisfactory for precise determinations because they reacted with or adsorbed some of the products of the combustion reaction. Although platinum was attacked slightly, it was used most generally as a lining material since corrections could be made easily for the thermal effect of the corrosion reaction. It was found that tantalum was not corroded significantly in the combustion process. However, tantalum crucibles were not used to contain combustion samples since this metal is oxidized at the high temperatures produced in the combustion zone.

As a result of the investigations outlined above, three methods have been developed by means of which the heats of combustion of organic chlorine compounds may be determined with reasonably high accuracy. Two, the quartz-spiral and glass-cloth methods, are static methods that may be used in most combustion laboratories. The third, the moving-bomb method, is more reliable; however, the special equipment required in its use is not available to many investigators. The remainder of this chapter will be devoted to descriptions of these three experimental methods and a comparison of the results obtained by each.

**2. Experimental.** Uncertainties are inherent in some degree in all of the experimental methods developed to date for determining the heats of combustion of chlorine compounds. Furthermore, adequate thermal data are not available for the reduction of the experimental results, however reliable, to the appropriate standard reference states. For this reason, it is not possible at this time to recommend a procedure for the determination of the heats of combustion of chlorine compounds with an accuracy comparable to that which may be attained in studies of hydrocarbons and organic oxygen, nitrogen, or sulfur compounds. Instead, the best available methods will be described in their present state of development.

(*a*) *Calorimetric System.* Use of the static methods in combustion experiments with chlorine compounds does not require a specialized calorimetric system. The systems used in the investigations to be described here were modifications of the constant temperature environment calorimetric system discussed by Dickinson (18). Descriptions of the more unique systems employed in moving-bomb experiments may be found in Chapter 7 and in the literature (3,12,14, 16,19,20).

(*b*) *Static Methods.* The two static methods best adapted for combustion experiments with chlorine compounds were designed to effect the complete and rapid reduction to chloride ion of the free chlorine formed in the combustion process. In both the quartz-spiral and glass-cloth methods, a reducing solution was supported by an absorbent material on the walls of the bomb. This technique was used to increase the rate of reduction of chlorine not only by increasing the area of contact between the reducing solution and the gas phase, but also by maintaining the reducing solution in close proximity to the combustion zone. The experimental techniques employed in the two static procedures are outlined in the following paragraphs.

The quartz-spiral method developed by Smith and co-workers at the University of Lund has been described in numerous publications (2,4,8–12), but the essential features of the method will be discussed briefly.

The Lund investigators used in their experiments a two-piece Julius Peters bomb which was completely lined with platinum. All internal fittings and parts of the bomb were also fabricated from platinum and, if necessary, welded with pure gold. To protect the fittings in the head of the bomb from the combustion blast, a shield was fixed approximately 3 cm above the crucible that contained the combustion samples.

Smith and his co-workers used a solution of arsenious oxide as a reducing agent for chlorine. The solution was supported on a bundle of loose quartz fibers wound in an open spiral on the upper part of the bomb wall. The total surface covered by the spiral of quartz fibers and its interspaces amounts to 50–60 per cent of the inner wall of the bomb. The reducing solution, 20 ml of 0.35 $N$ arsenious oxide solution, was poured over the quartz spiral immediately before a combustion sample was placed in the bomb. Not all the solution was retained on the quartz spiral, and the excess drained to the bottom of the bomb.

The calorimetric observations were divided into initial, reaction, and final periods, each of 5 min duration (see later discussion). At the conclusion of the observations, the bomb was removed from the calorimeter, discharged and opened.

To define the final state of the bomb process, the contents of the bomb were analyzed. It was necessary to determine the amounts of dissolved gold and platinum, of excess arsenious oxide, and of nitric acid (formed from nitrogen impurity in the oxygen). Dissolved noble metals were found only in the condensate formed on the electrodes, shield, crucible, and lid of the bomb. Consequently, the condensate was separately analyzed for noble metals only. About 0.5 mg gold and 2–5 mg platinum were found in the condensate after each combustion. The remainder of the solution in the bomb was analyzed for arsenious oxide and nitric acid; the quantity of hydrochloric acid present in the bomb solution was calculated from the amount of chlorine contained in the combustion sample.

This analytical procedure gave a knowledge of the final bomb state, provided that all free chlorine formed in the combustion process was reduced to chloride ion. Tests for the presence of chlorine in the bomb gases were made as described in reference (11) or (2). The bomb gases were discharged through a sodium hydroxide solution, which was then analyzed for chloride ion by the Volhard method. Less than 0.1 per cent of the chlorine present in a combustion sample was found in the absorbing solution.

Details of the experimental procedure used in the quartz-spiral method may be summarized as follows. The energy equivalent of the calorimetric system was determined by combustion of benzoic acid in experiments in which 20 ml of $0.35N$ arsenious oxide solution was added to the quartz spiral in the bomb.

In preparation for a combustion experiment, an approximately 4-g bundle of loose quartz fibers (0.01–0.02 mm diam.) was wound in a spiral on the bomb wall from the height of the crucible and upwards. The spiral was usually put in place dry. However, an easier procedure was to put it in place wet, in which case the water was evaporated in an oven before the experiment was started.

Several methods were used to obtain the mass of the combustion sample. Nonvolatile solid samples were pelleted and weighed in an open crucible. Liquid or volatile solid samples were handled by either: (a) the method described by Roth and Wallasch (21), in which the sample was weighed in a crucible covered by a cellophane lid; (b) the unsealed ampoule technique described by Verkade and Coops (22) as modified by Eftring (11); or (c) the sealed ampoule technique originally described by Richards and Jesse (23).

A paraffin oil, of known mass and heat of combustion, was used as an auxiliary kindling material. A fuse, a 35-mm length of cotton thread also of known mass and heat of combustion, was placed in the kindling material and attached to a platinum ignition wire 0.05 mm in diameter.

After the combustion charge had been prepared, 20 ml of 0.35$N$ arsenious oxide solution was poured over the quartz spiral in the bomb. The bomb was then closed and the air it contained flushed out with about 2 liters of oxygen. Finally the bomb was charged with oxygen to a pressure of 25 atm, and the calorimetric system was assembled. The calorimetric observations were started after a 20-min equilibration period and were divided into initial, reaction, and final periods, each of 5 min duration.* The combustion sample was ignited by connecting an 8-volt battery across the ignition wire. The platinum wire melted in less than 0.5 sec, and the ignition energy was only about 0.1 cal. The temperature of the calorimeter was measured every 30 sec with a calibrated Beckmann thermometer. The total heat evolved in the combustion process was always approximately 5000 cal, which produced a temperature increment of about 1.7°C in the calorimetric system. Most of the calorimetric measurements were made in a constant temperature room at 20°C.

As mentioned above, the contents of the bomb were divided into two portions: the condensate that collected on the electrodes, shield, crucible, and lid of the bomb and the residue of the bomb solution. Since the quantity of dissolved noble metals was small and essentially the same for each of a series of combustion experiments, the condensates from several experiments were washed into a single flask. The solution so obtained contained all of the dissolved gold and platinum formed in the experiments. To determine the amount of dissolved gold, the condensate solution was made basic and heated; the gold was then precipitated by hydrogen peroxide. After removal of the gold, the solution was acidified with hydrochloric acid and boiled; the platinum, as the sulfide, was then precipitated with hydrogen sulfide. Subsequently, the sulfide was ignited to convert it to metallic platinum. The amounts of noble metal dissolved in each combustion experiment were approximately 0.5 mg gold and 2–5 mg platinum. The reducing solution found in the bomb after an experiment contained hydrochloric acid, nitric acid, the unused arsenious oxide, arsenic oxide, and dissolved carbon dioxide. This solution was rinsed from the quartz

---

* Analyses of the gas phase in the bomb after a combustion and observations of the time-temperature curve have shown (2,4,11) that the reduction of free chlorine to chloride ion is usually complete 5 min after ignition of the sample. Therefore, the main period was usually 5 min long. An initial period of the same length was considered adequate and a final period of 5 min or more was used.

spiral and wall of the bomb with *hot water* into a 250-ml volumetric flask and then, for analysis, divided into 50-ml aliquot portions. One aliquot was acidified with 10 ml of 50 per cent sulfuric acid and boiled. The amount of arsenious oxide present was determined by titration of the boiling solution with $0.1N$ potassium permanganate solution. To minimize analytical errors, the arsenious oxide reducing solution was standardized under similar conditions; i.e., by addition of hydrochloric acid, the concentration of chloride ion in the standard reducing solution was made essentially the same as in the final bomb solution. Another of the aliquot portions of the diluted bomb solution was used for determining the quantity of nitric acid formed in the combustion process. The solution was boiled to remove $CO_2$, and the amount of nitric acid was then determined colorimetrically with diphenylamine (24). Since the amount of nitric acid formed was small, this colorimetric method was found satisfactory. The quantity of chloride ion present was assumed to be equivalent to the amount of chlorine contained in the combustion sample.

The glass-cloth, hydrazine-dihydrochloride method for the determination of heats of combustion of chlorine compounds has been described by Hubbard, Knowlton, and Huffman (13). These investigators also used a calorimetic system (25) similar to that described by Dickinson (18), except that the calorimeter well was not covered by a water-jacketed lid but was completely submerged in a constant-temperature bath. Two calorimetric bombs were used. That used in the earlier investigations was lined with platinum and the internal fittings were fabricated from the same material. The principal differences between this bomb and the one used in the quartz-spiral method are: (*a*) a shield was not used to protect the fittings in the head of the bomb; and (*b*) gold was not used in fabricating the bomb. Later in the studies described in reference (13), a more unique bomb was developed to minimize corrosion that occurs during the combustion process. This second bomb was lined with tantalum and equipped with fittings made from the same material. As mentioned previously, it was necessary to use platinum crucibles since tantalum crucibles were oxidized in the combustion zone. To protect the bomb fittings from the combustion blast, the tantalum-lined bomb was *inverted* and the crucible supported from beneath. It was possible to use a "Teflon" (polytetrafluoroethylene) gasket to seal the bomb, since the gasket of the inverted bomb was below the combustion zone.*

Hubbard *et al.* used a hydrazine dihydrochloride solution to reduce the chlorine formed in a combustion experiment. The reducing solution was supported on coarsely woven glass filter cloth that completely lined the inner wall of the bomb. To ensure rapid thermal equilibration, it was necessary to place the glass-cloth lining in as close contact with the wall as possible. The reducing solution was added to the lining immediately before a weighed combustion sample was placed in the bomb. The quantity of reducing solution added was adjusted to provide at least 25 per cent more reductant than would be consumed. If appreciably less reductant was used, attainment of thermal equilibrium was slow or incomplete. However, all of the reducing solution was held by the glass-cloth lining, and none drained to the bottom of the bomb.

In the combustion experiments, it was found that the duration of the reaction period depended on the compound under investigation. Although the reaction period was usually about 12 min, it was occasionally as long as 20 min. The criterion used to decide that the bomb reaction was complete and that "equilibrium" had been obtained was that the same corrected temperature increment could be calculated from observations made in different portions of the final period.

At the conclusion of an experiment, the combustion gases were discharged through a starch-iodide solution to establish that the reduction of free chlorine had been complete. To determine the extent of the side reactions that occurred in the experiment and make the necessary thermochemical corrections to the observed energy of the bomb process, it was necessary to analyze the liquid contents of the bomb. As in the quartz-spiral method, the condensate that formed on exposed platinum parts contained dissolved platinum. The condensate was kept separate from the remainder of the bomb liquid until the excess reductant in the latter had been determined and removed. Then the two solutions were combined and the total amounts of dissolved platinum, ammonium ion, and nitrate ion were determined analytically. When the tantalum-lined bomb was used, the crucible was the only part attacked by chlorine and the amount of

* In laboratories of the Bureau of Mines at Bartlesville, Okla., and the National Bureau of Standards, Washington, D. C., Teflon gaskets have failed occasionally in combustion experiments with the usual upright bomb.

dissolved platinum was determined simply from the loss in weight of the crucible. Analysis for the constituents mentioned above served to define the final state in the combustion reaction.

Further details of the procedure used in the glass-cloth method were as follows. The calorimetric system was calibrated essentially as described in Chapter 3. In all experiments, the combustion sample was contained and weighed in thin-walled, soft-glass, flat-bottomed ampoules, the stems of which were drawn down to very fine capillaries and bent in an inverted "U" shape (26). The neck of the ampoule was inserted in a hole in the end of a strip of ashless filter paper which served as a fuse. The other end of the fuse was inserted in a loop in a 0.006-in. diameter platinum ignition wire. A small amount of hydrocarbon oil was used as an auxiliary kindling material to initiate the combustion. After the sample, auxiliary material, and fuse were weighed and assembled, the hydrazine dihydrochloride reducing solution was placed in the bomb, and the bomb was sealed. The air in the bomb was swept out with oxygen, the bomb was charged with oxygen to a pressure of 30 atm, and the calorimetric system was assembled. Measurements of the temperature of the calorimeter were made with a calibrated platinum resistance thermometer in conjunction with a Mueller bridge. After the system reached equilibrium, temperature readings of the initial period were made; the combustion sample was then ignited by passing an electrical current through the ignition wire for a predetermined length of time. The ignition wire did not fuse, but the electrical ignition energy was the same for each experiment, about 1.28 cal. The calorimetric observations were terminated after a 10- to 20-min reaction period and a final period of sufficient duration (about 15 min) to establish that thermal equilibrium had been attained. Then, the combustion bomb was removed from the calorimeter, discharged, and opened. Additional details of the procedure outlined above for analysis of the bomb contents are given in the following paragraph.

The bomb gases were discharged through a starch-iodide solution, and if this test indicated no chlorine was contained in the bomb gases, all of the chlorine contained in the combustion sample was assumed to have been converted to the chloride ion. Immediately after the bomb was opened, the glass-cloth lining was removed and placed in a special titration vessel. The condensate on the exposed platinum parts was washed into a separate vessel, and liquid on the remaining portions of the bomb was rinsed into the titration vessel that contained the glass-cloth lining. It was necessary to keep the two solutions separate, since the excess reductant on the glass-cloth lining would reduce the dissolved platinum in the condensate. The amount of excess hydrazine on the glass-cloth lining and in the bomb washings was determined in the special titration vessel by the direct iodine method (27). After this determination, the solution in the titration vessel was combined with the condensate solution that contained dissolved platinum, and the mixture was divided into two equal parts. The quantity of dissolved platinum in one portion was determined by precipitation of the metal with formic acid. The other portion was used to determine the quantities of, first, ammonium ion by Kjeldahl distillation, and, immediately afterwards in the same apparatus, of nitrate ion by Devarda's method. In experiments in which the tantalum-lined bomb was used, the amount of platinum ion in solution was determined directly from the loss in weight of the crucible. Therefore, after the amount of excess hydrazine was determined, the entire bomb solution was used to determine the quantities of ammonium and nitrate ions present.

(c) *Moving-Bomb Method.* The moving-bomb method for determining heats of combustion of organic halogen compounds was introduced first by Popoff and Schirokich (14). The combustion bomb was fastened in a ring equipped with extending axles that were supported at the walls of the calorimeter. The bomb was rocked on these axles by means of two strings attached to a wheel on one of the axles. In an effort to prevent corrosion in the combustion process, the interior of the bomb was coated by electrolytically deposited silver chloride.

Popoff and Schirokich used an arsenious oxide solution to reduce the chlorine formed in the combustion reaction to chloride ion. Before the bomb was assembled 30 to 40 ml of the reducing solution were added to it. Throughout the initial period of calorimetric observations and through the first few observations of the reaction period, the bomb was stationary. Then the rocking motion was started at a rate of $5 \frac{1}{2}$ complete swings per minute and continued for the remainder of the experiment. The amount of heat generated by the rocking motion was determined in separate experiments, and a correction for this thermal effect was applied to the results of the combustion experiments.

At the University of Lund three moving-bomb systems have been used to determine the heats of combustion of several chlorine-containing compounds. The first was a swinging-bomb system (3) similar to that of Popoff and Schirokich except that motion was imparted to the bomb by a lever arrangement. The second was a rotating-bomb system (3, see also 16) and the third (12,17, and 20) was a modification of the first with both a swinging and rotating motion. Further details concerning this last-named moving-bomb system are given in Chapter 9.

The experimental and analytical procedures used were the same as those of the quartz-spiral method; but, of course, it was not necessary to use a supporting material for the reducing solution, and the bomb was rotated in a part of the reaction period. The studies were not extensive but were designed principally to establish the reliability of the quartz-spiral method, since the moving-bomb method is theoretically more reliable.

**3. Thermodynamic states and appropriate thermal corrections.** For interpretation of the results obtained by any of the methods described, it was only necessary to define precisely the initial and final states of the bomb contents. The chemical reactions that occurred in the bomb process were complex, but to interpret the calorimetric results, a set of arbitrary reactions that is consistent with the actual final and initial states could be assumed. All of the calorimetric methods described were designed to permit determination of the change in internal energy for the idealized combustion reaction represented by the following equation:

$$C_aH_bO_cCl_d(c \text{ or liq.}) + [a + (b - d)/4 - c/2] \, O_2(g)$$
$$+ [dn - (b - d)/2]H_2O(liq.) \longrightarrow aCO_2(g) + d[HCl \cdot nH_2O](liq.). \quad (1)$$

To compute values of the standard heat of reaction from the experimental data, it was necessary to correct the observed values for the energy of the combustion process for the effects due to various side reactions. Actually, part of the chlorine compound reacted according to the following equation:

$$C_aH_bO_cCl_d(c \text{ or liq.}) + [a + b/4 - c/2] \, O_2(g)$$
$$\longrightarrow aCO_2(g) + b/2H_2O(liq.) + d/2Cl_2(g). \quad (2)$$

The chlorine formed by reaction 2 was then reduced to chloride ion, by $As_2O_3$ for example, according to the following reaction:

$d/2Cl_2(g) + d/4As_2O_3(aq.) + d/2H_2O(liq.)$

$$\longrightarrow d/4As_2O_5(aq.) + dHCl(aq.). \quad (3$$

It may be seen that the sum of Equations 2 and 3 is equal to the sum of Equation 1 and $d/4$ times the following equation:

$$As_2O_3(aq.) + O_2(g) \longrightarrow As_2O_5(aq.). \tag{4}$$

Therefore, it is correct to consider that all of the chlorine compound reacted as shown in Equation 1 and that all of the arsenious oxide reacted according to Equation 4. By an analogous treatment, it may be seen that, when hydrazine dihydrochloride was used as a reductant, all of the hydrazine consumed in the combustion process could be considered to have reacted according to the following equations:

$$N_2H_4 \cdot 2HCl(aq.) + O_2(g) \longrightarrow N_2(g) + 2H_2O(liq.) + 2HCl(aq.). \quad (5)$$

$$^1/_2[N_2H_4 \cdot 2HCl](aq.) + ^1/_2H_2O(liq.) \longrightarrow NH_4Cl(aq.) + ^1/_4O_2(g). \quad (6)$$

In addition to the above chemical reactions, the following side reactions were assumed to occur in the combustion experiments with chlorine compounds.

$$6HCl(aq.) + O_2(g) + Pt(c) \longrightarrow H_2PtCl_6(aq.) + 2H_2O(liq.). \quad (7)$$

$$3HCl(aq.) + ^3/_4O_2(g) + Au(c) \longrightarrow AuCl_3(aq.) + ^3/_2H_2O(liq.). \quad (8)$$

$$^1/_2N_2(g) + ^5/_4O_2(g) + ^1/_2H_2O(liq.) \longrightarrow HNO_3(aq.). \quad (9)$$

The true oxidation state of the dissolved gold and platinum in the bomb solution has not been definitely determined. However, Eftring (11) conducted experiments that showed the tetravalent oxidation state of platinum to predominate in the diluted condensate, and concluded that it was probable that only $H_2PtCl_6$ was formed in the actual combustion process. The exact oxidation state of the dissolved gold was not important because of the small correction involved.

The analytical procedures used in the quartz-spiral and moving-bomb methods, in which arsenious oxide was used as a reductant, were designed to permit determination of the extents of reactions 1, 4, 7, 8, and 9. In the glass-cloth method, in which hydrazine-dihydrochloride was the reductant, the extents of reactions 1, 5, 6, 7, and 9 were determined from the analytical results. Appropriate thermal corrections for these auxiliary combustion reactions were then applied to the observed values for the energy of the bomb process by use of the data in Table 2. The data of Table 2 are strictly applicable only for the specified reaction in pure water. For rigorous application of the necessary thermal corrections, data applicable to the actual bomb solutions should have been used, but such detailed thermochemical data were not available. However, the errors that resulted from use of the tabulated data were probably small.

TABLE 2

Change in Internal Energy[a] for the Auxiliary Combustion Reactions, at 25 °C, in Kcal/Mole

| | | | Reaction no. | | |
| 4 | 5 | 6 | 7 | 8 | 9 |
|---|---|---|---|---|---|
| −74.4 | −132.68 | +4.25 | −63.20 | −14.76 | −14.074 |

[a] Computed from data given in reference (28).

In addition to these corrections for side reactions, it was necessary to adjust the result of each experiment for deviation from an *arbitrarily chosen* final concentration of hydrochloric acid. The data (28) used to make the dilution corrections are given in Table 3.

TABLE 3

Heat of Formation of HCl in $n$ moles $H_2O$, at 25 °C, in Kcal/Mole

| $n$ | $\Delta E°$ | $n$ | $\Delta E°$ |
|---|---|---|---|
| 20 | −39.218 | 100 | −39.713 |
| 25 | −39.335 | 200 | −39.798 |
| 30 | −39.413 | 300 | −39.837 |
| 40 | −39.516 | 400 | −39.859 |
| 50 | −39.577 | 500 | −39.874 |
| 75 | −39.665 | 600 | −39.881 |

Finally, by application of appropriate corrections the results were reduced to approximately those for the idealized combustion process, in which both reactants and products in Equation 1 are in their standard reference states. The strict application of Washburn (29) corrections could not be made. However, approximate and, in part, empirical Washburn corrections were made.

Smith (12) used an empirical relationship to correct data obtained by the quartz-spiral method for the thermal effect due to solution of carbon dioxide, the most important of the Washburn corrections. He found that the analytically determined amount of carbon dioxide dissolved in the final bomb solution could be represented by the empirical equation,

$$(CO_2 \text{ diss.}) = 0.632a + 0.620 \text{ mg,} \qquad (10)$$

where $a$ denotes milliatoms of carbon burned. By use of this relationship and a value of 4.5 kcal/mole for the heat of solution of $CO_2$, Smith (12) applied corrections for dissolved $CO_2$ to all the data determined at the University of Lund. He also determined the following empirical equation to correct the heat-of-combustion data for dilution of hydrochloric acid to the "standard" concentration, $HCl \cdot 600H_2O$,

$$\text{corr. (HCl)} = 0.29d - 0.46 \text{ cal.,} \qquad (11)$$

where $d$ is the milliatoms of chlorine in a combustion sample. Equation 11 was based on determinations of the amount of hydrochloric acid found in varying concentrations at different points in the bomb.

The amounts of dissolved carbon dioxide and hydrochloric acid were not determined in the investigations with the glass-cloth method. Therefore, approximate Washburn corrections were calculated by assuming (a) that the final bomb solution was homogeneous and in equilibrium with the gas phase, and (b) that the solubility and heat of solution of the bomb gases in the bomb solution were the same as in pure water.

In the investigations in which the moving-bomb method was used, the final state of the bomb contents more closely approached true thermodynamic equilibrium. Therefore, in principle, a rigorous application of the Washburn corrections should be possible. As noted above, however, some of the thermochemical data required to make these corrections accurately were not available. (See discussion at the end of Chapter 5.)

**4. Application of the method of comparative measurements.** Use of the method of comparative measurements to minimize experimental uncertainties in determinations of the heats of formation of organic sulfur compounds is discussed in Chapter 7. Although this method has not been used to determine heats of formation of chlorine compounds, its application may be desirable in future investigations. Consequently, a suggested procedure for making the necessary comparative measurements will be described briefly, as follows:

(i) The calibration experiments should be made precisely as recommended by the standardizing laboratory.

(ii) Combustion experiments with an organic chlorine compound should be made with an appropriate reducing solution in the combustion bomb, as follows:

TABLE 4

Standard Change in Internal Energy for Reaction 1, in kcal/mole, at 20 °C, with $n = 600$

| Compound | Quartz-spiral-As₂O₃ method with cellophane cover | Quartz-spiral-As₂O₃ method with glass ampoule | Glass-cloth-N₂H₄·2HCl method with glass ampoule | Moving-bomb-As₂O₃ method with glass ampoule |
|---|---|---|---|---|
| n-Propyl chloroacetate | 4820.9 ± 2 (8,9,12) | | | 4828.3 ± 2.6 (12) |
| n-Butyl chloroacetate | 5406.8 ± 0.5 (8,9,12) | | | 5419.1 ± 2.2 (12) |
| n-Amyl chloride | | 7498.9 ± 2 (11,12) | | 7499  ± 5   (12) |
| 1,2,3-Trichloropropane | | 2800.1 ± 3 (11,12) | | 2808.0 ± 1.3 (12) |
| p-Chlorobenzoic acid[a] | | 4680.8 ± 2 (4,12) | | 4680.8 ± 2.3 (12) |
| o-Dichlorobenzene | 4808.5 ± 2 (4,12) | 4814.1 ± 3.5 (12) | 4815.9 ± 1 (13) | 4817.3 ± 2.9 (12) |
| m-Dichlorobenzene | 4800.1 ± 2 (4,12) | | 4811.2 ± 1 (13) | |
| p-Dichlorobenzene | 4777.6 ± 1 (4,12) | | 4775.4 ± 1 (13) | |
| Chlorobenzene | | 6601.3 ± 3 (4,12) | 6599.1 ± 1 (13) | |

[a] No ampoule used.

$C_aH_bO_cCl_d$(c or liq.) + $(a + b/4 - c/2 - d/4 + 1/2)O_2$(g)
+ $R \cdot (nd - b/2 + d/2)H_2O$(liq.) = $aCO_2$ (g) + $RO \cdot d(HCl \cdot nH_2O)$(liq.). (12)

In Equation 12, R denotes the reducing agent and RO its oxidation product. The reaction of the reductant may be represented by

$$R + 1/2O_2 = RO. \qquad (13)$$

(iii) Combustion experiments with a hydrocarbon oil (taken as $CH_2$ for purposes of illustration) should be made with a solution in the bomb so constituted that the final state of the combustion process will be nearly identical with that obtained in experiments with the chlorine compound as follows:

$aCH_2$(liq.) + $3a/2O_2$(g) + $RO \cdot [dHCl \cdot (dn - a)H_2O]$(liq.)
$= aCO_2$(g) + $RO \cdot d(HCl \cdot nH_2O)$(liq.). (14)

(iv) The heat of the following reaction 15 may then be computed as the difference between the heats of reactions 12 and 14, minus the heat of reaction 13:

$C_aH_bO_cCl_d$(c or liq.) + $(b/4 - a/2 - c/2 - d/4)O_2$(g)
+ $(nd - b/2 + d/2)H_2O$(liq.) = $aCH_2$(liq.) + $d(HCl \cdot (dn - a)H_2O)$(liq.). (15)

The heat of formation of the chlorine compound may be calculated from the heat of reaction 15 by the usual thermochemical methods. Since the systematic errors associated with determinations of the heats of reactions 12 and 14 are nearly identical, they tend to cancel in the calculation of the heat of reaction 15. Consequently, it is evident that the use of the principle of comparative measurements, as proposed here, should reduce the uncertainty in values of the heats of formation of organic chlorine compounds.

**5. Comparison of data obtained by the different methods.** Some of the published data obtained by the quartz-spiral, glass-cloth, and moving-bomb methods have been reduced to a common basis as described in Section 3 of this chapter. These heat-of-combustion data are recorded in Table 4 to permit a comparison of the several methods. The results determined by the quartz-spiral method have been divided into two groups according to the type of container used for the combustion sample. Two changes have been made in the data of reference (12): (a) A revised correction for dissolved noble metals was applied to the data of Karlsson and Schjanberg; and (b) an estimated Washburn correction of +0.4 cal g$^{-1}$ was used [see reference (12)].

Because of the uncertainty of the Washburn corrections applied and because of probable differences in the purities of the combustion samples used in the various investigations, a precise comparison of the experimental data is not possible.   Nevertheless, two general conclusions may be made.   First, it is apparent that the use of a cellophane-covered crucible to contain a liquid combustion sample having a boiling point lower than about 200° usually resulted in heat-of-combustion values significantly lower than those obtained when glass ampoules were used.   Second, the results obtained by the quartz-spiral (with glass ampoules), glass-cloth, and moving-bomb methods generally agreed within the precision uncertainty of the experimental data.   Unfortunately, a comparison of all methods is afforded only by the results tabulated for o-dichlorobenzene.   However, the data for this compound are in good agreement, with the exception of the datum obtained by the quartz-spiral method with a cellophane-covered crucible.

**6. Discussion.**   It has been shown in the foregoing section that the three methods developed to determine the heats of combustion of chlorine compounds yield results of comparable accuracy.   The methods discussed involve several variations in apparatus and procedure.   First, two quite different calorimetric systems were used: a moving-bomb system and conventional static systems.   Second, two different reducing solutions were employed: arsenious-oxide and hydrazine dihydrochloride solutions.   Third, two different methods to support the reducing solution were developed: a spiral of quartz fibers and a sleeve of coarsely woven glass cloth.   Fourth, two materials were used to fabricate the internal parts of the combustion bomb: platinum and tantalum.   The most satisfactory combination of these various techniques cannot be definitely recommended on the basis of available experimental evidence.   Also, the most satisfactory combination of design features and procedures for a particular investigation will depend largely on the availability of equipment and materials and on the accuracy required.   Consequently, a discussion of the several variables is given in the following paragraphs to aid investigators in this field who must choose the procedure most appropriate for their requirements.   Some general and tentative recommendations are given in the last paragraph of this section.

(a) *Comparison of Reductants.*   Both of the reductants discussed above—arsenious oxide and hydrazine dihydrochloride—effectively reduced free chlorine formed in a combustion reaction to chloride ion.* Consequently, a comparison of the two reductants need involve only (i) the magnitude of their thermal effects on the combustion reaction, (ii) the uncertainties caused by their presence in the bomb, and (iii) their relative stabilities.

(i) Thermal effect. The thermal effect of the reduction of chlorine by arsenious oxide is only about one-sixth that involved in the use of hydrazine dihydrochloride. Consequently, the correction to the energy of the bomb process for the oxidation of the reductant could be made more reliably if the former reductant was used in a combustion experiment.

(ii) Uncertainties introduced. The addition of relatively large amounts of solution to a bomb used in combustion experiments unavoidably introduced uncertainties associated with the corrections for the heats of solution of the bomb gases in the bomb liquid. In this respect, the use of hydrazine dihydrochloride had a definite advantage since it is more soluble in water than is arsenious oxide. As a result of the greater solubility of hydrazine dihydrochloride, a smaller volume of reducing solution was used, and the corrections for solution of bomb gases in the liquid were smaller. Smith (12) has stated that half of the volume of reductant actually used in the quartz-spiral, arsenious oxide method would provide satisfactory reduction of chlorine. However, a change in the volume of reductant would necessitate redetermination of the empirical correction (Equations 10 and 11). It is evident that use of a gas phase reduction of chlorine to chloride ion would minimize uncertainties connected with the use of liquid reducing solutions. Although experiments have been made (13) in which carbon monoxide and formic acid vapors were used as reducing agents, the results were not satisfactory, and further investigations of gas phase reductants have not been attempted.

(iii) Stability of reductant. A reductant for use in bomb calorimetry must be stable in the presence of oxygen at pressures used in combustion experiments. It has been found that both arsenious oxide (12) and hydrazine dihydrochloride (13) solutions react slightly with oxygen. For both reductants, however, the magnitude of the thermal effect of the small amount of oxidation that occurred was

* In fact, Smith (2) found that pure water alone effected partial reduction of chlorine, probably as a result of the following reaction: $2H_2O + 2Cl_2 = 4HCl + O_2$.

shown to be insignificant. Additional discussion of the stability of reductants is given in Chapter 9.

(b) *Supporting Materials.* The material used to support a reducing solution in combustion experiments with chlorine compounds should undergo no thermally significant change of state in the combustion process. It has been established that the quartz fibers used in the quartz-spiral method were completely inert (12). The supporting material used in the glass-cloth method was not completely inert to the combustion process, but the thermal effect of the slight reaction that occurred was of only borderline significance (13). The presence of the supporting material on the walls of the bomb may delay the transfer of heat from the bomb to the calorimeter water. It has been shown that only a slight delay is caused by a quartz spiral. The delay caused by a glass-cloth lining is greater particularly if the lining is not placed in good contact with the walls of the bomb.

(c) *Equilibrium and Homogeneity.* The use of relatively large amounts of liquid in combustion experiments makes difficult the attainment of thermodynamic equilibrium in the final state of the combustion process. The moving-bomb method was undoubtedly the most effective in producing an equilibrium final state. In neither of the static methods was the final bomb solution completely homogeneous and in equilibrium with the gas phase. However, errors due to nonequilibrium and inhomogeneity were partially eliminated in the quartz-spiral method by use of empirical methods to reduce the data to standard states (12). Lack of homogeneity and equilibrium was not as serious in the glass-cloth method since (a) less than half the volume of reducing solution was required, and (b) the solution was entirely supported on the glass cloth. Although the extent of homogeneity and equilibrium was not investigated in the experiments with the glass-cloth method, calorimetric measurements showed that thermal effects due to nonequilibrium in the final state were not large (13).

(d) *Conclusions.* Undoubtedly, the moving-bomb method is, in principle, the most satisfactory method for the accurate determination of heat-of-combustion data for chlorine compounds, but unavailability of the specialized equipment required will prevent its use in many laboratories. The static methods have been shown to yield results of reasonably high accuracy, and the methods may be adapted for use in most heat-of-combustion laboratories. Therefore, on the basis of the investigations described in this chapter, some general recommendations will be made as to the static-bomb combustion procedure that appears to be most satisfactory. In most cases, the advantage of any one procedure over another is very slight.

Conventional combustion bombs have proved to be suitable for experiments with chlorine compounds if the bomb-lining and internal fittings are constructed of either platinum or tantalum. Use of the latter metal may be slightly more convenient since corrosion effects are smaller and easier to determine.

Principally because of the small thermal effect associated with its oxidation, use of arsenious oxide as a reducing agent is judged to be preferable to use of hydrazine dihydrochloride.

The supporting material for the reducing solution should be fabricated from quartz fibers as inert as those used in the quartz-spiral method. However, the material should support all of the bomb solution. Any glass or quartz material used should be thoroughly tested for inertness in the combustion process.

The criterion used in the glass-cloth method to establish that the combustion process was completed and "equilibrium" attained in the bomb should be employed. However, as in the quartz-spiral method, the liquid from various parts of the bomb should be analyzed for dissolved carbon dioxide and hydrochloric acid and, if necessary, appropriate corrections applied for nonequilibrium and inhomogeneity.

**7. Summary.** Since the work of Berthelot and Matignon in 1891, three methods have been developed for determining reasonably accurate values of the heats of combustion of organic chlorine compounds: two were static methods in which conventional calorimetric systems were used; the other was the moving-bomb method for which a specialized calorimetric system was designed. In each of these methods the two major problems were attacked in the same manner: a definite final state of the combustion process was obtained by use of a reducing agent in the bomb to convert the free chlorine formed to chloride ion; and indeterminable corrosion effects were eliminated by use of either platinum or tantalum for fabrication of the interior parts of the bomb. The moving-bomb method is, in principle, capable of highly accurate results. The static methods are less reliable because of uncertainties inherent in the use of a large amount of liquid in a stationary bomb. However, no method for the determination of heats of combustion of chlorine compounds has yet been developed to a point such that the accuracy of the results obtainable is comparable to the existing body of thermochemical data for hydrocarbons.

Critical re-examination of the over-all chemistry of the combustion process will be required to improve further the methods discussed in this chapter. In addition, the determination, for conditions of the combustion experiments, of the thermochemical data required in interpretation of calorimetric results will be necessary if heat-of-combustion data of highest accuracy are to be obtained in future investigations. Finally, a reference substance that contains only carbon, hydrogen, oxygen, and chlorine and has the proper physical characteristics (30) should be selected to permit reliable intercomparison of data obtained in different laboratories. Smith has suggested that *p*-chlorobenzoic acid be used as a reference standard, but further studies of its suitability are needed.

## References

1. F. Swarts, *J. chim. phys.* **17**, 3 (1919) and preceding papers by Swarts *et al.*
2. L. Smith and E. Schjanberg, *Svensk Kem. Tidskr.* **43**, 213 (1931).
3. L. Smith and S. Sunner, *The Svedberg Mem. Vol.*, Almqvist and Wiksells Boktryckeri, Uppsala, Sweden, 1944, p. 352.
4. K. J. Karlsson (now Karrman), Thesis, University of Lund. Carl Bloms Boktryckeri, Lund, Sweden, 1941.
5. M. P. E. Berthelot and C. Matignon, *Ann. chim. phys.* [6s] **23**, 507 (1891).
6. L. Smith, *Svensk Kem. Tidskr.* **40**, 297 (1928).
7. L. Smith, *Svensk Kem. Tidskr.* **41**, 272 (1929).
8. E. Schjanberg, Thesis, University of Lund. Berlingska Boktryckeriet, Lund, Sweden, 1934.
9. E. Schjanberg, *Z. physik. Chem.* **A172**, 197 (1935).
10. G. Sjostrom, *Svensk Kem. Tidskr.* **48**, 121 (1936).
11. E. Eftring, Thesis, University of Lund. Carl Bloms Boktryckeri, Lund, Sweden, 1938.
12. L. Smith, L. Bjellerup, S. Krook, and H. Westermark, *Acta Chem. Scand.* **7**, 65 (1953).
13. W. N. Hubbard, J. W. Knowlton, and H. M. Huffman, *J. Phys. Chem.* **58**, 396 (1954).
14. M. M. Popoff and P. K. Schirokich, *Z. physik. Chem.* **A167**, 183 (1933).
15. W. A. Roth, *Z. Electrochem.* **43**, 355 (1935).
16. S. Sunner, Thesis, University of Lund. Carl Bloms Boktryckeri, Lund, Sweden, 1949.
17. L. Smith and L. Bjellerup, *Acta Chem. Scand.* **1**, 566 (1947).
18. H. C. Dickinson, *Bull. Natl. Bur. Standards* **11**, 189 (1915).
19. W. N. Hubbard, C. Katz, and G. Waddington, *J. Phys. Chem.* **58**, 142 (1954).
20. L. Bjellerup, Thesis, University of Lund. To be published.

21. W. A. Roth and H. Wallasch, *Lieb. Ann.* **407**, 134 (1915).
22. P. E. Verkade and J. Coops, *Rec. trav. chim.* **45**, 545 (1926).
23. T. W. Richards and R. H. Jesse, *J. Am. Chem. Soc.* **32**, 268 (1910).
24. L. Smith, *Svensk Kem. Tidskr.* **45**, 110 (1933).
25. W. N. Hubbard, J. W. Knowlton, and H. M. Huffman, *J. Am. Chem. Soc.* **70**, 3259 (1948).
26. G. Waddington, J. W. Knowlton, D. W. Scott, G. D. Oliver, S. S. Todd, W. N. Hubbard, J. C. Smith, and H. M. Huffman, *J. Am. Chem. Soc.* **71**, 797 (1949).
27. R. A. Penneman and L. F. Audrieth, *Anal. Chem.* **20**, 1058 (1948).
28. F. D. Rossini, D. D. Wagman, W. H. Evans, S. Levine, and I. Jaffe, *Natl. Bur. Standards Circ.* 500 (1952).
29. E. W. Washburn, *J. Research Natl. Bur. Standards* **10**, 525 (1933).
30. H. M. Huffman, *J. Am. Chem. Soc.* **60**, 1171 (1938).

# CHAPTER 9

# Combustion in a Bomb of Organic Bromine Compounds

LENNART SMITH AND LARS BJELLERUP

**1. Introduction and historical development.** The general nature of the problems encountered in measurements of the heats of combustion of organic halogen compounds was discussed in Chapter 8. Since the problems met in studies of both chlorine and bromine compounds are similar, attempts were made to use the same experimental methods for both classes of compound. However, the static methods that were reasonably satisfactory for studies of chlorine compounds were found unsuitable for use with bromine compounds (1). Because a large amount of free halogen is formed in combustion experiments with the latter materials (see Table 1, Chapter 8), complete reduction to bromide ion was not possible by use of the static techniques. The moving-bomb method, however, proved to be adaptable to investigations on bromine compounds; the development of that method will be described in this chapter.

As mentioned in Chapter 8, Popoff and Schirokich (2) described in 1933 the first moving-bomb apparatus for determining the heats of combustion of halogen compounds. These investigators reported results obtained for several bromine compounds. The principal aim of their investigation was to develop the unique "oscillating-bomb" calorimeter, and the precision of their results was low, 0.1 to 0.5 per cent. After Smith and Sunner (1) had shown static techniques impractical for experiments with bromine compounds, Smith, Sunner and Bjellerup, in the same laboratory, made extensive studies of the moving-bomb method (1,3-5). These investigators developed three different types of moving bomb: (*a*) a rocking bomb (1) similar to that of Popoff and Schirokich (2); (b) a rotating bomb, designed by Sunner primarily for use with sulfur compounds (5); and (c) a bomb with an oscillatory-rotatory motion designed by Smith and Bjellerup (3,4). As the several moving-bomb techniques were developed and improved, results of increasingly high precision were obtained. The oscillatory-rotatory motion of the bomb designed by Smith and Bjellerup effectively provided the agitation and mixing required to reduce the free bromine formed in a combustion reaction. The results obtained with the most recent modification of this technique were comparable in precision (0.01 to 0.04 per cent) to those obtained by the best methods available for heats of combustion of organic oxygen and organic sulfur compounds.

**2. Experimental apparatus and procedure.**  Of existing techniques, only the moving-bomb methods may be considered satisfactory for the determination of the heats of combustion of bromine-containing compounds. The calorimetric system and experimental techniques used by Smith and Bjellerup (3,4) are well suited for this purpose. Consequently, in this section, in addition to remarks of a general nature, some specific details of Bjellerup's (4) apparatus and procedure will be presented. However, it should be emphasized that, in general, any high precision techniques may be used for handling the sample, igniting the charge, sufficiently agitating the bomb contents to accomplish the reduction, or making the calorimetric observations. Any of the dynamic calorimetric systems described in Chapters 7 and 8 and in references (1–6) should be adaptable to meet adequately the problems involved in combustion experiments with bromine compounds.

Since the problems involved in studies of chlorine and bromine containing compounds are similar, the procedures outlined here may also serve as a guide for the determination of the heats of combustion of chlorine-containing compounds by the moving-bomb method.

(a) *The Reducing Agent.*  Regardless of the type of calorimetric system employed, a suitable reducing agent must be used in a bomb for experiments with chlorine and bromine compounds. In 1936, the former Commission for Thermochemistry suggested (7) three reducing agents for possible use in combustion experiments with halogenated organic substances: arsenious oxide, formic acid, and hydrazine *mono*-hydrochloride. The use of arsenious oxide and hydrazine *di*-hydrochloride in experiments with chlorine compounds has been described in Chapter 8, and the advantages and disadvantages of each were discussed.

One of the principal requirements for a reducing agent is that it should not react with the oxygen present in the bomb in either the initial or final period of the calorimetric observations.* It has been found that hydrazine monohydrochloride (8) and hydrazine dihydrochloride (9) are both oxidized in varying amounts under the initial conditions of static-bomb experiments in which the reducing solution is supported on a quartz spiral or glass cloth. Karlsson (10) found that small and varying amounts of arsenious oxide were lost in his combustions of halogen-free substances with the quartz-spiral method. Smith and co-workers (8), however, found no loss of arsenious oxide in their combustions of paraffin oil with the quartz-spiral method. Bjellerup (4) also investigated the stability of arsenious oxide solutions and found the reductant to be completely stable during combustions of benzoic acid and paraffin oil with the moving-bomb method. Because of its stability and other advantages discussed in Chapter 8, Bjellerup chose arsenious oxide as a reductant in his bomb-calorimetric investigations with bromine compounds.

(b) *Calorimetric System.* The calorimetric system used by Bjellerup was of the constant temperature environment type, and was designed in such a manner that there was space within the calorimeter vessel for a complete end-over-end rotation of the bomb. The temperature measurements were made with the improved ocular scale Beckmann thermometer technique described by Sunner (5).

Bjellerup found that the bomb could be of conventional design— preferably of the three-part type†—and equipped with two valves to permit thorough flushing of air from the bomb. To minimize corrosion the bomb lining and internal fittings were constructed from platinum and, where necessary, welded with gold. In combustion experiments with bromine compounds, the noble metals were only slightly attacked by the combustion products. The thermal effect of the corrosion was less than 0.1 cal per combustion experiment.

The oscillatory-rotatory combustion bomb-calorimetric system described by Smith and Bjellerup provides a very effective agitation

* Oxidation, if any, of the reductant during the reaction period is automatically considered in applying the correction for side reaction 5 discussed in Section 3.

† Use of a three-part bomb facilitates installation of a noble metal lining and gasket.

of the bomb solution. Such thorough agitation of the solution and combustion products is particularly necessary in bromine compound studies because it is difficult to reduce the large amount of elemental bromine formed in the experiment in a reasonably short reaction period.

The combustion bomb was supported by a ring equipped with axles and bearings so designed that the bomb could be either oscillated or completely rotated about a horizontal axis. Arrangement was also made such that the bomb could be turned 90° in the support ring at a predetermined time. The sequence of motions used in a combustion experiment was as follows. First, the bomb was oscillated back and forth about a horizontal axis over an arc slightly larger than 180°. After 12 complete oscillations, the bomb was rotated about the same horizontal axis for five complete revolutions. It was then turned 90° on its longitudinal axis and again rotated for five complete revolutions about the horizontal axis. The whole series of operations was accomplished by means of a fine copper wire wound both around a pulley on one axle of the supporting ring and back and forth around appropriately located pins on the bomb-rotating mechanism. The time required for this sequence of motions was 130 sec. The motion of the bomb insured that a solution in the bomb was thoroughly agitated and that all the internal surfaces of the bomb were rinsed by the bomb liquid if the volume of the bomb solution was 30 ml.

(c) *Calorimetric Procedure.* Some of the details of the calorimetric procedure used by Bjellerup follow.

For combustions of volatile liquids the samples were sealed in soft-glass ampoules and paraffin oil was used as the auxiliary material.* After the sample, auxiliary material, and fuse had been weighed and assembled in the crucible, 30 ml of $0.0625M$ arsenious oxide solution was added to the bomb. The bomb was sealed and the air flushed out with oxygen to minimize the quantity of nitrogen oxides formed in the combustion process. The bomb was then charged with oxygen† to 30 atm pressure and installed in the calorimeter.

---

* No nonvolatile solid bromine compounds were studied, but, for combustions of such materials, the sample should be pelleted. Some solid compounds of high bromine content should also require use of an auxiliary oil to insure complete combustion.

† The oxygen used contained 0.3 per cent nitrogen as impurity, but no detectable hydrogen.

After the calorimetric system was assembled and at thermal equilibrium, observations of the temperature of the calorimeter were made in a 10-min initial period. The combustion sample was then ignited, and 40 sec later,* the sequence of oscillatory-rotatory motions of the bomb was started. It was found that the time required for completion of the reaction period was 21.5 min. The unusual length of the reaction period was partly owing to the fact that use of an ebony lid for the calorimeter vessel delayed attainment of thermal equilibrium.

After the reaction period, the temperature of the calorimeter was observed for a final period of fifteen minutes.

(d) *Analytical Chemical Procedure.* The analytical procedures used by Bjellerup in his experiments with bromine compounds were similar to those used at the University of Lund in studies of chlorine compounds (see Chapter 8). To define the final state of the combustion process it was necessary (i) to establish that all free bromine was reduced to bromide ion, (ii) to determine the amount of arsenious oxide consumed in the reaction, (iii) to determine the amount of nitric acid formed, and (iv) to determine the amount of platinum and gold dissolved in the bomb solution. Briefly, the procedure employed was as follows:

(i) After some of the combustion experiments, the bomb gases—at the end of the reaction period—were discharged through a starch-iodide solution to detect free bromine. In none of the experiments in which the test was made was the presence of free bromine established. Consequently, it was assumed that the reduction to bromide ion was complete in all the experiments. To obtain further verification of this assumption, the bromide ion concentration in the bomb solution was determined after all combustion experiments by potentiometric titration with silver nitrate solution.

(ii) The liquid contents of the bomb were transferred quantitatively to a volumetric flask and diluted to 250 ml. A 50-ml aliquot portion of the diluted solution was titrated with potassium permanganate in the presence of a trace of potassium iodide to determine the amount of excess arsenious oxide in the bomb solution and, by difference from the quantity originally added, the amount consumed was calculated (12, see also Chapter 8).

* By direct measurement of the temperature in the combustion zone, it was shown that most of the combustion reaction was completed within 15 sec after ignition of the sample (11, cf. Chapter 7).

(iii) The amount of nitric acid in the bomb solution was determined colorimetrically by the diphenylamine method (13). It was found that about 0.15 millimol nitric acid was formed in each experiment.

(iv) The small amounts of platinum and gold dissolved in the bomb solution were determined by the techniques used in the quartz-spiral method for chlorine compounds, as described in Chapter 8.

**3. Thermodynamic states and appropriate thermal corrections.** If the results of combustion experiments are to be most useful, they must be so interpreted as to obtain a value for the change in internal energy of an idealized combustion reaction. For this purpose, it is necessary that the chemistry of the bomb process be well understood in order that appropriate thermochemical corrections may be applied to the observed energy of the bomb process.

(*a*) *Chemistry of the Bomb Process.* The nature of the chemical process that occurs in combustion experiments made in a moving bomb is well established for organic bromine compounds. The primary chemical reaction is the oxidation of the compound to form carbon dioxide, elemental bromine, and hydrobromic acid solution:

$$C_aH_bO_cBr_d(c \text{ or liq.}) + [a - c/2 + (b - d)/4 + x/2]O_2(g) = aCO_2(g)$$
$$+ xBr_2(g) + (d - 2x)HBr\cdot(b/2 - d/2 + x)H_2O(aq.). \qquad (1)$$

The elemental bromine formed is then reduced to hydrobromic acid by the arsenious oxide solution present in the bomb:

$$xBr_2(g) + x/2As_2O_3(aq.) + xH_2O(liq.) = 2xHBr(aq.) + x/2As_2O_5(aq.). \qquad (2)$$

The amount of elemental bromine formed according to Equation 1 has been found (1,3,4) to comprise from 90 to 97 per cent of the bromine content of the sample (Table 1, Chapter 8) and to depend on various experimental conditions such as the amount of bromine in the sample, the quantity of auxiliary oil used, the temperature of the combustion, and the position of the crucible. However, the moving-bomb–arsenious oxide method has been shown to reduce effectively the bromine formed in a combustion experiment. The tests described in the preceding section of this chapter showed that significant concentrations of bromine were not present in the gas phase; and analysis (4) of the liquid phase showed that 99.5 to 99.8 per cent of the bromine contained in a combustion sample was present as $Br^-$ in the final bomb solution and that about 0.2 per cent was present as $Au Br_4^-$.

In addition to the reactions shown in Equations 1 and 2, several side reactions take place in the combustion process. One of these side reactions involves the combustion of the auxiliary material used to ignite samples enclosed in glass ampoules. Other side reactions involve oxidation of the nitrogen present as impurity in the oxygen and corrosion of noble metals in the bomb.

(b) *Thermochemical Corrections and Reduction to Standard States.* On the basis of the preceding discussion, the contents of a combustion bomb after experiments with a bromine compound in a moving-bomb system may be described qualitatively as follows: a homogeneous gas phase that contains oxygen, carbon dioxide, and a small amount of **nitrogen** and that is saturated with water vapor; and a homogeneous liquid phase that consists of an aqueous solution of arsenious oxide, arsenic oxide, hydrogen bromide, carbon dioxide, nitric acid, oxygen, and dissolved gold and platinum. A quantitative description of this final state of the bomb process may be obtained by the analytical procedures discussed in the preceding section. Consequently, by application of appropriate thermochemical corrections, the standard change in internal energy for the following idealized combustion reaction may be computed from the observed energy of the bomb process:

$$C_aH_bO_cBr_d(c \text{ or liq.}) + (a + b/4 - c/2)O_2(g)$$
$$= aCO_2(g) + b/2H_2O(\text{liq.}) + d/2Br_2(\text{liq.}). \quad (3)$$

where both reactants and products are in their appropriate standard reference state.

The thermal corrections required to compute the change in internal energy of reaction 3 may be determined in a manner analogous to that described in Chapter 8 for experiments with chlorine compounds. For the purpose of the calculations, the following hypothetical combustion process may be considered instead of a more realistic process represented by Equations 1 and 2:

$$C_aH_bO_cBr_d(c \text{ or liq.}) + [a - c/2 + (b - d)/4]O_2(g)$$
$$= aCO_2(g) + dHBr \cdot (b - d)/2H_2O(\text{aq.}). \quad (4)$$
$$As_2O_3(\text{aq.}) + O_2(g) = As_2O_5(\text{aq.}). \quad (5)$$

It may be seen that the sum of reaction 4 and $x/2$ times reaction 5 is the equivalent to the sum of reactions 1 and 2. Furthermore, the sum of reaction 4 and $d$ times reaction 6 is equivalent to reaction 3.

$$HBr(aq.) + \tfrac{1}{4}O_2 = \tfrac{1}{2}H_2O(liq.) + \tfrac{1}{2}Br_2(liq.). \hspace{2em} (6)$$

The extent of reaction 5 may be determined from the amount of arsenious oxide consumed in the combustion reaction; and the extent of reaction 6 may be computed from the composition and mass of the combustion sample. Thus, except for the effects of side reactions and deviations from standard states, the change in internal energy of reaction 3 may be computed from the observed energy of the bomb process by subtraction of the energy of oxidation of arsenious oxide (Equation 5) and addition of the energy of oxidation of hydrobromic acid (Equation 6).

To make these calculations requires thermochemical data for reactions 5 and 6. Unfortunately, the change in internal energy for the oxidation of arsenious oxide (Equation 5) is not well established, but, until a more reliable value becomes available, use of the following datum (14a) is recommended for the sake of consistency:*  −74.3 kcal/mole for the change in internal energy at 25°C. The value to be used for the change in internal energy of reaction 6 depends on the concentration of hydrobromic acid in the final bomb solution. Table 1 contains values of $\Delta E°$ at 25°C (reaction 6) as a function of the concentration of hydrobromic acid (14b,c).

To determine the change in internal energy of reaction 3, it is

TABLE 1

| $\dfrac{n(H_2O)}{n(HBr)}$ | $\Delta E°$ at 25°C, kcal/mole |
|---|---|
| 20 | −5.76 |
| 30 | −5.60 |
| 40 | −5.53 |
| 50 | −5.47 |
| 75 | −5.40 |
| 100 | −5.36 |
| 200 | −5.30 |
| 300 | −5.27 |
| 400 | −5.25 |
| 500 | −5.24 |
| 700 | −5.23 |

* From calorimetric measurements of the heat of reaction of arsenious oxide and bromine in aqueous solution and the established heats of formation of water and solutions of bromine and hydrobromic acid, Smith and Sunner (1) found $\Delta E°$ at 20°C for reaction 5 to be −77.2 kcal/mole.

necessary to correct the observed energy of the bomb process for the thermal effects of the various side reactions. Corrections for the energy of combustion of the auxiliary oil and fuse and for the ignition energy may be applied in the conventional manner (Chapter 3). Corrections must also be made for the effects of the following side reactions:

$$^1/_2N_2(g) + {}^5/_4O_2(g) + {}^1/_2H_2O(liq.) = HNO_3(aq.\ 0.1N) \tag{7}$$

$$\Delta E°(\text{reaction 7}) = -14.074 \text{ kcal/mole at } 25°C \text{ (14c,d).}$$

$$6\ HBr(aq.) + O_2(g) + Pt(c) = H_2Pt\ Br_6(aq.) + 2H_2O(liq.) \tag{8}$$

$$\Delta E°(\text{reaction 8}) = -79.64 \text{ kcal/mole at } 25°C \text{ (14b,c,e)}$$

$$4\ HBr(aq.) + {}^3/_4O_2(g) + Au(c) \longrightarrow HAuBr_4(aq.) + {}^3/_2H_2O(liq.) \tag{9}$$

$$\Delta E°(\text{reaction 9}) = -31.93 \text{ kcal/mole at } 25°C(14b,c,f).$$

The appropriate corrections for reactions 7, 8, and 9 may be made from the thermochemical data given and the experimentally determined amounts of nitric acid and dissolved metals in the final bomb solution. The actual nature and energetics of side reactions 8 and 9 are not well established, but the thermal effects involved are small; i.e., the total correction is usually less than 0.1 cal.

The problem of reduction to standard states (at 25°C) of calorimetric heat-of-combustion data is discussed in Chapter 5, and a convenient computation form was presented there. As mentioned in that chapter, some of the auxiliary data required to make the corrections to standard states are lacking and must be estimated to interpret the results of combustion experiments with chlorine or bromine compounds. The data that must be determined before the strict reduction to standard states can be made are discussed.

Bjellerup (4) has determined the necessary auxiliary data at 20°C. His results should be very useful as a guide in estimating the thermal data needed at 25°C. Since most of the corrections are small, the estimates of their magnitudes can usually be made with moderate accuracy. The largest of the so-called Washburn (15) corrections is that for the heat of solution of carbon dioxide in the bomb liquid. This correction is particularly large in combustion experiments with bromine compounds since the volume of liquid used in the moving-bomb may be as much as 40 times that recommended for use in combustion calorimeters (16,17). Bjellerup (4) used the method of Sunner (5) to determine the heat of solution of carbon dioxide in solutions similar in composition to those found in his combustion experiments. For the conditions of Bjellerup's combustion experiments, the correction for the heat of solution of carbon dioxide was found to be about 0.3 per cent of the total energy evolved in the bomb process. The results of an investigation primarily concerned with possible errors related to the evaluation of this energy effect have been discussed by Sunner and Bjellerup (18).

(c) *Summary.* By application of corrections determined as discussed in the preceding paragraphs, the standard change in internal energy at 25°C for the idealized combustion reaction 3 may be computed with moderate accuracy from the observed energy of the actual combustion process. To show the magnitudes of some of these corrections, representative data from Bjellerup's investigation of the heat of combustion of $n$-butyl bromide are given in Table 2.

TABLE 2

| Item No.[a] | Quantity | Value | Units |
|---|---|---|---|
| 2 | $m'$, mass of $n$-butyl bromide | 0.60492 | g |
| 8 | $m''$, mass of auxiliary oil, $CH_{1.97}$ | 0.15996 | g |
| 38a | $n^f(As_2O_5)$, moles of arsenic oxide in the final solution | 0.001057 | mole |
| 91a | $\Delta E^f_{decomp.}(A_2sO_5)$ | 78.6 | cal |
| $-97 + 92$ | $-n'''\Delta E^\circ_c(\text{fuse}) + \Delta E^f_{decomp.}(HNO_3)$ | 19.5 | cal |
| 87 | $\Delta E^f_{soln.}(CO_2)$ | 13.4 | cal |
| [b] | $\Delta E(\text{reaction } 6)n^f(HBr)$ | $-23.2$ | cal |
| | The sum of the remaining corrections to standard states | 0.4 | cal |
| 99 | $\dfrac{n'\Delta E_c{}^\circ(n\text{-butyl bromide})}{m'}$ | $-4733.4$ | cal g$^{-1}$ |

[a] Item numbers concerning standard states, in Chapter 5.

[b] Item number 91 plus a correction for the oxidation of HBr to liquid bromine and water.

## 4. Application of the method of comparative measurements.

By use of the moving-bomb method described in this chapter, values of the heats of combustion of organic bromine compounds may be determined with high precision. However, because of uncertainties inherent in the method or the lack of certain auxiliary thermal data, the absolute accuracy of the results may not be as high. To minimize uncertainties, it is desirable to employ a procedure in the calibration and combustion experiments such that systematic errors partially cancel in calculating heats of combustion and/or formation from data obtained by bomb calorimetry.

The principal systematic errors that must be considered are caused by the differences between the bomb conditions encountered in conventional calibration experiments (Chapter 3) and those in combustion experiments with bromine compounds. In the latter experiments, the amount of solution present in the bomb is much larger than in the former. Consequently, significant systematic errors in evaluating the thermal effects due to a large amount of liquid in the bomb would lead to error in the final results if conventional calibration procedures were used. For this reason, Smith and Bjellerup (3,4) adopted a modified calibration procedure. In their calibration experiments with benzoic acid, these investigators added to the combustion bomb an arsenious oxide solution of the same volume and composition as that used in their combustion experiments. Thus, the initial states in the calibration and combustion experiments were nearly identical, and the final states did not differ radically. By means of this procedure systematic errors due to the use of a large volume of liquid in the bomb were partially canceled. However, it was necessary to evaluate the thermal effects associated with the deviation of the *actual* from the *standard* calibration experiments, and the difference in the final states of the calibration and the combustion experiments. To date, this procedure has been used exclusively in studies of the heats of combustion of bromine compounds.

Two other procedures designed to eliminate similar systematic errors have been described in the chapters on sulfur (Chapter 7) and chlorine compounds (Chapter 8). Either or both of these methods should be adaptable for use in studies of bromine compounds, but neither has been used in actual experiments with halogenated materials. A careful investigation of these two possible techniques must be made before the most satisfactory procedure can be established. A complete investigation with one compound by all three methods would yield considerable information concerning the existence of systematic errors in determinations of the heats of combustion of bromine-containing compounds.

**5. Evaluation of the method of Smith and Bjellerup.** The method of Smith and Bjellerup (3,4), as described in preceding sections of this chapter, has been used to obtain high-precision heat-of-combustion data for bromine compounds. Unfortunately, no directly measured data of comparable precision have been reported by other investigators, and, therefore, an evaluation of the method must be considered tentative only.

As with most thermal measurements it is difficult to establish the absolute accuracy of the results obtainable by the application of a given procedure for the determination of the heats of combustion of halogen-containing compounds. Use of the method by different investigators for studies on identical samples of a substance is desirable since it would introduce variations of procedure and a critical examination of significant variables. Another check available in some situations is the utilization of the resulting heats of formation for the calculation of chemical equilibria which have been accurately established by other means. A third approach is to seek a calorimetrically determined heat of reaction which may be compared with the results of the combustion experiments. An example of this method is the comparison which has been made by Rossini (19) of the directly determined heat of hydrogenation of ethylene (20) and the indirect evaluation of this datum from directly determined heats of combustion (21). Conn, Kistiakowsky, and Smith (22) have determined the heat of bromination of ethylene and propylene and Lacher *et al.* (23,24) have determined the heat of reaction of hydrogen bromide with cyclopropane, propene, and the isomeric butenes to give 1-bromopropane, 2-bromopropane, and 2-bromobutane, respectively. These results have been compared (25) with direct determinations of the heats of combustion of 1-bromopropane, 2-bromopropane, and 2-bromobutane (4). The heats of formation of these bromoalkanes calculated from the results of the independent investigations mentioned above are given in Table 3. The table shows that only in the case of 1-bromopropane was the discrepancy in the heats of formation obtained very much greater than the combined uncertainties of the several methods.

The use of an ebony lid on the calorimeter can which delays thermal equilibrium, and the use of 30 ml of water in the bomb might lead to significant errors. However, Sunner and Bjellerup (18) showed that errors from these causes did not lead to errors in their results. The heat of combustion of paraffin oil obtained with Bjellerup's system (4) was in excellent agreement with a corresponding value obtained with Sunner's system (5) in which the amount of water added was one third and the length of reaction period was one half of that necessary for Bjellerup's system.

By use of the method of Smith and Bjellerup (3,4), accurate values, can, in principle, be obtained for the heats of combustion and formation of organic bromine compounds. However, since some of the auxiliary thermochemical data required to interpret the experimental combustion data are not well established, the accuracy that actually

TABLE 3

Comparison of Heats of Formation of Organic Bromine Compounds from Several Methods

| | Heat of formation at 25°C in kcal/mole | | |
|---|---|---|---|
| | From heat of hydrobromination data[a] | From heat of combustion data | From heat of hydrogenation and bromination data[b] |
| 1-Bromopropane | $-18.5 \pm 0.3$ | $-21.3 \pm 0.4$ | — |
| 2-Bromopropane | $-23.8 \pm 0.4$ | $-22.7 \pm 0.5$ | $-22.5 \pm 0.4$ |
| 2-Bromobutane | $-28.6 \pm 0.4$ | $-28.0 \pm 0.4$ | $-27.4 \pm 0.4$ |

[a] The hydrobromination data given by Lacher et al. have been recalculated to 298°K. The value given for 2-bromobutane is the mean of the three values calculated from the heats of hydrobromination of the three butenes.

[b] The values were calculated from the heats of hydrobromination of propene and 1-butene estimated according to the method proposed by Kistiakowsky et al. (22).

can be obtained at the present time may not be as high as that of which the method is inherently capable. In addition to the need for more reliable auxiliary data, further study of some of the details of the experimental method would be desirable. Some aspects of the method that require further study are indicated in the following paragraphs.

(i) Additional systematic investigations should be made of the chemical and thermodynamic properties of various reducing agents for use as reductants in combustion calorimetry with halogen compounds.

(ii) The application of experimental techniques that have proved valuable in studies of other types of compounds should be considered. These would include the use of an inverted bomb (see Chapters 7 and 8).

(iii) Investigations should be made of the several methods for making comparative measurements mentioned in Section 4 of this chapter.

Application in a single laboratory of all the procedures described should permit a decision as to the most reliable method.

(iv) To minimize uncertainties in application of the various thermal corrections discussed in Section 3 of this chapter, accurate values of some of the auxiliary thermal data, such as the heats of reactions 5 and 6, should be determined for conditions similar to those encountered in the actual combustion experiments. Furthermore certain other auxiliary data which are discussed in Chapter 5 (Section 5 and 7) need to be obtained.

**6. Summary.** A method has been described in this chapter by means of which highly reproducible values of the heats of combustion and formation of organic bromine compounds may be obtained. Although the procedure and apparatus were developed particularly for experiments with bromine compounds, the method should be easily adaptable for bomb-calorimetric investigations of organic chlorine compounds and halogen compounds in general. Within a few years, it is probable that further minor improvements in the experimental technique will be made and that most of the auxiliary thermal data required for accurate interpretation of experimental results will be determined. None of the problems that require further investigation (see Section 5, this chapter) are insoluble by presently available techniques, and their solution should be provided in investigations currently in progress or planned. Therefore, it may be expected confidently that a general method will soon be available for determining the heats of combustion and formation of organic halogen compounds with an accuracy comparable to that of the existing body of precise thermochemical data.

### References

1. L. Smith and S. Sunner, *The Svedberg Mem. Vol.*, Almqvist och Wiksells Boktryckeri, Uppsala, Sweden, 1944, p. 352.
2. M. M. Popoff and P. K. Schirokich, *Z. physik. Chem.* **A167,** 183 (1933).
3. L. Smith and L. Bjellerup, *Acta Chem. Scand.* **1,** 566 (1947).
4. L. Bjellerup. To be published.
5. S. Sunner, Thesis, University of Lund, Carl Bloms Boktryckeri, Lund, Sweden, 1949.
6. W. N. Hubbard, C. Katz, and G. Waddington, *J. Phys. Chem.* **58,** 142 (1954).
7. Union Internationale de Chimie, Commission Permanente de Thermochimie, *Appendices au Premier Rapport de la Commission*, Paris, 1936.
8. L. Smith, L. Bjellerup, S. Krook, and H. Westermark, *Acta Chem. Scand.* **7,** 65 (1953).

9. W. N. Hubbard, J. W. Knowlton, and H. M. Huffman, *J. Phys. Chem.* **58,** 396 (1954).
10. K. J. Karlsson, Thesis, University of Lund, Carl Bloms Boktryckeri, Lund, Sweden, 1941.
11. S. Sunner, Unpublished measurements.
12. I. M. Kolthoff and E. B. Sandell, *Textbook of Quantitative Inorganic Analysis,* rev. ed., Macmillan, New York, 1943, p. 594.
13. L. Smith, *Svensk Kem. Tidskr.* **45,** 110 (1933).
14. F. D. Rossini, D. D. Wagman, W. H. Evans, S. Levine, and I. Jaffe, *Natl. Bur. Standards Circ.* 500 (1952). (*a*) Series 1, Table 20; (*b*) Series 1, Table 11; (*c*) Series 1, Table 8; (*d*) Series 1, Table 18; (*e*) Series 1, Table 37; (*f*) Series 1, Table 36.
15. E. W. Washburn, *J. Research Natl. Bur. Standards,* **10,** 525 (1933).
16. Union Internationale de Chimie, Commission Permanente de Thermochimie, *Premier Rapport,* Paris, 1934.
17. "Provisional Certificate of Analysis of Standard Sample 39g, Benzoic Acid," Natl. Bur. Standards, Washington, D. C., 1949.
18. S. Sunner and L. Bjellerup, *Acta Chem. Scand.* **5,** 261 (1951).
19. F. D. Rossini, *J. Research Natl. Bur. Standards* **17,** 629 (1936).
20. G. B. Kistiakowsky, H. Romeyn, Jr., J. R. Ruhoff, H. A. Smith, and W. E. Vaughan, *J. Am. Chem. Soc.* **57,** 65 (1935).
21. F. D. Rossini and J. W. Knowlton, *J. Research Natl. Bur. Standards* **19,** 249 (1937).
22. J. B. Conn, G. B. Kistiakowsky, and E. A. Smith, *J. Am. Chem. Soc.* **60,** 2764 (1938).
23. J. R. Lacher, C. H. Walden, K. R. Lea, and J. D. Park, *J. Am. Chem. Soc.* **72,** 331 (1950).
24. J. R. Lacher, T. J. Billings, D. E. Campion, K. R. Lea, and J. D. Park, *J. Am. Chem. Soc.* **74,** 5291 (1952).
25. L. Bjellerup, *XIIIth International Congress of Pure and Applied Chemistry Abstracts of Papers,* 1953, p. 8.

# CHAPTER 10

## Combustion in a Bomb of Organic Iodine Compounds

LENNART SMITH

**1. Introduction.** Measurement of the heat of combustion of an organic iodine compound does not involve the severe technical difficulties encountered in bomb-calorimetric investigations of chlorine and bromine compounds. In combustion experiments with the last two types of compounds, the halogen content of a combustion sample is found in the reaction products in two oxidation states; but in experiments with iodine-containing materials, only elemental iodine appears among the products of the combustion reaction (Table 1, Chapter 8). Thus, investigations of the heats of combustion of iodine compounds do not require such special techniques as were used in studies of chlorine and bromine compounds to obtain a definable final state of the combustion process. For this reason, relatively conventional procedures were used in the few investigations that have been made on iodine compounds.

Since the early bomb-calorimetric combustion studies of organic iodine compounds made by Berthelot (1), only three similar investigations have been reported in the literature. In 1921, Roth and Macheleidt (2) determined the heat of combustion of iodo-aniline. In 1941, Karlsson (3) published in his dissertation heat-of-combustion data for nineteen iodine-containing derivatives of benzene. Roth's (4) determination in 1944 of the heat of combustion of $\beta$-iodo propionic acid is the last reported work on iodine compounds. Some of the unique features of these investigations will be described in this chapter.

**2. Experimental apparatus and procedure.** It has been found

221

that the conventional apparatus and procedures of bomb-calorimetry are satisfactory for use in determining the heats of combustion of organic iodine compounds. Consequently, the procedures discussed in earlier chapters of this book for calibrating calorimetric systems, handling combustion samples, and making experimental observations are applicable to studies of iodine compounds. For this reason, it will not be necessary to discuss in detail the procedures that were described in references (1–4). However, the following observations reported by Roth and Karlsson deserve mention:

Both Roth (2,4) and Karlsson (3) found that use of a combustion bomb lined with platinum and equipped with platinum fittings eliminated significant corrosion of the bomb parts by the products of combustion.

Roth (4) added only 1 ml of water to the bomb before a combustion experiment. Consequently, systematic errors connected with the presence of a large volume of liquid in the bomb were minimized in his determinations.

Roth (4) stated that for the conditions of his experiments with iodine compounds the rate of change of temperature did not become constant until 11 min after firing, whereas for halogen-free compounds the rate became constant from 8 to 9 min after firing. Consequently, care must be taken that the reaction period is sufficiently long.

Both investigators found that the elemental iodine formed in the combustion reaction was distributed among the aqueous, vapor and solid phases with the bulk of the material being present as solid iodine.

To secure evidence regarding the assumption that only elemental iodine is formed in combustion experiments with iodine compounds, both Karlsson and Roth determined the total iodine distributed among the three phases of the combustion products and found it to agree with the calculated amount.*

On the basis of the investigations mentioned above, the following general procedure can be recommended for bomb-calorimetric studies with organic iodine compounds:

A conventional static-bomb calorimetric system may be employed.

---

* Iodine in the vapor phase was condensed from the bomb gases (Karlsson) or dissolved in KI solution (Roth). These amounts were added to washings of the remainder of the bomb contents. Total iodine in the combined solutions was determined by thiosulfate titration.

A bomb lined with platinum should be used.

Calibration of the calorimetric system should conform to the recommendations that accompany standard sample benzoic acid (see Chapter 3).

The combustion experiments should be conducted under the same conditions as the calibration experiments.

Conventional analytical procedures may be employed to establish the final state of the combustion process. If it is assumed that only elemental iodine is formed, determination of the amount of nitric acid, if any, in the final bomb solution will suffice to define the final state. However, determination of the total amount of free iodine in the bomb is advisable to verify the assumption that only elemental iodine is formed in the combustion reaction.

**3. Chemistry of the bomb process.** The principal problem encountered in bomb-calorimetric studies with iodine compounds has been to determine the oxidation state of iodine in the products of combustion. Berthelot (1) assumed that only elemental iodine was formed in the combustion process, but Roth (5) pointed out that such an assumption may not be valid.

In their investigations, both Roth (4) and Karlsson (3) attempted to determine the precise state of the iodine present in the combustion products. These investigators found that the total amount of elemental iodine present in the bomb after an experiment—in the gas phase, in water solution, and as a solid—agreed well with the theoretical iodine content of the combustion sample. If their samples of iodine compounds were of sufficiently high purity, these results indicate that essentially all of the iodine appeared in the final bomb state as the free element. However, these tests did not provide positive evidence for the absence of hydriodic, iodic, or periodic acids. For this reason, Roth (4) analyzed the products of some of his combustion experiments for iodic acid. He found that thermally significant quantities of this acid were not formed in the usual combustion process.*

* Roth reported that 0.0015 millimole iodic acid was formed in one of two special experiments designed to favor the formation of the acid. In these experiments, an atmosphere of air was left in the bomb intentionally in order that the nitrogen oxides formed in the combustion process might catalyze the formation of iodic acid. The thermal effect of the formation of 0.0015 millimole iodic acid was only 0.04 cal for the conditions of Roth's experiments.

The results of Roth and Karlsson's investigations of the chemistry of the bomb process strongly favor the conclusion that only elemental iodine is formed in the combustion reaction.

**4. Thermodynamic states and appropriate thermal corrections.** The final state in a combustion bomb after experiments with organic iodine compounds may be defined more precisely than that found in experiments with chlorine or bromine compounds. In fact, the final state obtained with iodine compounds differs from that obtained with carbon-hydrogen-oxygen compounds in the following respects only: (a) the gas phase contains iodine vapor; (b) the liquid phase contains dissolved iodine; and (c) a solid iodine phase is present. If the three phases are homogeneous and in thermodynamic equilibrium with one another, the procedure described in Chapter 5 may be used to compute the change in internal energy of the following idealized combustion reaction:

$$C_aH_bO_cI_d(c \text{ or liq.}) + (a + b/4 - c/2)O_2(g)$$
$$= aCO_2(g) + b/2H_2O(liq.) + d/2I_2(c) \quad (1)$$

in which the reactants and products are in the appropriate standard reference states. The only unusual thermochemical corrections that must be applied are those for the energy of sublimation of the iodine in the gas phase and the energy of solution of iodine in the liquid phase. The corrections for these two thermal effects are relatively insignificant—0.03 and 0.01 cal per combustion for Roth and 0.05 and 0.1 for Karlsson, respectively. For Karlsson's values also, a correction must be applied for the heat of solution of carbon dioxide in the liquid phase of volume (20 ml) (6).

**5. Discussion.** The heats of combustion of organic iodine compounds may be determined with relatively high accuracy by the conventional methods of bomb calorimetry that are referred to in this chapter. However, additional investigations of the chemistry of the bomb process are needed to further substantiate two assumptions that have been made in interpreting the experimental results. First, it should be established definitely whether or not elemental iodine is the only form of iodine produced in significant amounts in the combustion process. Second, it should be established that the three phases of the final state of the bomb process are in equilibrium with one another and that the liquid phase is homogeneous.

Although no experiments on iodine-containing compounds have

been made by the moving-bomb method, it is possible that this method would provide a means of estimating the accuracy of results obtained by the static-bomb method. However, it should be emphasized that, in all probability, carefully executed experiments with the static method would produce results as accurate as could be obtained by the moving-bomb method.

## References

1. M. P. E. Berthelot, *Ann. chim. phys.* (7) **21**, 296 (1900).
2. W. A. Roth and G. Macheleidt, Dissertation, Braunschweig (1921).
3. K. J. Karlsson (now K. J. Karrman), Thesis, Univ. of Lund, Carl Bloms Boktryckeri, Lund, Sweden. 1941.
4. W. A. Roth, *Ber.* **77B**, 535 (1944).
5. W. A. Roth, *Z. Elektrochem.* **45**, 341 (1939).
6. L. Smith, *Acta Chem. Scand.* To be published.

# CHAPTER 11

# Thermochemistry of Reactions Other Than Combustion

H. A. Skinner

**1. Introduction.** The contribution of the thermochemist to physical chemistry is essentially that of providing numerical values for the heats of formation of chemical compounds under defined conditions of temperature and pressure. The field is a vast one to which the experimenter may contribute either by improving the accuracy of existing data, or by extending the boundaries to cover some of the numerous compounds for which data are yet lacking. In general it is not practicable to obtain the heat of formation of a chemical compound by *direct* measurement of its formation from its constituent elements, and a more usual procedure is to measure the heat associated with a reaction of the compound in which it is decomposed into products of known heat content. Although there is no restriction in principle on the type of chemical reaction chosen for thermochemical study, it is necessary that the stoichiometry of the reaction be known precisely, and this requirement places a high premium on reactions that proceed cleanly in one direction to yield easily analyzable products.

It is a historical fact that thermochemists interested in the organic compounds of carbon have given most attention to one particular type of reaction, namely, the degradative oxidation reactions occurring as a result of combustion in gaseous oxygen. As a consequence, the techniques of combustion calorimetry have now been developed to a high degree of efficiency and accuracy, and a large number of "heats of combustion" of different compounds have been recorded in the literature. The predominant position occupied by combustion

227

calorimetry in thermochemistry is undoubtedly due to the wide-spread applicability of the combustion method, particularly in organic chemistry. Nevertheless, it is important to stress that the combustion methods are not universally applicable.

Experience has firmly established the usefulness of the combustion methods for study of hydrocarbons; of compounds containing carbon, hydrogen, and oxygen; and of compounds containing carbon, hydrogen, and nitrogen. In earlier chapters, some of the difficulties of combustion of organic sulfur compounds and organic halogen compounds have been discussed. In view of active research investigations now in progress, the reader may feel optimistic for the future of the combustion method in its application to both sulfur- and halogen-containing compounds. But the chemistry of the combustion processes in compounds containing other elements, e.g., phosphorus, boron, arsenic, and many of the metals is virtually an uninvestigated field; and although degradative oxidation remains *potentially* the most promising type of reaction from the viewpoint of generality of application, much pioneering work must be done before its capabilities are fully defined.

No other type of reaction carries so great a degree of potential worth as that of degradative oxidation. But there are many reactions of more limited scope which can be used, either to supplement or confirm data obtainable from combustion experiments, or to provide data for compounds to which combustion methods are at present unsuitable or impracticable. It is our purpose in this chapter to draw attention to some of the reactions, *other* than combustion, that are of value in thermochemical studies.

**2. Reduction.** It is perhaps natural to begin by turning from oxidation reactions to those of reduction. We might first discriminate between direct reduction by hydrogen gas, and reduction by chemical reducing agents in general. The former method has been used extensively by Kistiakowsky and his co-workers (1) in a series of measurements of the heats of hydrogenation of *unsaturated* hydrocarbons, alcohols, aldehydes, and ethers. The various reactions were carried out by passing a mixture of excess hydrogen and the unsaturated substance to be reduced into a reaction chamber containing some suitable catalyst (usually copper, platinum, or cobalt-nickel). The catalyst chamber was contained in a calorimeter using diethylene glycol as calorimeter fluid, enabling operations to be carried out at temperatures as high as 150°C. The suitability of the gaseous hydrogenation reaction as a model for thermal study was established by careful analysis of the products which revealed both the completeness of the reduction process and the absence of side reactions. A successful extension of the Kistiakowsky technique to the study of liquid-phase hydrogenation has been described by Williams (2).

The hiatus brought about by World War II cut short studies on the hydrogenation method, and it is probable that the full potentialities of the method have not yet been realized. It seems certain that it will find further application in the study of *addition reduction* (i.e., reactions of the type $R—CH{=}CH—Y + H_2 \rightarrow R{\cdot}CH_2{\cdot}CH_2{\cdot}Y$), but whether or not the method could be applied to *displacement reductions*, i.e., reactions of the type

$$R—C{\underset{Z}{\overset{X}{\diagup}}}Y + H_2 \longrightarrow R—C{\underset{H}{\overset{X}{\diagup}}}Y + HZ;$$

$$R—C{\underset{H}{\overset{X}{\diagup}}}Y + H_2 \longrightarrow R—C{\underset{H}{\overset{X}{\diagup}}}H + HY;\ \text{etc.})$$

is questionable.

It may be that the successful study of displacement reduction reactions, which should be of far-reaching thermochemical interest, will be found in the use of chemical reducing agents other than hydrogen. The discovery in recent years of new and powerful reducing agents such as lithium aluminum hydride (3) lends color to this view. Already it appears from the work of several investigators that $LiAlH_4$ in ether solution is a highly successful reducing agent of both organic and inorganic compounds. One might, for example, refer to the paper of Nystrom and Brown (4) in which they describe the reduction of various organic compounds, including alkyl halides→ hydrocarbons, aliphatic nitriles→primary amines, aromatic nitro- and azoxy-compounds→azo-compounds. Systematic study of the stoichiometry and cleanliness of reactions of this type is needed prior to their adoption as models for thermochemical study, but the field is a promising one and deserving of attention.

**3. Halogenation.** The difficulties of the combustion process with halogen-containing compounds make for special interest in alternative methods of deriving thermal data on this class of compound. Direct halogenation presents itself as the most general approach, and has been used with success in determining heats of formation of a number of inorganic halides. In organic chemistry, direct halogenation, as with hydrogenation, divides into addition and replacement halogenation. Both these types of reaction have proved valuable, although halogenation reactions often present difficulties to the thermochemist.

Additive halogenation depends for its success on the completeness of the addition reaction and on the absence of competing and contaminating substitution reactions by the halogen. Not all additive halogenation reactions comply with these requirements, so that the method is of limited applicability. It has been used successfully by Conn, Kistiakowsky, and Smith (5) (heats of addition of chlorine and bromine to gaseous olefins), by Lister (6) (heats of addition of bromine to cyclic olefins in carbon tetrachloride solution), and more recently by Lacher and co-workers (7) (vapor-phase chlorination of fluoro- and chloro-fluorinated olefins). These examples illustrate the promise of the method, the usefulness of which has not yet been fully explored.

The majority of organic halogen replacement reactions are unsuitable for thermal study, due to side reactions resulting in a complex mixture of halogenated products. The problems vary with the halogen. In the case of fluorination, the main difficulty is that of controlling the vigor of the reactions; conversely, in the case of iodination, the major difficulty is often that of persuading the replacement reaction to occur. Chlorination and bromination reactions are frequently difficult to localize, i.e., halogen substitution occurs at several points simultaneously, leading to a mixture of products.

These difficulties impose severe limitations on the method, and only two examples of its use will be quoted here. The first of these makes use of the mild reactivity of fluorinating agents, relative to that of fluorine itself. The second depends upon a choice of reaction in which halogenation is rapid and localized. Jessup, Brickwedde, and Wechsler (8) measured the heat of fluorination of $C_6H_4(CF_3)_2$, using $CoF_3$ as fluorinating agent.

$$C_6H_4(CF_3)_2 + 14CoF_3 \longrightarrow C_6F_{10}(CF_3)_2 + 14CoF_2 + 4HF.$$

The experiment was only partially successful, the main reaction being accompanied by some unknown side reactions. Despite this disappointment, the method used by Jessup is suggestive, and one can anticipate that in due course successful thermal study of fluorination reactions will be achieved, aided perhaps by improvements in fluorination technique or by happier choice of fluorinating agent. Skinner and co-workers (9) have measured the heats of bromination and iodination of a number of metallic alkyls. In these reactions the halogen attacks preferentially at a single point in the molecule, e.g., at a metal-carbon bond in the zinc, cadmium, and mercury alkyls, at the As-As bond in cacodyl, so that by suitable control of the experimental conditions the halogen attack is localized and clean-cut halogenation achieved.

Some halogenation reactions can be effected other than by direct reaction with the halogen. The outstanding example is the formation of inorganic halides by dissolution of metal or basic oxide in a halogen acid; the corresponding reaction in organic chemistry, that of esterification, has received surprisingly scant attention from thermochemists. Examples of organic reactions with the halogen hydracids that have been studied thermally include the addition of hydrogen bromide to propylene, cyclopropane, and the isomeric butenes by Lacher (10), the hydrobromination of simple fluorolefins by Lacher (11), the addition of hydrogen chloride to ethylene oxide by Berthelot (12), and the replacement reactions of hydrogen bromide and hydrogen iodide with boron tributyl by Skinner (13).

**4. Hydrolysis.** Hydrolysis reactions of both inorganic and organic compounds have been frequently used by thermochemists. In many cases the hydrolyses are simple to investigate, and proceed cleanly and quantitatively at room temperature. The more difficult case of slow hydrolysis becomes increasingly amenable to study with recent developments in design and operation of calorimeters suitable for slow processes (14) (see also Chapter 12). Among the many hydrolysis reactions that have been studied, mention may be made of the following:

(a) Hydrolysis of inorganic halides (e.g., of B, Al, Si, Ge, P) and of inorganic oxyhalides (e.g., of P, S); for several references to these, see Bichowsky and Rossini (15); for more recent references see (16).

(b) Hydrolysis of inorganic hydrides, e.g., $B_2H_6$ by Prosen (17): hydrides of Ca, Sr, Ba (15); borohydrides of Na and Li and aluminohydride of Li by Stegeman (18).

(c) Hydrolysis of metal alkyls, e.g., alkyls of Zn and Cd, by Skinner (9a, b).

(d)  Hydrolysis of acid amides by Calvet (19).

(e)  Hydrolysis of acid anhydrides by Kistiakowsky (20).

(f)  Hydrolysis of acyl halides by Skinner (21).

(g)  Hydrolysis of esters, e.g., ethyl acetate by Berenger-Calvet (22); esters of boric acid by Skinner (23); esters of arsenious acid by Skinner (24).

(h)  Hydrolysis of various halides, e.g., trichloroborazole, by van Artsdalen (25), dibutyl borine halides by Skinner (13), allyl and benzyl halides by Skinner (26).

(i)  Hydrolysis of phosphates, e.g., creatine phosphoric acid, adenyl pyrophosphoric acid by Mayerhof (27).

**5. Specific reactions.**  In addition to the general types of reaction we have so far discussed, the thermochemist can from time to time make use of some of the more specific reactions characteristic of a given compound, or group of compounds.  Some of these specific reactions are special cases of oxidation, reduction, halogenation, or hydrolysis reactions: examples include the direct addition of $O_2$ to hexaphenylethane (28), the oxidation of dimethyl sulphide by $H_2O_2$ (29), the ozonolysis of a number of unsaturated aromatic compounds (30), the reduction of $CF_4$ by potassium (31), the "hydrolysis" of ketene (32), and of chloral and bromal (33) by aqueous caustic soda, the chlorination of diborane (34), and the iodination of phenyl arsine (35).  Examples less easy to classify include the studies by Swietoslawski (36) on diazotization, by Tong and Kenyon (37) on polymerization reactions, by Ubbelohde (38) on Grignard reactions, by Eley (39) on addition complexes of aluminum chloride, by Brown (40) on the addition complexes of $BF_3$ and $BMe_3$ with pyridine and various pyridine bases, by Prosen (41) on the thermal decomposition of diborane, by Hieber (42) on metallic carbonyls and their derivatives and the "burning" of gaseous oxygen in excess sulfur vapor by Eckman and Rossini (44).  This list is by no means exhaustive but serves to show the versatility and range of reaction calorimetric studies that have been made in recent years.

**6. General remarks.**  Earlier, we identified the *ultimate* aim of thermochemical measurement with the attainment of accurate values of the heats of formation of the chemical compounds from their elements.  Now the translation of a heat of reaction into heat content terms presupposes knowledge of values of heats of formation for the other entities taking part in, and resulting from, the reactions.  Only in the case of direct synthesis from the elements (or the converse process of decomposition into elements) is the heat of reaction a *direct* measure of the required heat of formation.  The merit of combustion calorimetry (from this point of view) lies in the drastic degradative power of combustion reactions, thus giving products that are usually simple compounds ($H_2O$, $CO_2$, etc.) having well-established values of heats of formation.  The noncombustion reactions, on the other hand, are far less drastic, and the reaction products may be relatively complex; this limits the thermochemical value of some types of reaction for it must be borne in mind that the heat of formation information latent in a measured heat of reaction carries not only the inaccuracy of the measurement itself, but also the uncertainties present in the heat-of-formation values presumed known, or requiring independent determination.

For purposes other than the primary one of the determination of heat of formation, heats of reaction may be of value per se.  An important example occurs in the calculation of equilibrium constants from thermal data, for which reaction heats are required with the minimum of error.  Generally, a direct measurement of a reaction heat is *potentially* of higher over-all accuracy than an indirect one, since it involves the experimental error of a single process and not the cumulative errors of several processes.  One might give as examples the direct measurement of the heat of hydrogenation of ethylene by Kistiakowsky (1), and the indirect determination of this same reaction heat from the heats of combustion of $C_2H_4$, $H_2$, and $C_2H_6$ by Rossini (43).  Now it may be that Rossini's indirect measurement is, in fact, more nearly true than Kistiakowsky's direct measurement (for Rossini may have used reactants of higher purity, and had the advantage of a calorimetric technique capable of a higher degree of precision), but the indirect route in this case involves *three* heat measurements, each of which is considerably more exothermic (in terms of cal/mole of reactant) than the single measurement required of the direct process.  Given *equal* over-all precision, the direct route has a twentyfold advantage in potential accuracy.

It is not, however, our intention to set up reaction and combustion calorimetry in opposition to one another; on the contrary, each possesses an area of advantage between which there is a large tract of common ground.  One might venture further and argue the growing need for a closer unity between these two forms of calorimetric study.

Herein lies the method of cross-checking on the accuracy of thermochemical data. This point has been elaborated in Chapter 9 in the discussion on the evaluation of the combustion method applied to bromine containing compounds.

Little has been said in this report of the design and operation of calorimeters. The reason is that there is no "standard" calorimetric procedure applicable to so varied a range of reactions, and in general the investigator must adapt his calorimetry to the peculiarities of the reaction he chooses to study. But in one respect reaction calorimetry is less demanding than is combustion calorimetry, in that the heats to be measured (per gram-mole of reactant) are normally significantly smaller—sometimes by a factor of as much as 100—than are heats of combustion. Indeed the limits of accuracy in reaction calorimetry are usually set by the imperfections in analysis of the chemistry of the reaction studied than by inadequacies in the calorimetric technique employed.

## References

1. (a) G. B. Kistiakowsky, H. Romeyn, J. R. Ruhoff, H. A. Smith, and W. E. Vaughan, *J. Am. Chem. Soc.* **57**, 65 (1935); (b) G. B. Kistiakowsky, J. R. Ruhoff, H. A. Smith, and W. E. Vaughan, *J. Am. Chem. Soc.* **57**, 876 (1935) and **58**, 137, 146 (1936); (c) M. A. Dolliver, T. L. Gresham, G. B. Kistiakowsky, E. A. Smith, and W. E. Vaughan, *J. Am. Chem. Soc.* **60**, 440 (1938); (d) M. A. Dolliver, T. L. Gresham, G. B. Kistiakowsky, and W. E. Vaughan, *J. Am. Chem. Soc.* **59**, 831 (1937).

2. R. B. Williams, *J. Am. Chem. Soc.* **64**, 1395 (1942).

3. A. E. Finholt, A. C. Bond, and H. I. Schlesinger, *J. Am. Chem. Soc.* **69**, 1199 (1947).

4. R. F. Nystrom and W. G. Brown, *J. Am. Chem. Soc.* **70**, 3738 (1948).

5. J. B. Conn, G. B. Kistiakowsky, and E. A. Smith, *J. Am. Chem. Soc.* **60**, 2764 (1938).

6. M. W. Lister, *J. Am. Chem. Soc.* **63**, 143 (1941).

7. J. R. Lacher, J. J. McKinley, C. Walden, K. Lea, and J. D. Park, *J. Am. Chem. Soc.* **71**, 1334 (1949).

8. R. S. Jessup, F. G. Brickwedde, and M. T. Wechsler, *J. Research Natl. Bur. Standards* **44**, 457 (1950).

9. (a) A. S. Carson, K. Hartley, and H. A. Skinner, *Proc. Royal Soc. (London)* **195A**, 500 (1949); (b) A. S. Carson, K. Hartley, and H. A. Skinner, *Trans. Faraday Soc.* **45**, 1159 (1949); (c) K. Hartley, H. O. Pritchard, and H. A. Skinner, *Trans. Faraday Soc.* **46**, 1019 (1950) and **47**, 254 (1951); (d) C. T. Mortimer, H. O. Pritchard, and H. A. Skinner, *Trans. Faraday Soc.* **48**, 220 (1952); (e) C. T. Mortimer and H. A. Skinner, *J. Chem. Soc.* 4331 (1952).

10. (a) J. R. Lacher, C. H. Walden, K. R. Lea, and J. D. Park, *J. Am. Chem. Soc.* **72**, 331 (1950); (b) J. R. Lacher, T. J. Billings, D. E. Campion, K. R. Lea, and J. D. Park, *J. Am. Chem. Soc.* **74**, 5291 (1952).

11. J. R. Lacher, K. R. Lea, C. H. Walden, G. G. Olson, and J. D. Park, *J. Am. Chem. Soc.* **72**, 3231 (1950).

12. M. Berthelot, *Ann. chim. phys.* (5) **27**, 383 (1882).

13. H. A. Skinner and T. F. S. Tees, *J. Chem. Soc.* 2378 (1953).

14. J. M. Sturtevant, *Physical Methods of Organic Chemistry*, Part 1, Chap. 14, Interscience, New York, 1949.

15. F. R. Bichowsky and F. D. Rossini, *Thermochemistry of Chemical Substances*, Reinhold, New York, 1936.

16. (a) D. F. Evans and R. E. Richards, *J. Chem. Soc.* 1292 (1952); (b) T. Charnley and H. A. Skinner, *J. Chem. Soc.* 450 (1953); (c) H. A. Skinner and N. B. Smith, *Trans. Faraday Soc.* **49**, 601 (1953).

17. E. J. Prosen, W. H. Johnson, and F. Y. Pergiel, *Natl. Bur. Standards Rept.* No. 1552, March, 1952.

18. W. D. Davis, L. S. Mason, and G. Stegeman, *J. Am. Chem. Soc.* **71**, 2775 (1949).

19. (a) E. Calvet, *Compt. rend.* **189**, 530 (1929); (b) E. Calvet, *J. chim. phys.* **30**, 1, 140, 198 (1933).

20. J. B. Conn, G. B. Kistiakowsky, R. M. Roberts, and E. A. Smith, *J. Am. Chem. Soc.* **64**, 1747 (1942).

21. (a) A. S. Carson and H. A. Skinner, *J. Chem. Soc.* 936 (1949); (b) H. O. Pritchard and H. A. Skinner, *J. Chem. Soc.* 272, 1099 (1950); (c) A. S. Carson, H. O. Pritchard, and H. A. Skinner, *J. Chem. Soc.* 656 (1950).

22. Mme. Berenger-Calvet, *J. chim. phys.* **24**, 325 (1927).

23. T. Charnley, H. A. Skinner, and N. B. Smith, *J. Chem. Soc.* 2288 (1952).

24. T. Charnley, C. T. Mortimer, and H. A. Skinner, *J. Chem. Soc.* 1181 (1953).

25. E. R. van Artsdalen and A. S. Dworkin, *J. Am. Chem. Soc.* **74**, 3401 (1952).

26. O. H. Gellner and H. A. Skinner, *J. Chem. Soc.* 1145 (1949).

27. O. Mayerhof and H. Lehmann, *Biochem. Z.* **253**, 431 (1932).

28. H. E. Bent, G. R. Cuthbertson, M. Dorfman, and R. E. Leary, *J. Am. Chem. Soc.* **58**, 165 (1936).

29. T. B. Douglas, *J. Am. Chem. Soc.* **68**, 1072 (1946).

30. (a) E. Briner, K. Ryffel, and S. de Nemitz, *Helv. Chim. Acta* **21**, 257 (1938), (b) E. Briner, D. Frank, and E. Perrottet, *Helv. Chim. Acta* **21**, 1312 (1938).

31. H. v. Wartenberg, *Nach. Akad. Wiss. Göttingen* 55 (1946).

32. F. O. Rice and J. Greenberg, *J. Am. Chem. Soc.* **56**, 2268 (1934).

33. H. O. Pritchard and H. A. Skinner, *J. Chem. Soc.* 1928 (1950).

34. J. R. Lacher, R. E. Scruby, and J. D. Park, *J. Am. Chem. Soc.* **74**, 5292 (1952).

35. C. T. Mortimer and H. A. Skinner, *J. Chem. Soc.* 3189 (1953).

36. W. Swietoslawski, *Roczniki Chem.* **5**, 214 (1925).

37. L. K. J. Tong and W. O. Kenyon, *J. Am. Chem. Soc.* **67**, 1278 (1945).

38. (a) H. Mackle and A. R. Ubbelohde, *J. Chem. Soc.* 1161 (1948), (b) R. J. Nichol and A. R. Ubbelohde, *J. Chem. Soc.* 415 (1952).

39. M. H. Dilke, D. D. Eley, and M. G. Sheppard, *Trans. Faraday Soc.* **46**, 261 (1950).

40. (a) H. C. Brown and R. H. Horowitz, unpublished; (b) H. C. Brown and D. Gintis, unpublished.
41. E. J. Prosen, W. H. Johnson, and F. A. Yenchius, *Natl. Bur. Standards Report, to U. S. Office of Naval Research,* Project NA-onr-8-47, Sept. 30, 1948.
42. (a) W. Hieber, H. Appel, and A. Woerner, *Z. Elektrochem.* **40**, 262 (1934), (b) W. Hieber and A. Woerner, *Z. Elektrochem.* **40**, 287 (1934).
43. F. D. Rossini, *J. Research Natl. Bur. Standards* **17**, 629 (1936).
44. J. R. Eckman and F. D. Rossini, *J. Research Natl. Bur. Standards* **3**, 597 (1929).

# CHAPTER 12

# Microcalorimetry of Slow Phenomena

EDOUARD CALVET

**1. Interest in microcalorimetry of slow phenomena.** At the present time it is possible to construct a calorimeter of such sensitivity and accuracy that one can study closely the thermal effects which accompany slow phenomena. These thermal effects can be treated either from a static or kinetic point of view.

The total quantity of heat given off from the very beginning to the end of the transformation can be determined; one thus obtains a basic thermodynamic quantity, namely, the change of heat content or enthalpy of the system.

Alternately, from the rate of generation of heat with time, one can study the thermokinetics of the phenomenon. For most calorimeters, intended for measurements of long duration, one obtains the approximate relation (in which $q$ is heat and $t$ is time)

$$\frac{dq}{dt} = f(t).$$

But in order to obtain a precise curve, without the distortion which would be due largely to the thermal inertia of the apparatus, it is necessary for certain known corrections to be made to the recorded curve. It is clear that knowledge of the curve allows us to obtain, through integration, the total quantity of heat given off in the course of the transformation.

Thus a calorimeter capable of registering the heat flow with respect to time is of considerable interest. For example, it allows us to follow a large number of physical phenomena which are slow, such as adsorption, dissolution, gelatinization, changes in structure, etc. It has been used with excellent results in the study of slow chemical reactions such as many of those of organic chemistry. In biology, vital activity is characterized by the evolution of heat. For example, one can study the germination of seeds in a calorimeter, and can identify bacteria by their thermogenetic curve, etc. In the field of biological sciences, the microcalorimeter, adapted for the measurement of slow phenomena, seems to have unlimited scope.

In the thermokinetic study of chemical reactions, all measurements of chemical kinetics of interest to us are clearly in evidence. The advantage of this study is that there is no disturbance in the course of the experiment; this study gives us continuous recordings in which the most minute details are clearly shown.

But from the thermodynamic point of view we may wonder whether the direct measurement of slow heats of reaction are of interest and whether instead of making particular measurements for each reaction, often under difficult conditions, it would not be better to calculate the heat of reaction by starting with the heat of the formation of reacting substances and products. We already know that the heat of a chemical reaction is the difference between the sum of the heats of formation of the products and the sum of the heats of formation of the reactants.

Let us consider the heat given off in the esterification of ethyl alcohol by acetic acid:

$$C_2H_5OH + CH_3COOH = CH_3COOC_2H_5 + H_2O,$$

all the substances being in the liquid state. If the values of the heats of formation of the first three substances were obtained from modern heats of combustion, the uncertainties in the several values would be, assuming the highest precision available today, approximately $\pm 0.06$, $\pm 0.05$, and $\pm 0.11$ kcal/mole. Assuming the uncertainty in the heat of formation of water to be negligible in relation to the other values, the uncertainty in the resulting value for the heat of the reaction becomes $\pm 0.14$ kcal/mole. However, a direct measurement of the heat of esterification of ethyl alcohol by acetic acid has been made by Bérenger-Calvet (1) and found to be $1.07 \pm 0.01$ kcal/mole. We thus see that the direct measurement of the heat of esterification yields a value with an uncertainty only $1/_{14}$ as large as would be obtained from even the best modern combustion data were they available. Actually, the use of the existing old data on heats of combustion to calculate the heat of esterification would be uncertain by perhaps 100 or 200 times the direct measurement and might even yield a value of incorrect sign.

Therefore, it seems most desirable to combine direct measurements of the kind mentioned with precise modern data on heats of combustion to obtain the best over-all values of heats of formation. For example, the values of the heats of formation of ethyl alcohol, acetic acid, and water could be known or determined from combustion data, leaving the direct measurement of the heat of reaction 1 to provide an accurate value for the heat of formation of the remaining component of the reaction, ethyl acetate.

That is, instead of measuring the heats of formation from the heats of combustion, for all substances, by means of the bomb, it would suffice to measure precisely the heats of combustion of a certain number of suitably chosen substances, from which, by use of direct measurements, we would deduce the heats of formation of the others.

We thus see that the direct measurements of heats of reaction will not only serve to verify the measurements made by the bomb of heats of combustion and formation, but also will complement them very effectively in the thermochemical tables. We feel that this immense task of reconstructing the thermochemical tables which give the heats of formation of all substances is quite necessary, and calls for making measurements of the heats of many reactions other than those of combustion.

**2. Calorimetric apparatus adapted to the study of slow phenomena.** The different types of calorimetric apparatus which have been used for the study of slow phenomena include apparatus for measuring change of state, adiabatic calorimeters, differential calorimeters, compensation calorimeters (2). The last three types are usually electrical calorimeters using thermoelectric piles, and having a very high sensitivity.

Since 1924, we have adopted A. Tian's (3–6) type of compensation microcalorimeter with Peltier and Joule effects, which we have improved and arranged as a differential apparatus. We will describe this apparatus, giving the theory of it and showing how it can be used. Then we will indicate how we were able to improve its sensitivity and above all its reliability. Finally, we will discuss ways of improving its accuracy of measurement.

Following is a description of a compensatory microcalorimetric element with Peltier and Joule effects. The peculiarities of this apparatus are as follows:

(i) It is a compensatory electrical apparatus in which Peltier and Joule effects are superimposed on the thermal phenomenon to be studied according to whether the heat given off is positive or negative. In this way the total calorific phenomenon is completely balanced. The compensatory method has the advantage of avoiding the necessity of knowing the exact calorific capacity of the calorimeter and its contents. Besides, Peltier and Joule effects are easily regulated and can be estimated with great accuracy.

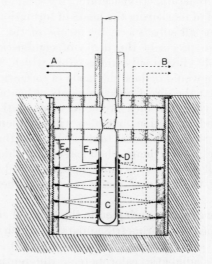

Figure 1. Diagram of calorimetric element.   A, thermoelectric pile for detection; B, Peltier effect; C, coppered glass cell; D, silver socket; $E_e$, external chamber; $E_i$, internal chamber.

(ii) It is a microcalorimeter. The Peltier effect only allows a very small quantity of heat to be absorbed. Therefore the thermal delivery itself should be very small, at the rate of 0.1 to 1 cal per hour. In Tian's original apparatus, the useful part of the cell containing the substances used in a calorimetric experiment is reduced to a cylinder with a cross-section of 1 cm² by 7 cm long (we are actually using cylindrical cells with a section of 2 cm² by 8 cm long).

(iii) This arrangement has the great advantage of avoiding agitation which, in ordinary calorimeters, involves an inaccurate correction. In a lengthy experiment this correction becomes as important as the effect to be measured.

A calorimetric element (Figure 1) consists of a cell C in which the calorific phenomenon is produced. This is thermally insulated from a quantity of water (Tian calorimeter) or metal (Calvet calorimeter) at a constant temperature, which surrounds it. The difference of temperature between the cell and its thermostated casing (external chamber) are revealed by means of a thermoelectric pile connected to a galvanometer, and recorded. The couples in contact with the surface of the cell are placed on a silver socket D (internal chamber), which the cell can enter with very little friction.

Another thermoelectric pile, arranged like the first one, is connected to a storage battery through a rheostat and a milliammeter. We can thus send a current through it, of direction and intensity suitable for compensating, by the Peltier effect, the positive heat produced in the cell.

On the contrary, when dealing with a negative thermal effect, compensation is made by the Joule effect, by means of a current sent through a resistance placed inside the cell.

The two thermoelectric piles are made of a different number of couples: 7 and 42 in A. Tian's apparatus and 16 and 128 couples in our latest apparatus. A switch permits the interchange of the roles detector and producer of the Peltier effect in the two thermoelectric piles, in order to vary the sensitivity.

Following is a discussion of the theory of the apparatus. First of all suppose that the cell is like a long cylinder, surrounded by the thermoelectric pile, and that the entire heat flow lost by this cell is transmitted by conductivity to the wires of the thermocouples. We wonder whether the electromotive force of the pile depends only on the total heat flow emanating from the cell and not also on the distribution of temperature on the cell surface. In fact, as we shall see later, the contents of the cell are often very heterogeneous and the distribution of temperature is hardly ever uniform on the cell surface.

It is easy to see that in the case of a cell completely surrounded by thermocouple junctions, which are uniformly distributed, there is a direct porportionality between the total heat flow emanating from the cell and the electromotive force of the thermoelectric pile.

In fact, the heat flow conducted by a thermocouple element is

$$\varphi_1 = c\Delta\theta_1,$$

$c$ being the thermal conductivity of a thermocouple wire and $\Delta\theta_1$ the difference between the temperature $\theta_1$ of the internal chamber near the internal junction and the uniform temperature $\theta_0$ of the external chamber. The thermocouples all being identical the total flow conducted by the $n$ thermocouples is

$$\Phi = c\sum_n \Delta\theta_1. \tag{1}$$

On the other hand, the electromotive force $e_1$ appearing in each thermocouple is:

$$e_1 = \mathcal{E}_0\Delta\theta_1$$

$\mathcal{E}_0$ being the thermoelectric power of an element for one degree difference between the junctions.

All the elements being in series, the total electromotive force is:

$$\mathcal{E} = \mathcal{E}_0\sum_n \Delta\theta_1 \tag{2}$$

From Equations 1 and 2 we get:

$$\mathcal{E} = \frac{\mathcal{E}_0}{c}\Phi.$$

In practice the thermocouple junctions do not cover the entire cell surface. In order to insulate them electrically one from another, we are obliged to leave a certain amount of space between them, and through this space, heat is lost by radiation or convection.

If we admit that these losses are also proportional to the difference of temperature $\Delta\theta$ between different parts of the cell surface and that of the external enclosure, we find an equation for the entire loss similar to Equation 1

$$\Phi' = \gamma\sum_n \Delta\theta_1.$$

When the losses in the wires by conductivity are

$$\Phi_c = c\sum_n \Delta\theta_1,$$

the total loss becomes

$$\Phi = \Phi' + \Phi_c,$$

and we deduce

$$\mathcal{E} = \frac{\mathcal{E}_0}{c + \gamma}\,\Phi. \tag{3}$$

Therefore, we see that the electromotive force is weaker than if the entire heat was conducted by the thermocouple wires.   We thus find it advantageous to weld the wires to small silver plates, which will be placed in thermal contact with the surface of the cylinder.   (We must however, insure electrical insulation between the plates and the silver cylinder.   This is done by covering the latter with a sheet of mica $1/_{100}$ mm. thick, stuck to the cylinder surface by means of a silicone varnish.)   The silver plates will be of such dimensions as to leave the smallest possible space between them, while still being electrically insulated from each other.

Unfortunately, it is nearly impossible to cover the entire surface of the cell with thermoelectric pile junctions.   In fact, the upper part of the cell must be closed by a stopper, through which the control rods of the apparatus pass.   Therefore there is a loss of heat in the upper part of the cell.

We will reduce those losses by using a long cell of small diameter (which, by the way, favors a decrease of thermal inertia in the cell). With a cell of 2 cm² section by 8 cm long, the stopper only takes up about 4 per cent of the total section.   In order to take such a loss into account, we must represent it by a known and the smallest possible fraction of the total loss $\Phi$ so that we can always have an equation of proportionality between E and $\Phi$.   The equation then becomes

$$\mathcal{E} = \frac{\mathcal{E}_0}{c + \gamma}\,(I - \epsilon)\Phi. \tag{4}$$

For this, we must first insure that the thermal contact between the glass cell and the silver cylinder carrying the thermocouple junctions is as perfect as possible.   We use a cell of platinum or very fine glass ($2/_{10}$ to $3/_{10}$ mm thick), metallized outside.   This part of the cell is topped by a portion in glass (nonmetallized), or in any other low thermal conducting material.   The thermocouples cover it to such a height as to absorb in their junctions the heat lost by conductivity through the nonmetallized upper part of the cell.   The stopper and the control rods passing through it are made of poor heat conducting material.   The depth of liquid in the cell (necessary to secure good heat conductivity) will always be the same (for example 6 cm in a cell of 8 cm useful depth), so that the fraction of total heat lost in the upper part of the cell will be invariable.

Finally we shall point out a difficulty which occurs when an electrical resistance is placed in the cell to insure its heating by the Joule effect. The wires connecting this resistance to the exterior of the calorimeter cause a thermal loss which can be considerable if the difference between the temperature of the interior of the cell and the exterior of the calorimeter is great, and if we neglect the following precaution: the wires must make thermal contact with the external chamber immediately they immerge from the cell. If the external chamber is made of a big block of copper, kept at an even temperature, the wires must be passed through this block (electrically insulated) before coming out of the calorimeter. Since the difference of temperature between the cell and the block (thermostat) is always very small (about a few thousandths of a degree), the loss due to conductivity in the heating wires becomes of the same order as the current in the thermocouples. This loss is constant and represents a well-defined fraction of the total loss. If, however, the heat conducted by the exterior wires is added to the block forming the thermostat, this loss will have no perceptible influence to the cell.

Following is a discussion of the *simplified theory in the hypothesis of a complete thermal uniformity of the cell and its casing*. The external chamber (thermostated block) is supposed to be at a constant temperature. We have seen that the temperature of the internal chamber is not usually uniform. However it is possible to define an average temperature $\theta_i$ of this internal chamber by the equation:

$$\mathcal{E} = n\mathcal{E}_0 \Delta\theta$$

and

$$\theta_i = \theta_0 + \Delta\theta,$$

$\mathcal{E}$ being the electromotive force of the thermoelectric pile, $n$ the number of couples, and $\mathcal{E}_0$ the thermoelectric power of the couples in volt/degree. This measured electromotive force $\mathcal{E}$ is, itself, proportional to the flow of heat given off by the internal chamber, as we have seen before.

Let $W$ be the calorific power released inside the cell at the moment $t$. During the time $dt$ the quantity of heat given off is $W\,dt$. This heat is partly compensated for by the Peltier effect, represented by $P\,dt$ and partly lost outside the cell, represented by $p(\theta_0 - \theta_i)\,dt$; $p$ being the calorific power exchanged for a difference of temperature of $1\,°C$ between the chambers; the rest of the heat is used to raise the temperature of the cell by $d\theta$ which brings into play the heat quantity $\mu \, d\theta$; $\mu$ being the calorific capacity of the cell and its contents.

Therefore we have

$$W \, dt = P \, dt + p(\theta_0 - \theta_i) \, dt + \mu \, d\theta$$

or

$$W = P + p(\theta_0 - \theta_i) + \mu \frac{d\theta}{dt}. \tag{5}$$

We note that the deviation $\Delta$ of the galvanometer connected to the detector thermoelectric pile is proportional to the electromotive force $\mathcal{E}$, that is to say

$$\Delta\theta = \theta_0 - \theta_i.$$

By neglecting the mechanical inertia of the moving parts of the galvanometer, we can write at the time $t$

$$\Delta = g(\theta_0 - \theta_i)$$

and

$$\frac{d\Delta}{dt} = g \frac{d\theta}{dt}.$$

Equation 5 becomes:

$$W = P + \frac{p}{g} \Delta + \frac{\mu}{g} \frac{d\Delta}{dt}, \tag{6}$$

which is the fundamental equation of Tian's apparatus and will be called Tian's equation.

Following is a discussion of the general case where thermal uniformity in the system being studied is not realized. The preceding equation can be generalized in the case where the cell and its contents are not at a uniform temperature corresponding to that of the thermocouples. This, incidentally, is always the case as thermal uniformity presumes that the substances constituting the cell and its contents have perfect thermal conductivity.

The flow of heat coming from the internal chamber has passed through various thermal resistance media (such as the glass cell with the silver tube, the glass cell itself, and different regions of the cell interior); this therefore presumes the existence of differences of temperature in the inside area of the surface occupied by the thermoelectric junctions.

The heat accumulates as a result of this thermal inequality. If, at a given time, the thermal conductivity of the material of the cell and its contents could be made infinite, a certain quantity of heat $q$ would have to be absorbed so that the spot of the galvanometer connected to the detector thermoelectric pile would not vary. Tian has called this quantity the "heat of internal thermal disequilibrium." This heat is the algebraic sum of the terms obtained by multiplying the heat capacity of the different parts of the cell contents by the temperature of these parts over that of the internal chamber $\theta_i$.

These excesses of temperature are proportional to the flow of heat $W$ which comes from the cell. The result is that the quotient $q/W = D$ is a constant characteristic of the calorific properties of the internal chamber. $D$ is the "coefficient of internal thermal disequilibrium"; this quantity has the dimensions of time.

We will see later how we can determine $D$ by experiment. Our measurements have shown that $D$ is a constant quantity for a cell in which the contents are well determined; it is remarkably independent of the sensitivity used and stays the same when we interchange the detector and producer of the Peltier effect of the two thermoelectric piles.

Following is a discussion of the *consequences of thermal disequilibrium and apparent growth of heat capacity*. An increase $dW$ of calorific power developed in the cell has the effect of raising the temperature of the detector junctions from $d\theta$ in such a way that $dW/p = d\theta$. If uniformity of temperature was insured, the heat gained by the cell would be

$$dQ = \mu \, d\theta,$$

but, owing to thermal disequilibrium, there is, over and above this, an accumulation of a quantity of heat $dq$ so that

$$dq = D \, dW = Dp \, d\theta.$$

Finally, the accumulation of heat in the cell is

$$dQ + dq = (\mu + Dp) \, d\theta.$$

The apparent increase of the heat capacity is $\Delta\mu = Dp$ and the relative growth is

$$\frac{\Delta\mu}{\mu} = D \, \frac{P}{\mu}.$$

Tian's fundamental equation remains valid, even when uniformity of temperature in the cell is not reached, provided the heat capacity is replaced by a corrected value taking into account the thermal disequilibrium.

As we shall see later, it is easy to measure the corrected heat capacity. The correction of heat capacity due to thermal disequilibrium is, by the way, small. For example, we have found, in a cell of Tian's calorimeter containing 5 cm$^3$ of water that $p/\mu = 0.0023$, $D = 0.35$ hr and $\Delta\mu/\mu = 0.08$ per cent. This correction becomes greater in certain cases, as for example, when the heat producing system is placed in a poor heat-conducting tube in the interior of the cell.

Following is a discussion of the *variation of the heat capacity of the system*. Whereas for calorimeters destined for short duration measurements, the heat capacity is a sufficiently well-defined quantity, such is not the case for calorimeters destined for the study of slow phenomena. In fact this heat capacity depends on the duration of the experiment. It is necessary to make a systematic study according to the duration of the experiments. For example, for a cell of Tian's type of calorimeter, we find a capacity of 13.6 cal/degree for a sudden phenomenon of 1 min duration, whereas with the same cell we find 15.0 cal/degree for a thermal phenomenon of the same intensity which has lasted for 24 hr. This comes from the fact that the quantity of heat produced in the cell is conveyed further and further from it as the experiment continues. However, it is possible to measure the heat capacities accurately enough and to correlate them with the known calorimeter operating rates, which permits us to know the exact value of the heat capacity at any moment during the course of an experiment.

Following is a discussion of the determination of the constants of a microcalorimetric element with compensation by Peltier and Joule effects. The simplest way to determine the coefficient $g$ of proportionality between the deviation and the difference in temperature $\theta - \theta_1$, is to calculate it. If the detector thermopile comprises $n$ couples whose thermoelectric value is $\mathcal{E}_0$ volts/degree, $R$ being the total resistance of the circuit, $S$ the intensity of current necessary to produce a 1-mm deviation of the galvanometer light spot on a scale placed at 1 m from the mirror (galvanometer sensitivity), we have

$$g = \frac{n\mathcal{E}_0}{RS}.$$

In the *measurement of the ratio p/g, the calibration by deviation* is most important. The ratio $p/g$ measures the constant calorific value producing a 1-mm deviation of the galvanometer light spot on a scale placed at 1 m from the mirror. In order to carry out this measurement we cause, mainly by the Joule effect, a constant calorific power $W$ to be given off in the cell, and we record the deviation of the galvanometer light spot. We measure this deviation $\Delta$ when the light spot has a stabilized position. We have

$$p/q = W/\Delta.$$

Figure 2 shows the recording obtained in such a determination. OA is the trace of the experimental zero. At point A we commenced heating the cell (Joule effect). Therefore the curve ABC then described, tends to become parallel to OA by approaching the ordinate asymptote Aa and we obtain a $\Delta$ value by underestimation.

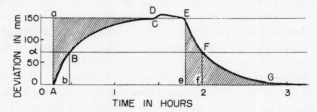

Figure 2. Record obtained in an experiment. See text for explanation.

At point C we have produced a slight increase in the heat given off followed by a return to the $W$ power previously obtained. After a fairly long period we obtain $\Delta$ value by overestimation. We take the average value $\Delta_0$ from the determinations (by under- and overestimation). Such measurements can be made without difficulty to an accuracy of $^5/_{1000}$. At point E we have abruptly cut off the cell heating and recorded the return curve to experimental zero.

$$0 = \frac{p}{g}\,\Delta + \frac{\mu}{g}\,\frac{d\Delta}{dt}.$$

$$\Delta = \Delta_0 e^{-\frac{p}{\mu}t}.$$

We now discuss the evaluation of the time of half-heating, $T_{1/2}$. In the preceding graph we trace the parallel to the time axis at ordinate $\Delta_0/2$ which crosses the curve at points B and F. We measure Ab

$= ef = T_{1/2}$. This half-deviation time characterizes the apparatus when employed as an oscillograph (intended for thermokinetic measurements). For example we find, in a Tian's type of calorimeter, $T_{1/2} = 8$ min. In our present apparatus we have notably reduced this half-heating time.

Next we discuss the measurement of the heat capacity of the internal chamber. We have seen that the heat capacity depends on the heating time when the same quantity of heat is furnished to a cell. Therefore we should obtain a value $\mu$ for the different speeds of heating. Usually we determine the limit values $\mu_0$ and $\mu_\infty$ corresponding to a very quick heating (of about 1 min), or a very slow one (of about 1 day).

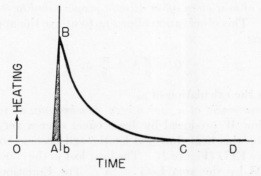

Figure 3. Record from an experiment with "quick" heating. See text for explanation.

In the *measurement of $\mu$ for a quick heating*, we use the apparatus as a "ballistic" one. During a very short time we produce the Joule effect in the cell (without compensation by Peltier effect). We record the curve OABCD in which AB corresponds to the period of heating. Let $Q$ be the total quantity of heat given off by the Joule effect. Tian's fundamental equation (in which $P = 0$), can be written

$$W \, dt = \frac{p}{g} \, \Delta \, dt + \frac{\mu}{g} \, d\Delta.$$

Let us say that zero is the moment when heating commences (point A), and $t$ is the moment heating ceases (point B). We have

$$\int_0^t W \, dt = \frac{p}{g} \int_0^t \Delta \, dt + \frac{\mu_0}{g} \int_0^t d\Delta. \tag{7}$$

$\int_0^t \Delta \, dt$ represents the area A contained between the portion AB of the recorded curve, the ordinate of B and the axis of time.

$\int_0^t d\Delta = \Delta_t - \Delta_0 = \Delta_t$ is the ordinate of the maximum B. $\int_0^t W \, dt = Q$. Therefore we have

$$Q = \frac{p}{g} A + \frac{\mu}{g} \Delta_t. \tag{8}$$

We notice that if the heating is very quick, the area A $= \int_0^t \Delta \, dt$ is negligible; the term $p/g$ A becomes negligible compared to $(\mu/g)\Delta t$ and we have directly

$$Q = \frac{\mu}{g} \Delta_t.$$

*The quantity of heat given off is directly proportional to the maximum deviation* $\Delta_t$. This observation allows us to utilize the apparatus as a "ballistic" one.

$$Q = \frac{p}{g} A + \frac{\mu_0}{g} \Delta_t.$$

This permits the calculation of $\mu_0$.

In *the measurement of* $\mu_\infty$ *for a very slow heating*, we record a constant heat flow $W$ produced by Joule effect over a very long time. Then, we stop this heat flow and let the cell become cold. We record the curve EFG (Figure 2). The heat lost in the course of cooling is represented by the area EeG $= A'$. The Equation 7 in which $\int W \, dt = 0$ gives us

$$p \int_0^t \Delta \, dt = -\mu \int_0^t d\Delta$$

or

$$pA' = \mu_\infty \Delta_t.$$

$\Delta_t$ represents the constant deviation of the spot light before stopping the flow of heat.

$$\mu_\infty = \frac{pA'}{\Delta_t}.$$

For a cell of Tian's calorimeter containing 5 cm³ of water we have found $\mu_0 = 13.6$ cal/degree; $\mu_\infty = 15.0$ cal/degree. It is important to note that the value $\mu_\infty$ thus found represents an apparent heat capacity. It should be corrected for the thermal disequilibrium in order to obtain the true capacity.

In the *measurement of the Peltier effect constant*, the calorific power $P_0$ absorbed by Peltier effect is proportional to the intensity $i$ of the current traversing the junctions.    We have

$$P_0 = \pi i.$$

$\pi$ is the Peltier effect constant.    It is connected with the thermoelectric power E by the thermodynamic equation.

$$\pi = \frac{T}{J}\frac{d\varepsilon}{dt}.$$

This last equation would allow the calculation of $\pi$.    It is better to measure $\pi$ experimentally because the heat absorbed by the junctions is not transmitted entirely to the internal chamber.    The measurement of $\pi$ under identical experimental conditions thus gives a more correct result.    But when a current $i$ is passed through the thermocouples, to cause a Peltier effect, it produces at the same time a Joule effect.    The junctions behave as if they represented an "apparent resistance $\rho$ and the total thermal power absorbed in the junctions is only

$$P = \pi i - \rho i^2.$$

We see that $P = 0$ for a certain value $I$ of current $i$ and then

$$\pi I = \rho I^2$$

$$I = \frac{\pi}{\rho}.$$

This current $I$, for which the Peltier effect is exactly compensated by the Joule effect produced in the junctions, is easy to measure.    It suffices to increase the intensity of current $i$ until the galvanometer deviation becomes zero.    For example we find in a Tian apparatus $I$ = 90 ma.

The calorific power absorbed by the Peltier effect is, therefore, generally

$$P = \pi i - \rho i^2 = \pi i\left(1 - \frac{\rho}{\pi}i\right) = \pi i\left(1 - \frac{i}{I}\right). \tag{9}$$

It is in this last form that we use the Peltier effect.    For example, to measure $\pi$, we produce a constant and known heat $W$ in the cell by Joule effect, and exactly compensate it by the Peltier effect produced by a current $i$ determined by trying various values.    Following this we deduce $\pi$ from the preceding formula. This formula shows that the maximum power that can be absorbed by the Peltier effect is

$$\frac{\pi I}{2}.$$

This corresponds to about 0.3 cal per junction per hour with Tian's apparatus. In practice we use $i$ currents much lower than $I/2$; for example nearer $I/50$; the correction for the heating in the junctions is therefore always low and is known with sufficient accuracy. We notice that $\pi$ is a function of temperature. The calibration of the Peltier effect constant should, in consequence, be done at different temperatures.

To measure the *coefficient of internal thermal disequilibrium D* we must be able to estimate the quantity of heat $q$ accumulated in the internal chamber because of the nonuniformity of temperature and to measure the heat flow $W$ in the internal chamber. We have seen that

$$D = \frac{q}{W}.$$

For this determination we shall use an electrical resistance conveniently placed in the cell and shall pass a current through it which will produce a constant heat flow $W$ by the Joule effect. We shall, at the same time, produce a Peltier effect so that the two effects, Joule and Peltier, exactly compensate each other. When the preliminary regulation of currents producing the two contrary effects is obtained (in such a way that the galvanometer on the detector pile is steady at zero), we cut off the two currents producing the Joule and Peltier effects, at the same moment. We then have a record of heating which corresponds to the production of heat $q$ (thermal disequilibrium) stored in the internal chamber, owing to the nonuniformity of temperature. In fact, when the galvanometer has returned to zero, we shall record a cooling down, followed by a return to zero, producing simultaneously the two compensatory effects. This cooling down when the circuits producing the Peltier and Joule effects are closed is equal to the heating produced when the currents are cut off, if the compensation is perfect. If it is not perfect, we shall take the average of the heating and cooling down observed when the Peltier and Joule circuits are cut off or closed. Thus we have a simple and accurate method of estimating the coefficient of thermal disequilibrium

D. The results obtained show that $q$ is directly proportional to $W$. With these results, we can discover the best conditions suitable for diminishing the thermal disequilibrium (for example, they show the advantage of metallizing the surface of the glass cell in contact with the silver tube). Finally the knowledge of the heat of disequilibrium $q$ permits the correction of heat capacity determinations and in consequence allows measurements of specific heats. As an example of this we give certain results obtained with a cell from Tian's calorimeter (diameter 13.85 mm, length 70 mm): Values of $D$ in hours: coppered cell, 0.0283; noncoppered cell, 0.0383.

In the *employment of the calorimeter for compensation by the Peltier and Joule effects,* we distinguish between the two uses by the terms "integrator" and "oscillograph." In the former case, we propose to find the total quantity of heat given off in the course of a calorimetric experiment or between two given moments $t_1$ and $t_2$. In the latter case we want to study the calorific power produced in the cell as a function of time, that is to say:

$$W = \mathrm{f}(t).$$

Tian's fundamental Equation 6, after integration, gives an equation analogous to Equation 8, but in which the heat compensated by Joule and Peltier effects is present:

$$Q = \sum_{t_1}^{t_2} P \, \mathrm{d}t + \frac{p}{g} A + \frac{\mu}{g} (\Delta_2 - \Delta_1).$$

Therefore to estimate $Q$ we must add together three quantities of heat, as indicated. For the evaluation of the *heat compensated by Joule or Peltier effects,* $\sum_{t_2}^{t_1} P \, \mathrm{d}t$, in practice we give a constant value to the current $i$, which produces the compensating effect, so that the compensation will be too low in the first part of the experiment and too strong in the second part. The area $A$ contained between the recorded curve and the axis of time therefore includes two lots of contrary signs of which the algebraic sum is essentially zero, if the compensating current is properly chosen. We can also give several successive values to the current producing the compensating effect, taking care to note very exactly the time taken for the passage of these currents. We recall that the calculation of the power compensated for by the Peltier effect is done by means of Equation 9. The area A is measured on the recorded curve by a planimeter or by weight. Correction of the area can be reduced to less than 5 per cent of the compensated heat if the compensating currents have been properly chosen. In that case the measurement of about 2 per cent of the area A only causes an error of less than $1/_{1000}$ in the total quantity of heat to be measured. Correction of the heat capacity, $\mu/g$ $(\Delta_2 - \Delta_1)$, is cancelled when $\Delta_2 = \Delta_1$. We have seen how, in general cases, the apparent heat capacity $\mu$ (when the thermal disequilibrium is taken into account) should be estimated.

In the employment of the apparatus as oscillograph, the compensating Joule or Peltier effect is stopped. The apparatus records the curve

$$\Delta = f(t).$$

In order that this curve approaches the curve

$$W = f(t) = \frac{p}{g}\,\Delta + \frac{\mu}{g}\frac{d\Delta}{dt}.$$

by a constant factor, it is necessary that the term $(\mu/g)(d\Delta/dt)$ of Tian's Equation (6) should be zero. This term can be made very low if the variations of $\Delta$ with respect to time are very slow and if the heat capacity is small compared to the coefficient of loss $p$. This is tantamount to saying that the time constant $\mu/p$ should be as low as possible. Generally the recorded curves can be corrected in such a way as to represent the correct curve.

$$W = f(t) = \frac{p}{g}\,\Delta + \frac{\mu}{p}\frac{d\Delta}{dt}$$

It suffices to add algebraically the value $(\mu/p)(d\Delta/dt)$ to the ordinates of the different points of the curve

$$\Delta = f(t).$$

In reality, the heat capacity depends slightly on the heating speed of the cell. It is possible to measure $\mu$ for different heating speeds (in practice for quick, average, or slow heating) and to multiply the slope of the curve at each point $\mu/p$. We notice that the maxima and minima of the recorded curve are unchanged. Therefore it suffices to make the correction on some points of the recorded curve in order to be able to draw the curve $W = f(t)$ very accurately. We have often done such work, using the traced curve for each sensitivity and each different temperature and we have obtained the thermokinetic curves of the studied phenomena quite accurately.

Next we discuss *improvements on Tian's microcalorimetric apparatus and the methods of its employment.* Having used Tian's apparatus for a long time in very varied research work, we have been led to improve it, in order to increase its sensitivity and above all its reliability.   We are at present improving the accuracy of its measurements.   We have also perfected new methods of employing our apparatus.

In *searching for improved sensitivity,* we are only considering the employment of the apparatus as "integrator" and the case of a permanent delivery of heat $W$, uncompensated by the Peltier effect. When equilibrium is established, Equation 6 is reduced to:

$$W = \frac{p}{g}\,\Delta.$$

The deviation $\Delta$ is itself proportional to the intensity $I$ of the current passing through the galvanometer:

$$\Delta = sI$$

$$W = \frac{p}{g}\,sI.$$

We will define the sensitivity $\sigma$ of the calorimeter by the ratio

$$\sigma = \frac{I}{W}.$$

The calculation of intensity $I$ can be made easily for the difference of the temperature $\theta$ between the internal and external chambers with a knowledge of the electrical characteristics of the circuit.   The calculation of the power $W$ can be made for $\theta$ with a knowledge of the thermal characteristics of the medium between the internal and external chambers and with a knowledge also of the Peltier effect produced by the passage of current $I$ in the thermopile.   It is therefore theoretically possible to calculate the sensitivity of a calorimeter, having thermoelectric couples, and to seek the conditions that should be fulfilled in order to have the greatest possible sensitivity: optimum number of couples; nature, length, and section of the wires, etc. The calculation is easy in the case where the heat losses by the wires of the thermocouples are solely due to heat conduction, that is to say, in the case where radiation and convection are relatively negligible. We will confine ourselves to this simple case in which the wires are insulated by a material jacket which is thick enough, from the thermal point of view. The sensitivity of an integrator calorimeter is, by the way, considerably improved when the space between the chambers is filled with a thermal insulating material. We have established that a unit of Tian's type becomes 2 or 3 times more sensitive when the space between the two chambers is filled with cotton-wool. The increase in the time constant $\mu/p$ which results, makes this apparatus a poor oscillograph.

The calculation of optimum sensitivity is due to Mr. Persoz of the National Office of Aeronautical Study and Research, inspired by the works of Whipp (7) and Tonnelat (8). We will adopt the following annotations:

| | |
|---|---|
| $l$ | The common length of the wires of the two metals M and M' constituting a couple. |
| $n$ | The number of couples constituting the detector thermopile. |
| $S$ and $S'$ | Sections of the wires constituting the couples. |
| $r$ and $r'$ | The resistance of the wires constituting the couples. |
| $c$ and $c'$ | The heat conductivity of the wires constituting the couples. |
| $p$ | The loss of the calorimeter heat, per second and per degree caused by the difference in temperature between the two chambers. |
| $p_c$ | The loss of heat in the wires of the thermocouples, caused by conductivity. |
| $p_0$ | The loss of heat in the wires not due to conductivity. We have $p = p_0 + p_c$. |
| $\theta$ | Difference of temperature between the internal junctions and the outer chamber. |
| $\rho$ | Resistance of the galvanometer and the connecting wires. |
| $\varepsilon_0$ | Electromotive force of a couple per degree of difference between the junctions. |
| $\pi$ | Heat absorbed by the Peltier effect, in 1 sec, in each junction traversed by a current of 1 amp. |

Let

$$R = \frac{r}{S} + \frac{r'}{S'}$$

$$C = cS + c'S'.$$

Total electromotive force $\mathcal{E} = n\mathcal{E}_0\theta$. Circuit resistance $\rho + nlR$.

$$I = \frac{n\mathcal{E}_0\theta}{\rho + nlR}. \tag{10}$$

In the case of thermal equilibrium, the $W$ power is partly compensated for (a very minor part), by the Peltier effect produced by the current $I$ but for the major part is lost in the form of heat leakages.

$$W = n\pi I + p\theta \tag{11}$$

with

$$p = p_0 + p_c = p_0 + \frac{nC}{l}. \tag{12}$$

The sensitivity, $\sigma$, of the calorimeter is calculated by taking into account Equations 10, 11, and 12.

$$\sigma = \frac{I}{W} = \frac{n\mathcal{E}_0}{(\rho + nlR)\left(p + n\pi \dfrac{n\mathcal{E}_0}{\rho + nlR}\right)}$$

$$\sigma = \frac{\mathcal{E}_0}{n\pi\mathcal{E}_0 + \left(p_0 + \dfrac{n}{l}C\right)\left(\dfrac{\rho}{n} + lR\right)}. \tag{13}$$

A maximum for $\sigma$ is obtained when the denominator is a minimum.

As to the number of couples, by differentiating the denominator with respect to $n$ and equating this derivative to zero we find

$$n = \sqrt{\frac{\rho p_0}{\mathcal{E}_0\pi + CR}}. \tag{14}$$

As to the choice of the length of wires, the same operation done with respect to $l$ gives

$$l = \sqrt{\frac{\rho C}{p_c R}}. \tag{15}$$

As to the choice of the section of the wires, by equaling the derivative of the denominator with respect to $S$ and $S'$ to zero, we find:

$$S = \sqrt{\frac{p_0 l + nc'S'}{\rho S' + nr'l} \frac{lS'r}{c'}} \tag{16}$$

$$S' = \sqrt{\frac{p_0 l + ncS}{\rho S + nrl} \frac{lSr'}{c'}}. \tag{16a}$$

We notice that in Equation 14 the term $\varepsilon_0 \pi$ is negligible compared to $CR$. In fact with a microcalorimetric unit we have constructed, and which is composed of 144 iron constantan couples of 0.3-mm diameter wires, we have: iron, $r = 10.10^{-6}$ ohm-cm, $c = 0.161$ cal/sec-degree-cm, $S = 7.06 \times 10^{-4}$ cm²; constantan, $r' = 44.2 \times 10^{-6}$ ohm-cm, $c' = 0.054$ cal/sec-degree-cm, $S' = S = 7.06 \times 10^{-4}$ cm²,

$$R = \frac{r}{S} + \frac{r'}{S'} = 7.66 \times 10^{-2} \text{ ohm/cm}, \quad C = cS + c'S' = 1.52 \times 10^{-4}$$

cal cm/deg sec, $RC = 11.65 \times 10^{-6}$ ohm cal/deg sec.
On the other hand,

$$\varepsilon_0 = 50 \times 10^{-6} \text{ volt/degree}$$

$\pi$ is approximately equal to $10^{-3}$ cal/sec amp

$$\pi\varepsilon_0 = 50 \times 10^{-9} \frac{\text{cal ohm}}{\text{deg sec}}$$

We finally have therefore an error of $5/1.000$ by neglecting $\pi\varepsilon_0$ with respect to $RC$.    Equation 14 therefore becomes:

$$n = \sqrt{\frac{\rho P_0}{CR}}. \tag{14a}$$

*The case of two microcalorimetric units arranged in a differential apparatus,* as we shall see later, is most interesting as it allows the apparatus to give indications almost independent of variations in exterior temperature.    In such an arrangement we place the detector thermopiles in opposition by connecting the last internal junction of one of the two thermopiles with the last internal junction of the corresponding identical thermopile in the second calorimetric element.    The resistances of the thermopiles are added up and their electromotive forces are subtracted.    We suppose that the electromotive force in the reference element is nil.    Under these conditions we find the following equations in place of Equations 13, 14a, 15, 16, and 16a:

$$\sigma = \frac{\varepsilon_0}{2n\pi\varepsilon_0 + \dfrac{\rho p_0}{n} + \dfrac{\rho C}{l} + 2lRp_0 + 2nRC} \tag{17}$$

$$n = \sqrt{\frac{\rho p_0}{2RC}} \tag{18}$$

$$l = \sqrt{\frac{\rho C}{2p_0 R}} \tag{19}$$

$$S = \sqrt{\frac{lp_0 + nc'S'}{\rho S' + 2nr'l} \cdot \frac{2lrs'}{e}} = l\sqrt{\frac{2p_0 r}{\rho c}} \tag{20}$$

$$S' = \sqrt{\frac{lp_0 + ncS}{\rho S + 2nrl} \cdot \frac{2lr'S}{c'}} = l\sqrt{\frac{2p_0 r'}{\rho c'}}. \tag{20a}$$

Equation 19 is deduced from the two Equations 20 and 20a and finally for the four quantities $n, l, S, S'$ we have only three independent equations. If we fix the length $l$ as the length of the wire of the couples (taking into account the convenience of setting). Solving Equations 18, 20, and 20a gives:

$$n = \frac{\sqrt{\frac{\rho p_0}{2}}}{\sqrt{cr} + \sqrt{c'r'}}$$

$$S = l\sqrt{\frac{2p_0 r}{\rho c}}$$

$$S' = l\sqrt{\frac{2p_0 r'}{c'}}.$$

It is therefore possible, when we have the length of the wire $l$ fixed for the thermocouples, and the nature of the metals of which they are made, to find the optimum number of couples to be employed (independent, by the way, of the length $l$ of the wires) and the sections $S$ and $S'$ of the wires (these are independent on $l$).

In bringing these last values of $n, S, S'$ into the sensitivity expression $\sigma$ we find that the 4 terms of the denominator (omitting the term $2n\pi\mathcal{E}_0$), become equal.

$$\sigma = \frac{\mathcal{E}_0}{4\sqrt{2}\sqrt{\rho p_0}\,(\sqrt{cr} + \sqrt{c'r'})}. \tag{21}$$

For example, in our latest differential calorimeters we have adopted iron-constantan couples

$$l = 3 \text{ cm} \qquad p_0 = 0.0110 \qquad \rho = 35\omega$$

$$\sqrt{cr} + \sqrt{c'r'} = 2.82 \times 10^{-3}.$$

We find on applying Equation 21 that the number of couples giving the maximum sensitivity is $n = 156$ couples. For building convenience we have adopted 144 couples grouped around the cell in 12 rows of 12 couples each. This number of couples is very near the number calculated to give the optimum sensitivity. Equations 20 and 20a give for the section of the wires (length being equal to 3 cm):

iron $S = 6 \times 10^{-4}$ cm$^2$, i.e., a diameter of $2.8 \times 10^{-2}$ cm

constantan $S' = 21.3 \times 10^{-3}$ cm$^2$, i.e., a diameter of $5.3 \times 10^{-2}$ cm

We have adopted iron wires of 0.3 mm diameter and constantan wires of 0.5 mm diameter, thus approaching the conditions of optimum sensitivity. Thanks to a judicious choice of the number of couples and of the section of wires we have been able to improve materially the sensitivity of our original apparatus.

With regard to the choice of the *nature of the wires* for the thermocouples, in order to obtain the maximum sensitivity, we are led to seek metals which give the greatest quantity for:

$$\frac{\varepsilon_0}{\sqrt{cr} + \sqrt{c'r'}}.$$

Now the products $(cr)$ vary relatively little (Wiedemann and Franz Law). We are therefore led to consider above all the thermoelectric power $\varepsilon_0$. Yet it must be noted that substances for which the thermoelectric power is exceptionally high (tellurium, germanium, silicon, etc.) generally have a high resistivity, which leads to the use of thick sectional wires. Now in the case of very long measurements it is necessary to include a certain portion of the wires in the heat capacity of the calorimeter. If the bulk of these wires is large it causes a serious disadvantage in calculating the corrections to the heat capacity. We use chiefly iron-constantan couples electrically welded on little silver plates.

The ratio of sections of the wires, according to Whipp (7), should be

$$\frac{S}{S'} = \sqrt{\frac{r/c}{r'/c'}}.$$

We have seen that the maximum sensitivity is obtained when the four terms of the denominator in Equation 17 become equal

$$\frac{\rho p_0}{n} = \frac{\rho C}{l} = 2lRp_0 = 2nRC = \sqrt{2\rho p_0}\,(\sqrt{cr} + \sqrt{c'r'}).$$

This means, according to Tonnelat (8) (a) that the total resistance of the two series of couples should be equal to the resistance of the galvanometer because

$$\rho = 2nlR,$$

and (b) the heat losses for the couples should be equal to the other losses because

$$p_0 = \frac{nc}{l}.$$

The preceding calculations are only valid for wires that are heat insulated in such a way that the losses by radiation and convection are negligible with respect to the losses by conductivity. At any rate, experiment shows that heat insulating of the wires in an integrating apparatus, increases its sensitivity. It is evidently not so with an oscillographic apparatus, with which we seek large heat leakages and a very small heat capacity.

Next, we consider *improvements to increase the reliability of the apparatus*. When only one microcalorimetric unit is set up in a thermostat, to insure an even temperature in the outer chamber, it becomes impossible to use the maximum sensitivity of the apparatus. In fact, the variations of the thermostat temperature affect considerably the reliability of the apparatus. Tian arranged his microcalorimeter in the floor of a deep cellar where there was an even temperature of about 17 °C. This temperature varied less than $1/_{100}$ of a degree per day and about 1 deg per year. The variations were always very slow. In spite of these precautions, the recorded experimental zero underwent such variations that it became almost impossible to make experiments lasting longer than one day. On the other hand, it is often very embarrassing to be able to work only at a temperature of 17 °C. We have therefore constructed precision thermostats with multiple enclosures, which are capable of being regulated between 0 and 150 °C and insuring an even temperature to 0.001 °C. These thermostats are themselves placed in a thermostated room, in which the temperature varies less than $1/_{20}$ of a degree. In spite of these precautions it is still impossible to use the optimum sensitivity of a microcalorimetric unit alone. In fact, the electromotive force $e$ produced in the detector thermopile is:

$$e = k(t_1 - t_0), \tag{22}$$

$t_1$ being the temperature of the cell (inner chamber), and $t_0$ being that of the outer chamber.

But the temperature $t_0$ of the thermostat varies a little in time and its variations are only transmitted to the cell (heat insulated), very much later. The result is that the variations of $t_0$ considerably affect the electromotive force $e$; this is translated in the recorded curve as variations of the experimental zero. As an example, consider an apparatus provided with a detector thermopile of 20 iron-constantan couples, producing an electromotive force of $20 \times 50 \times 10^{-6} = 10^{-3}$ volt/degree. The resistance of the circuit being 100 ohms, the intensity of the current will be $10^{-5}$ ampere/degree. With a galvanometer of $10^{-10}$ amp sensitivity for a deviation of 1 mm on a scale placed at 1 m, it is possible to record by a deviation of 1 mm a difference of temperature of $\theta = t_1 - t_0$ of $10^{-5}$ degree. If we could read

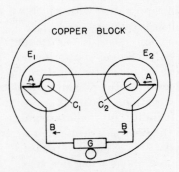

Figure 4. Diagram of the differential calorimeter. A, iron; B, constantan; $C_1$, $C_2$, cells; $E_1$, $E_2$, external chambers; G, galvanometer.

the scale to $^1/_{10}$ of a mm we should be able to attain a millionth of a degree. But no thermostat can insure the temperature in the outer chamber to $10^{-6}$ degree; in fact it is difficult to regulate a thermostat to about $0.001\,°C$. The reliability of the experimental zero of our apparatus being to a thousandth of a degree, the sensitivity to a millionth of a degree in our calorimeter is therefore illusory.

Next, we consider the differential setup of two calorimetric units. We considerably improve the reliability of the apparatus by arranging two identical microcalorimetric elements in two holes made in a big copper block, which is itself placed in the thermostat, and by connecting the detector thermopiles in opposition, according to the diagram of Figure 4 (differential setup). If the copper block is well designed, its temperature $t_0$ is uniform near the calorimetric units.

The temperature $t_0$ varies only slightly, but it is the same at all times in the outer chamber around the two calorimetric units. We will call the temperature of the two cells $t_1$ and $t_2$. The electromotive force $e_1$ and $e_2$ produced by the detector thermopiles of each unit are:

$$e_1 = k(t_1 - t_0)$$
$$e_2 = k(t_2 - t_0).$$

These thermopiles being in opposition, the resulting electromotive force is:

$$\mathcal{E} = e_1 - e_2 = k(t_1 - t_0). \tag{23}$$

We see that $\mathcal{E}$ does not depend any longer on the variations of $t_0$ with respect to time. The variations of $t_0$ in the course of time cause variations in the temperature of the two cells, but these variations are identical and have no effect on E, as is shown in Equation 23. This arrangement is of remarkable reliability. The variations of the experimental zero remain less than 1 mm on the galvanometer scale for quasi-unlimited periods and it becomes possible to make calorimetric experiments of unlimited duration.

We next discuss the application to the study of adsorption, involving continuous weighing by calorimetry in adsorption experiments. Since 1938 (9–25) we have been studying adsorption with the microcalorimeter. Numerous liquids have been adsorbed on soluble or insoluble substances, most of these adsorbents were crystalline, amorphous bodies or high polymers, such as nitrocellulose, bakelite, polyvinyl chloride, etc. We have already published numerous curves showing the evolution of heat produced during the course of the progressive adsorption of the vapors produced by these liquids.

The experiment was carried out in the following way: in a cell of differential microcalorimeter, a tube containing the adsorbent was placed (Figure 5). This tube is closed by a glass stopper which also acts as a stopcock and is controlled from the outside of the calorimeter. The stopcock allows the passage of the vapor from the liquid placed in the cell. When the stopcock is opened, a thermal effect is recorded as a result of the vaporization of the liquid and to the condensation of the vapor on the adsorbent. The heat of condensation of the liquid on the adsorbent is therefore measured directly. This method of working has given excellent results from the point of view of measuring the quantity of heat given off in the course of an adsorption. But it has the following shortcomings:

(i)   The weighing of the amount of substance adsorbed is hardly accurate for often it only means an increase of weight of about one mg or of a few milligrams over a long period (a day for instance).   In most of our determinations the measurement of the quantity of heat given off is obtained to within about 1 per cent, whereas the weighing (done with a balance to $1/_{100}$ mg at very long intervals) most frequently gives only a very poor accuracy.

(ii)   In order to do the weighing, it is necessary to stop the calori-

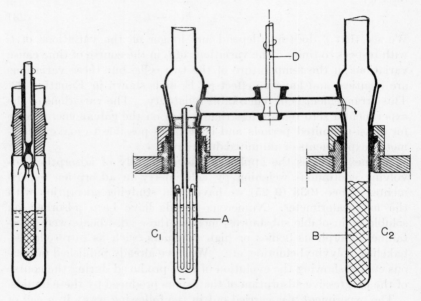

Figure 5. Microcalorimeter cell.   See text for details.
Figure 6. Arrangement of cells for an experiment on adsorption.   A, platinum pipe; B, adsorbent; $C_1$, $C_2$, cells; D, cock control.

metric experiment and remove the adsorption tube from the calorimeter.   This causes a waiting period of about half a day in order to restore the temperature equilibrium necessary for the continuation of the adsorption experiment.

The loss of time is considerable and the accuracy of the measurements is relatively poor.   There is therefore a great advantage in doing the automatic weighing inside the calorimeter while simultaneously measuring the heat given off.   The most sensitive means of evaluating, at any moment, the weight of liquid adsorbed is to record the flow of heat due to the vaporization of the liquid. We place the liquid to be adsorbed in the cell of the first unit $C_1$ and the adsorbent in the cell of the second unit $C_2$, the two cells being connected by a tube provided with a stopcock which can be regulated from outside the thermostat (Figure 6).

When we open the tap, the liquid distills from $C_1$ to $C_2$ into the adsorbent. There is cooling down in $C_1$ and heating in $C_2$. To measure the cooling down in $C_1$ we use the second thermopile (the one we usually use for the Peltier effect). This second pile is connected to a second galvanometer whose light spot is recorded. The recording allows the evaluation, at any moment, of the weight of the liquid evaporated, by integration of the recorded curve. Thus, if this liquid is water,

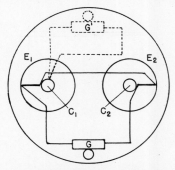

Figure 7. Diagram of the additional microcalorimeter. See text for details.

whose heat of vaporization is about 590 cal/g at 20°, it is possible to estimate at any moment the weight of water evaporated with an accuracy which no balance could give. In fact, the calorimeter, sensitive to $1/1000$ of a cal, used for 1 hr, allows the estimation of the weight of water distilled of the order of $1/500,000$ g per hr. But the elements $C_1$ and $C_2$ must no longer be connected differentially for we would record the difference of the algebraic values of the thermal effects produced in the two cells. Since these thermal effects have contrary signs, we would therefore record the sum of the absolute values. Now then, it is the difference of absolute values which interests us (adsorption heat). Therefore the apparatus must be set up as "additional," according to diagram in Figure 7. In this case we have for the resulting electromotive force:

$$\varepsilon = e_1 + e_2 = k(t_1 + t_2 - 2t_0). \qquad (24)$$

Unfortunately, we noticed that such a setup is doubly affected by variations in the temperature of the thermostat, in comparison with the calorimetric element used alone. In short, the system of two additional elements allows the simultaneous recording of the continuous weighing of liquid adsorbed and that of the adsorption heats; but the reliability of the measurements becomes uncertain, owing to variations in the temperature of the copper block, with time (imperfections of the thermostat).

*A device with four units permits setting up of two additional groups in differential.* We have already spoken of a calorimeter of four units, which we used initially to measure simultaneously two distinct calorimetric experiments (differential setups). By suitable coupling

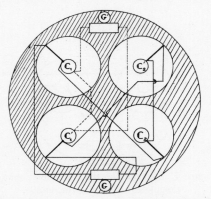

Figure 8. Additional differential system. See text for details.

the four calorimetric elements of such an apparatus we can keep the advantages of the preceding additional setup without having any of the inconveniences; that is to say, it becomes possible to get a reliable weighing of the substance adsorbed and a measurement of heat given off in the course of an adsorption, in spite of the variations in temperature of the copper block contained in the thermostat. To obtain this result, we must place the detector thermopiles of two calorimetric elements (laboratory elements) according to the preceding additional setup and those of the two other elements (reference elements) according to an identical setup; then we connect these two groups in opposition by interpolating the galvanometer in the circuit (Figure 8). The electromotive force E and E' produced in each group of two elements are substracted and we have:

$$\mathcal{E} = k(t_1 + t_2 - 2t_0)$$
$$\mathcal{E}' = k(t'_1 + t'_2 - 2t_0)$$
$$\mathcal{E} - \mathcal{E}' = k[(t_1 + t_2) - (t'_1 + t'_2)]. \tag{25}$$

If the elements are symmetrical, the disturbances coming from the variations of $t_0$ affect the temperatures of the cells $t_1$, $t_2$, $t'_1$, $t'_2$ in the same manner at any moment, and Equation 25 shows that the resulting electromotive force $\mathcal{E}-\mathcal{E}'$ becomes independent of these variations. Finally, we will set up the second thermopile of one of the two reference elements in opposition (differential system), with the pile being used for the determination of the weight of substances vaporized in such a way as to make the measurement independent of variations in temperature of the thermostat.

We have used this setup, differential coupling of two couples of calorimeters, each setup as additional. The results obtained have given great satisfaction from the point of view of the reliability of the apparatus. The sensitivity is a little diminished owing to the fact that the four resistances of the thermopiles are placed in series in the galvanometer circuit. But this slight diminution of sensitivity is largely compensated for by the excellent reliability of the apparatus.

The correct measurement of the heat of vaporization of a liquid requires special precautions. It is necessary to make the vapor of the liquid pass into the interior of the liquid in order to bring its temperature back to that of the liquid. To this end we have constructed a little heat exchanger represented in Figure 6.

We notice that the preceding set up can be used not only for the study of adsorption but also for that of other phenomena, such as isothermal distillation of a pure solvent to a solution. The weight of the vaporized liquid being deduced from the quantity of heat (recorded) required for the vaporization of the solvent.

The accuracy of our microcalorimetric measurements depends, first of all on that of the calibration of the apparatus which must be done under similar conditions to those of the calorimetric experiments. Of course it also depends on the accuracy of the length measurements (deviations of the galvanometer spot light), of the weight of the substances used, of time (duration of the Peltier and Joule effects, integration of the heat flow as time curves), and the electric measurements made in the course of the calorimetric experiment.

The calibration of the apparatus requires electrical resistance or electromotive force measurements and measurements of length and time. All these measurements can be made with an accuracy of better than $1/1000$.

Unhappily electrical measurements are not always perfectly comparable with thermochemical measurements: Thus, when a certain heating power is produced by the Joule effect in the cell, the temperature distribution in the cell (heat disequilibrium), is not the same as when an identical power is furnished by a chemical reaction in a liquid homogeneous phase. Now then, the thermal leakages from the two wires connecting the electric resistance in the cell to the rest of the circuit on the outside depend on the distribution of temperature in the cell and are not the same for a Joule effect or the case of a chemical effect of the same power in a homogeneous phase. We reduce this shortcoming by making the two lead wires pass through the interior of the copper block constituting the external enclosure in such a way as to place them in thermal contact with this block, while electrically insulating them. In this way we have only to take into consideration the transmission of heat due to the difference of temperature between the two chambers, whatever the outside temperature.

The best solution consists in calibration of the calorimetric apparatus by means of a slow chemical reaction or a slow phenomenon in which the heat given off is well known. At present we are endeavoring to calibrate our calorimeters by the measurement of heat adsorbed in the vaporization of a liquid, the vapor escaping from the cell being condensed outside the calorimeter in a low temperature trap. We are seeking a suitable solution to this problem, that is the calibration by a perfectly reproducible chemical reaction.

The accuracy of our measurements of heat quantities is of the order of $1/100$; we are trying to better this. But this accuracy is often superior to that of the determination of the weight of the reactants and products.

Thus, as we shall see later, we can measure to about 1 per cent the heat produced by the formation of a monomolecular film on a powdered substance whereas we are unable to attain this accuracy in the weighing of the adsorbed substance constituting this film. This is why, as we have shown previously, we would like to use the calorimeter itself to obtain the weight of adsorbed substance.

**3. Heat of solution, dilution, mixtures, and gelatinization.** The early measurements carried out with Tian's apparatus were made by Bérenger-Calvet (1). Their primary object was to check the reliability of the apparatus and discover the range of application. They were concerned with checking the well established heats of solution (for instance the heat of solution of $KNO_3$ in water) and heats of dilution of very dilute solutions (about 1 molecule of salt for 100 to 500 moles of water).

For these measurements, 5 cm³ of solvent are put in the cell in which is immersed a thin small glass tube containing the substance to be dissolved; this tube is closed at the bottom by a very brittle tapered point and it is connected on top to a capillary topped by a little rubber bulb (a rubber tube closed with a stopper). A heating resistance immersed in petroleum is also put in a thin glass tube inside the cell. To start the experiment, the tube, containing the substance to be dissolved, is pressed so as to break the tapered glass point. The rubber tube is opened in order to allow the liquid to go up in the glass tube which contains the crystals to be dissolved; then the stopper is replaced closing the rubber bulb which is squeezed to empty the capillary. When the pressure in the bulb is released, the liquid re-enters the tube; it is repeatedly emptied. Usually the whole solution process takes place after two or three emptyings of the tube. Of course, the method of handling must be studied beforehand so as to minimize the disturbances due to agitation, air bubbles, etc. The heats given out by broken glass points, agitation, etc., are measured by several separate experiments. With practice, these disturbances can be made less than $1/100$ of the thermal effect to be measured and, by knowing them to within 10 per cent, an error of less than $1/1000$ is made. Since one disturbance has to do with cooling, compensation by the Joule effect is indispensable. Compensation current intensity and time are adjusted in order to record a curve the area of which includes a negative part obviously equal to a positive part. The early mounting used by Bérenger-Calvet and copy of a curve recorded during the solution of $KNO_3$ in water are shown in Figure 9.

Since these first tests, many measurements of heats of solution, dilution, liquid mixtures and gelatinization of macromolecular substances have been made. The setup used varies with solution speed and the volatility of the liquids studied. Indeed, one must take into account variations of liquid vapor pressure (owing to solution) in the space not occupied by the liquid in the cell; these variations produce vaporization or condensation of the liquid accompanied by appreciable thermal effects compared to the one which will be evaluated.

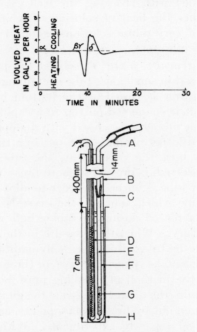

Figure 9. Device for measuring the heat of solution, with a copy of an experimental curve. A, rubber; B, cell; C, rubber connection; D, petroleum; E, tube with fragile pointed end containing the salt to be dissolved; F, water; G, salt to be dissolved; H, socket. See text for details.

Absolute variations in vapor pressure are more important as the liquid used is more volatile. In the case of very volatile liquids, it is necessary to eliminate space which can be occupied by vapor.

Figure 10 shows a device designed to measure heats of volatile liquid mixtures. If the rod R is pushed downward, the tail of bulb A slips into the stopper which closes tube E; the tapered point of bulb A is broken on the base of the rod R; mercury, contained in the cell, then enters bulb A to flush out the liquid in tube T.   The mixing occurs in tube T without any vapor being present above the liquid.

When solution is very slow, devices analogous to those shown in Figures 11 and 12 are adopted.   In Figure 11, the solution of nitrocellulose in acetone, when the nickel wire is pulled up, the bundle of nitrocellulose comes into the acetone.   In Figure 12, when the rod Q is pushed down, stopper B is removed and the small plates P containing the substance to be dissolved are immersed.   A similar device has

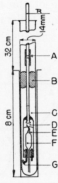

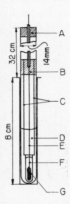

Figure 10. Device for measuring the heat of mixing volatile liquids.   A, connection; B, cork; C, mercury; D, alcohol; E, mercury; F, ether bulb; G, tubing for alcohol injection.   See text for details.

Figure 11. Device for measuring the heat of solution of nitrocellulose in acetone.   A, cork; B, cork; C, wire holding small tube; D, acetone; E, stiff nickel wire; F, mercury; G, small bundle of nitrocellulose attached to the nickel wire.   See text for details.

been used to transfer bacterial strains in culture media into the microcalorimeter.   Of course, other devices can be worked out. But it is always necessary to use a simple operation for starting the experiment so as to produce a very slight thermal effect which is reproducible in a blank experiment.

**4. Heats of adsorption of soluble, insoluble, and macromolecular substances.**   Devices have made possible the measurements of heats of adsorption of various liquids by means of solids with a transitional vapor state (Figures 5 and 6).   In particular, these studies are interesting from the thermokinetic point of view.

An examination of the records of heat flow with time for the very slow adsorption of a liquid on a dry substance has shown a remarkable phenomenon that we could explain only recently: in the curve recorded, there is an abrupt break corresponding to the end of monomolecular film formation. From this observation there results a very simple and new method of measuring the true surface energy of a pulverized substance (without having to degas it). It is only necessary to read the increase in weight of the adsorbent at the very moment of the break. If the area occupied by a molecule of the adsorbed substance is known, the specific surface of the adsorbent is deduced as in the B-E-T (Brunauer, Emmett, and Teller) method.

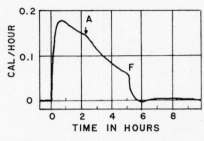

Figure 12. Device for measuring the heat of solution of amorphous alumina in aqueous sodium hydroxide.

Figure 13. Adsorption of water by anatase. At A, 0.32 per cent of water had been adsorbed, and the end of formation of the molecular film occurs. F marks the time of sealing of the adsorption tube.

Our early measurements were concerned with a sample of $TiO_2$ "anatase" whose specific surface was well known. It was similar to the sample used by Laporte (27) concerning the measurement of surface energy by the Harkins and Jura wetting method. The curve of heat flow with time corresponding to the adsorption of water by dried powder (but not degassed) reveals an abrupt change in slope for 0.24 per cent water adsorption (Figure 13). If the surface covered by a water molecule is 10.6 square Angstrom units, $A^2$, a value of 8.5m$^2$/g is found for the area occupied by a monomolecular film (Laporte found 9 m$^2$/g).

Later, the same experiments were carried out with samples of alumina ("boehmite" and "hydrargillite") whose specific surfaces

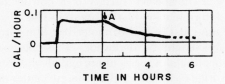

Figure 14. Adsorption of water by Gibbsite. At A, approximately 0.3 per cent of water had been adsorbed.

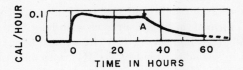

Figure 15. Adsorption of water by activated alumina. At A, 4.9 per cent of water had been adsorbed.

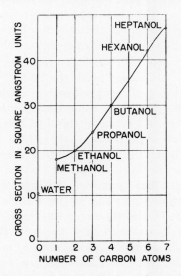

Figure 16. Cross section of molecules. See text for details.

were measured previously by the B-E-T method. The adsorption curves recorded by the microcalorimeter show very sharp breaks and allow the calculation of the specific surfaces which agree with other classical methods by less than 5 per cent (Figures 14 and 15). On the contrary if the specific surface of a powder is known beforehand, and if a determination of the break in the adsorption curve of heat flow with time at the end of molecular film formation is made, molecular surfaces could be deduced. This method has been applied to the adsorption of a series of normal alcohols on alumina.

The graph in Figure 16 shows that the molecular surface increases with the number of carbon atoms in the alcohol at least in the $C_1$ to $C_7$ range studied. This increase of molecular surface is 6 $A^2$ from $C_3$ to $C_7$, showing that the molecule is approximately lying flat on the adsorptive surface of the solid and not perpendicular to the latter as occurs in films formed on liquid surfaces with long-chain molecules of carbon atoms. This increase of 6 $A^2$ in surface area corresponds to the projection in space occupied by a $CH_2$ group on a plane including carbon atoms of the chain.

Our records show that adsorption goes on very much further than monomolecular film formation, chiefly in such cases as the adsorption of water by alumina. But the heat of adsorption for the first layer is much greater than that for the others. It was not possible to single out the formation of successive layers from the first one.

If an adsorptive powder is placed in a narrow cylindrical tube the diameter of which is about one tenth the height, it is thought that the upper part of the powdered substance adsorbs more moisture than the lower part. The same thing happens if the stopcock connecting the adsorbent and vapor of the liquid has a wide bore. In that case, the curve recorded proves that the heat flow is a decreasing function of time (Figure 13). The negative slope of that curve becomes greater as the stopcock is opened further. However, at the end of monomolecular film formation, the break is always observed. But then it corresponds to a value of the surface which is too large since the upper part of the tube contains several molecular layers whereas the lower part contains only one. On the contrary, if the stopcock has a small bore, a plateau (Figures 14 and 15) ended by an abrupt break is observed. In that case, the required area is determined very exactly. In order that the measurement may be correct, it is necessary, at the outset of the experiment, to adjust the stopcock controlling the adsorption speed so as to obtain a uniform heat flow.

Examples of soluble bodies that we have been studying include the adsorption of solvents such as water, ethyl alcohol, benzene, carbon sulfide, hexane, and acetone by solid substances such as urea, amides, saccharose, iodine, naphthalene, phenols, etc. In all cases, increases in the adsorption of a solvent by a dry substance produces a definite evolution of heat when the quantity of solvent adsorbed is large enough, even when solution accompanied by cooling, then occurs. It follows that all curves giving the heat emitted $Q$ by the adsorption of a solvent in increasing quantities $X$ pass through a maximum.

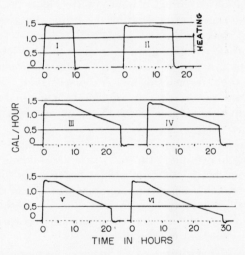

Figure 17. Record of heat evolved as a function of time by adsorption of water on urea. The quantity of urea is 1.8 g. These curves show the different phases of adsorption interrupted by intervals of two days: I, 6.85 mg; II, 11.55 mg; III, 13.95 mg; IV, 12.75 mg; V, 7.0 mg; VI, 6.5 mg.

The curves recorded of heat flow with time show the following characteristics in the case of soluble substances:

(i)    If the adsorption is made very slowly, we first notice a plateau ended by a break; secondly, a curve showing that heat flow decreases with time. If the experiment is shut down (by closing the adsorption tube) and then started again one or two days later, a new curve with the same slope is recorded whose plateau is shorter; but the ordinate of the plateau remains the same: quite the reverse of what happens in the case of insoluble substances (Figure 17).

(ii) In the case of water and urea for instance, it is possible in this way to adsorb to within 10 per cent of the tested adsorbent weight. That enormous number would correspond to a surface out of proportion to the outer surface of the urea crystals (even when they are crushed roughly). It is to be noted that there is a proportionality between the heat given out and the quantity of absorbed solvent for the very duration of adsorption which precedes solution. These observations show that water soaks into the urea crystal, without liquid phase formation. In other words, the crystal is spongy. After surface adsorption (recorded plateau), a very slow penetration takes place inside the crystal after short local solutions have occurred which open gaps and clefts in the crystal.

When adsorption begins again one or two days later, uncovered clefts and gaps are first covered with a film (new plateau of same ordinate) and the slow penetration takes place again. We could have checked that the penetration of water is very slight for molten and crushed sodium chloride monocrystals whereas it is large enough for ordinary sodium chloride crystals.

In the case of very soluble substances (example: phenols, di-phenylmethane in acetone) (18,20,21) it is very difficult to make adsorption evident before solution occurs because the liquid phase is produced very quickly before any monomolecular film can be formed. In that case it is impossible to record a break in the calorimetric adsorption curve. The existence of partial adsorption occurring before solution could however be proved.

In the case of gelatinization of macromolecular substances, the adsorption of acetone, acetic esters, alcohol–ether mixtures and methyl nitrate by nitrocelluloses has been studied in the micro-calorimeter (11,12,13,14); likewise the adsorption of acetone by methylcellobiose nitrates (15), and the adsorption of polyvinyl chloride solvents on bakelite (23).

The curves giving the quantity of heat released $Q$ as a function of the number of adsorbed molecules $n$ referred to a link of macromolec-ular substance, show that adsorption is always occurring with heat delivery. This seems higher at the beginning of adsorption as the adsorbed liquid is a better solvent. The slope at the origin indeed increases with dissolving power. These curves are linear at the beginning, as in the case of crystalline substances and indicate deep penetration of the solvent inside the adsorptive substance. The slope decreases when the expansion appears. The curves often show an abrupt change in the slope indicating the occurrence of solvation. In the case of the nitro-celluloses for instance, we get a sharp break in the curve for 6 mol of acetone per $C_6$ link and for 2 mol of methyl nitrate or acetic ester per $C_6$ link. Perhaps these abrupt variations of adsorption heat with respect to increasing amounts of absorbed liquid take rise in the fact that the solvent penetrates into a macro-molecular substance completely and tends to form a layer surrounding each molecule. Finally the curves $Q = f(n)$ always pass through a maximum as is the case for soluble substances (Figure 18).

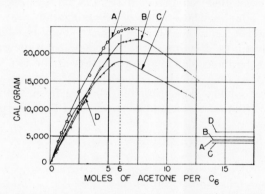

Figure 18. Heat of adsorption of acetone on nitrocellulose. A, film containing 14 per cent nitrogen; B, nitroramie containing 11.47 per cent nitrogen; C, film containing 11.5 per cent nitrogen; D, nitroramie containing 14.0 per cent nitrogen. On the scale at the lower right are given the total heats of solution for the same substances.

The studies about the thermokinetics of adsorption seem of great interest. For insoluble substances, they allow evaluation of the surface of powders and determination of the activated fraction of surfaces; for soluble substances, they allow a separation of the very general phenomenon of adsorption preceding solution and a partial explanation of the mechanism of solution; for macromolecular substances, they allow a classification of solvents or gelatinizing substances according to their activity, a study of expansion and the complexities of solvation, etc.

**5. Heats of change of state.** Suppose we have two allotropic varieties of a pure substance and use samples which each contain a single variety. They have dissolved in the same solvent and the final state is supposed to be the same for the two varieties. The difference between the molecular heats of solution will allow us to evaluate the heat required to change one variety to the other, the heat of transition. If we have no samples of each pure allotropic variety but only one containing a mixture (known composition) of the two varieties, it is only necessary to dissolve two samples of different (but known) composition so as to find the heats of solution required.

This method has been especially applied to the determination of the rate of crystallization of celluloses (28,29). Suppose we have two cellulose samples whose rates of crystallization are: $a$ (known) for the one and $x$ (unknown) for the other. They have dissolved in the same solvent (a diamine cupric–ethylene solution was chosen). Let $Q_0$ and $Q_1$ be molecular heats of solution of the two samples (in order to get the same solution concentration). Let us call $W_{cr}$ the molecular heat of crystallization of cellulose from the amorphous state and $W_a$ the molecular heat of solution of the amorphous state. We have:

$$-aW_{cr} + W_a = Q_0$$
$$-xW_{cr} + W_a = Q_1.$$

From these two equations $x$ can be calculated if $W_{cr}$ and $a$ are known. Conversely, if the rates of crystallization $a$ and $x$ are known, $W_{cr}$ can be calculated. Such measurements have been made and it has been found that

$$W_{cr} = 4100 \pm 200 \text{ cal/mole.}$$

The determination of the rate of crystallization of alumina gels is described in references (28,29). Gels initiating the precipitation of alumina from sodium aluminate solutions are more active as the rate of crystallization is smaller. This has been proved in a recent work (34). After having dried the gel at a suitable temperature (about 100°C), one may, by means of a simple solution in soda made in the microcalorimeter, evaluate approximately its rate of crystallization and therefore its value as a precipitation initiator. Indeed, solution of the amorphous part is abrupt and exothermal. The curves recorded are similar in type to Figure 19a when the gel is quite amorphous and simliar in type to Figure 19b when the gel is partially crystalline. In these curves, it is easy to determine the part corresponding to solution of the amorphous portion (exothermal point) and to solution of the crystalline portion (endothermal branch).

**6. Heats of slow reactions.** The early measurements of heats of slow reactions have been made with Tian's apparatus by Bérenger-Calvet (1). They were related to the heat of esterification of ethanol by acetic acid and the heat of hydrolysis of ethyl acetate.

Such thermochemical measurements are complicated for the following reason: during the reaction the new substances formed have

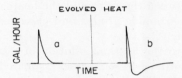

Figure 19. Rate of crystallization of alumina gels. See text for details.

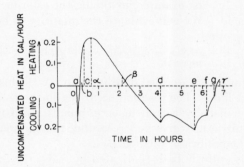

Figure 20. Saponification of acetamide by sodium hydroxide. See text for details.

dissolved in the existing medium whereas other substances are missing from this medium. Thermochemical measurement gives a value which should be corrected by the difference between the heats of solution of the reactants and products. This correction is important if the heat of reaction is low. A practical method by Bérenger-Calvet allows the evaluation of these heat quantities and for esterification and hydrolysis she obtained two values, agreeing well, with unlike signs (+1.07 kcal at 20°C for esterification).

Figure 20 shows the curve recorded during the saponification of acetamide in an investigation by the writer. The reaction here is exothermal. Compensation of the heat given out has been brought about by the Peltier effect. In the curve recorded, it will be noted that the Peltier effect was changed four times during the measurement (cusp in curve). In that investigation, we took into account corrections due to the heats of solution of reactants and products in the medium; a reference system has been used to allow a knowledge of the state of the system reacting in the calorimeter at each moment.

A comparison between the rates and the heats of saponification of aliphatic amides, benzamide groups and chloroacetamides has been made by the author.

Corrections due to the heats of dilution of reactants or products can be of great importance in some cases compared to the quantity of heat to be evaluated. This is especially true in the case of the heat of esterification of cellulose by nitric acid or nitric–sulfuric acids. To illustrate the importance of these corrections we are going to give some details of this last example, involving the esterification of cellulose by nitric acid. We will evaluate the quantity of heat given out by following reaction:

$$\text{cotton} + n\text{HNO}_3 = \text{nitrocellulose} + n\text{H}_2\text{O} + X \text{ cal} \tag{26}$$
$$\text{(dry)} \quad \text{(liquid)} \qquad \text{(dry)} \qquad \text{(liquid)}$$

$n$ being the number of esterified hydroxyls and $X$ the heat of reaction per cellulose $C_6$ link. The reaction occurring in the calorimeter consisted in immersing dry cotton in large quantities of nitric–sulfuric acids or acetonitric mixtures and recording the thermal phenomena produced until equilibrium was reached.

With a nitric–sulfuric bath (indicated by S.N.) the following reaction is obtained:

$$\text{cotton} + \text{bath S.N.} = \text{immersed nitrocellulose} + Q \text{ cal} \tag{27}$$
$$\text{(dry)} \quad \text{(initial)} \qquad \text{(in waste bath)}$$

To get $X$ from $Q$ with suitable complemental measurements, the following set of four transformations will be investigated.*

dry cotton + S.N.$_i$ $\xrightarrow{\alpha}$ dry cotton + ($n\text{HNO}_3$ + S.N.$_i$ from which $n\text{HNO}_3$

was taken out) $\xrightarrow{\beta}$ dry nitrocellulose + $n\text{H}_2\text{O}$ + (S.N.$_i$ from which $n\text{HNO}_3$

was taken out) $\xrightarrow{\gamma}$ dry nitrocellulose + S.N.$_r$ $\xrightarrow{\delta}$ nitrocellulose immersed in waste bath

* The nitric-sulfuric initial bath is called S.N.$_i$ and waste bath is called S.N.$_r$).

Reaction $\alpha$ calls into play the heat quantity $D_1$ produced when $n\text{HNO}_3$ is taken out of a large bath of S.N.$_i$. If $\gamma$ is called the differential heat of dilution when a molecule of $\text{HNO}_3$ is added to an infinite quantity of S.N. mixture, we get:

$$D_1 = -n\nu.$$

Reaction $\beta$ is nothing else than the reaction of esterification of cellulose by nitric acid. It calls into play $X$ cal. Reaction $\gamma$ calls into play the heat quantity $D_2$ produced when $n$ molecules of water are added to a large quantity of the S.N. bath used earlier. If $e$ is called the differential heat of dilution when one molecule of water is added to much S.N., we get:

$$D_2 = ne.$$

Reaction $\delta$ corresponds to the heat of immersion $I$ of a $C_6$ link of dry nitrocellulose in the final S.N. bath. The complete reaction is merely reaction (27), releasing $Q$ cal. Then we have:

$$Q = -n\nu + X + ne + I$$
$$X = Q + n(\gamma - e) - I.$$

Heat quantities, $Q$, $I$, $\nu$, and $e$ have been measured directly.

For esterified —OH groups an average value of $2000 \pm 200$ cal is obtained. The same result has been found again by the use of acetonitric mixtures instead of nitric–sulfuric acids. This heat of esterification is low. However, it is twice as high as the heat of esterification of ethyl alcohol by acetic acid. It is curious to note that the large and abrupt thermal effect produced when cotton is immersed in nitric–sulfuric acid, is due mostly to dilution phenomena (disappearance of nitric acid and formation of water) and also to the heat of immersion of cellulose nitrate in the waste bath. These thermal effects are responsible for about 70 per cent (for bath B) of the apparent heat of reaction $Q$.

The heat of saponification of methyl nitrate by potash has been measured (37). After having made corrections owing to dilution heats, we got for following reaction

$$\text{CH}_3\text{NO}_3 + \text{KOH} = \text{KNO}_3 + \text{CH}_3\text{OH} + X \text{ cal}$$
(infinite dilution      (solid)      (liquid)
in methanol)

the value $X = 11,850$ cal. Whence the value $2000 \pm 200$ cal is deduced for the heat of esterification of the methyl nitrate. This last value is the same, to within 10 per cent, as the one previously obtained for the esterification of an alcohol group of cellulose.

Precipitation of alumina from alumino-sodic solutions (called "decomposition") represents a phase of the formation of alumina by Bayer's process the mechanism of which is still not clear. We have been investigating this question by various methods; the ones which were most helpful were the study of the X-ray spectra of the products obtained and the microcalorimetric measurements. We could have recorded the thermokinetics of the "decomposition," occurring spontaneously or induced by crystalline nuclei or amorphous gels. These gels, and also half-crystalline gels ("pseudoboehmite" gels) proved the most active in starting the precipitation of alumina. It is known that the Bayer process requires a large amount of crystalline initiators (about 250 kg of alumina per $m^3$ of liquor); on the contrary, a very small quantity of amorphous alumina is sufficient to produce precipitation.

The formation of amorphous gels is then of great interest and an analysis of these gels with the microcalorimeter (by measuring the effects of solution in soda) was for us an excellent guide in forming gels which were especially active in initiating decomposition. By means of the microcalorimeter we have studied the aging of gels, measured heats of precipitation of crystalline varieties, etc. (34–36).

With regard to the mercerization of cellulose (37), curves can be drawn to give the heats released when cellulose is immersed in soda solutions of increasing concentration; the existence of cellulose–soda complexes of definite composition has been shown, and zones of reversibility of mercerization phenomenon could be studied, etc.

**7. Applications to biology.** The microcalorimeter allowed us to study heat changes occurring during seed germination and bacterial growth (40–42). The procedure for the thermogenesis of germination is as follows: seeds are put in the microcalorimeter cell. Germination is started when the tapered point of a tube containing some water is broken off. While, first of all the germination of wheat was being studied, the existence of a first phase was found: physicochemical thermogenesis corresponding to a moistening of the grain and reaching in a few minutes a maximum heat flow of 0.5 cal/hour for 1 g of grains. It is followed by a period of rest from the 10th till the 17th hour; then a second phase occurs: biological thermogenesis corresponding to a starting of the physiological phenomena of the germination (Figure 21). From this initial result, experimentation was continued in two directions.

(i) Keeping experimental conditions constant, the thermogenetic curves of many vegetable classes have been compared: corn (oats, rye, barley); cruciferous plants (radish, cabbage, turnip); cheno-podiaceae; leguminous plants; poppy tribe, etc. From these curves, specific characteristics could be singled out, especially the duration of physicochemical thermogenesis which seems to be a most stable characteristic. Varieties and series of seeds can be thus classed by their physiological properties. This is obviously of interest in agriculture.

(ii) Then working up a series of homogeneous seeds, experimental conditions are changed by the action of various physical and chemical factors. For instance, a little alcohol stops biological thermogenesis without changing physicochemical thermogenesis. Other substances

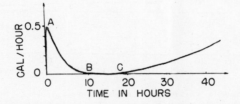

Figure 21. Thermogenesis of germination of wheat. See text for details.

on the contrary, such as hetero-auxins, promote the second phase at some concentrations. On the other hand, after the seeds are dried, two results are obtained. One, easily foreseen, is a marked increase in physicochemical thermogenesis; the other, *a priori* unforeseeable, is an acceleration of the beginning of biological thermogenesis. This is also of interest in agriculture as it indicates the possibility of promoting the beginning of seed germination after they have been dried under certain conditions.

The procedure for studying the thermogenesis during bacterial growth is as follows: miscellaneous bacterial strains have been introduced into well-defined culture media (kept in sealed bulbs) in the microcalorimeter cell. This can be done by using a kind of cup sealed to a long glass rod passing through the stopper of cell which can be handled from outside the calorimeter. Germs suspended in physiological water, for instance, are put in the cup at the density required under sterile conditions and immersed in the culture medium just as heat equilibrium is reached. We found that cultures of *B. Proteus* show a thermogenesis which first increases regularly till a maximum of about 0.16 cal/hour (at 17°C) is reached after 24 hr in the following conditions (8 ml of a peptone broth inoculated with 0.1 ml of a culture titrating 6 billion germs per milliliter). From this result, our researches have been directed, as in the case of seeds, in two directions.

(i) Keeping experimental conditions constant, we have ascertained that *every bacterial strain gives a specific thermogenetic curve.* For a rough indication, the curves obtained with *Eberthella typhosa* and *B. paratyphic* bacillus are shown here (Figure 22). Integrating the curves, it is possible to calculate the quantity of heat produced by various inocula in a similar culture medium. For instance, in the

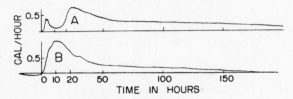

Figure 22. Specific curves of thermogenesis at 37.4°C. See text for details. A, *Eberthella typhosa;* B, paratyphic bacillus.

case of *Eberthella typhosa* at 37.4°C heat releases have been found to vary between 60 and 70 cal after 190 hours' waiting, for 10 ml of culture medium. At 17°C, the thermogenetic record of *Eberthella typhosa* could not be obtained. In the case of B. paratyphic bacillus at 37.4°C, we found 40 to 50 cal after 150 hr, whereas 2 cal was found at 17°C. Introduction of antibiotics decreases or cancels the growth of some pathogen bacteria. Thermogenesis decrease is therefore a quantitative measure of the inhibition power of the antibiotics.

(ii) On the other hand, working up a definite bacterial strain, we have changed experimental conditions. For instance, operating with more and more concentrated broths, a group of curves has been obtained with B. Proteus showing more and more prolonged thermogenesis and higher and higher maxima. If the broth concentration is doubled, the maximum is reached after 42 hr instead of 24 and gives a value of 0.3 cal/hour instead of 0.15 cal/hour. At that time, it seems that one of the nutritive elements of the culture medium becomes exhausted, therefore bacterial divisions are stopped.    This is shown by thermogenetic depression.    On the other hand, when inoculation with a less rich culture occurs, the time to reach the maximum heat flow is increased without, however, changing its value.    For instance, with a culture titrating inocula 10 millions per ml, that is six hundred times less than before, the maximum is reached after 52 hr, but it is still equal to 0.15 cal/hour.

It is to be noted that the material studied in a reaction can only after all be influenced by the heat changes occurring.    This is the best means at our disposal to discover its behavior in a continuous way without disturbing the existing medium.

**8. Conclusion.**    At the outset of this study, an interest in direct thermochemical measurements was shown in order to set up tables giving the heats of formation.    Precise measurements with the bomb are however still fundamental to establish any heats of formation that cannot be made by direct measurement; but it is desirable that direct measurements be made as often as possible.

A few applications previously described show the use of calorimetry in physics, chemistry, and biology.    Study of radioactive transformations can also be worked out in calorimeters fitted for slow phenomena.

The sensitivity and reliability of new microcalorimetric apparatus are such as to allow the measurement of very low heat flows (about 0.001 cal/hour) for almost unlimited time.    From the standpoint of both the thermodynamics and the kinetics of slow phenomena, it can be seen that great services to science will be rendered when laboratories well equipped for making microcalorimetric measurements will be at the disposal of physicochemists and biologists.

### References

1. Bérenger-Calvet, *J. chim. phys.* **24**, 325 (1927).
2. W. Swietoslawski, *Microcalorimetry*, Reinhold Publishing Corp., New York, 1946.
3. A. Tian, *Bull. soc. chim. France* **33**, 427 (1923).
4. A. Tian, *Compt. rend.* **178**, 705 (1924).
5. A. Tian, *J. chim. phys.* **30**, 665 (1933).
6. A. Tian, *Ann. fac. sci. Marseille* **6**, 3 (1933).
7. Whipp, *Phil. Mag.* **18**, 745 (1934).
8. Tonnelat, Thesis, University of Paris, Paris, 1945.
9. E. Calvet, *J. chim. phys.* **35**, 69 (1938).

10. E. Calvet, *J. chim. phys.* **35**, 286 (1938).
11. E. Calvet, *Compt. rend.* **212**, 542 (1941).
12. E. Calvet, *Compt. rend.* **213**, 126 (1941).
13. E. Calvet, *Compt. rend.* **214**, 716 (1942).
14. E. Calvet and J. Coutelle, *Compt. rend.* **215**, 138 (1942).
15. E. Calvet and Maurizot, *Compt. rend.* **216**, 51 (1943).
16. E. Calvet, *Compt. rend.* **217**, 482 (1943).
17. E. Calvet, *Soc. française phys., Section Mediterranée* **15**, 11 (1943).
18. E. Calvet, *J. Phys.* **6**, 398 (1945).
19. E. Calvet, *Bull. soc. chim. France, Series* 5, **12**, 553 (1945).
20. E. Calvet and G. Sebille, *Bull. soc. chim. France, Series* 5, **14**, 188 (1947).
21. E. Calvet and G. Sebille, *Bull. soc. chim. France, Series* 5, **14**, 286 (1947).
22. E. Calvet, *Mém. services chim. état (Paris)* **32**, 168 (1946).
23. E. Calvet, R. Dalbert, and J. Chedin, *Mém. services chim. état (Paris)* **32**, 220 (1946).
24. E. Calvet and G. Sebille, *Compt. rend.* **222**, 84 (1946).
25. E. Calvet, *Compt. rend.* **232**, 964 (1951).
26. E. Calvet, *J. Polymer Sci.* **8**, 163 (1952).
27. F. Laporte, Thesis, University of Paris, 1949.
28. E. Calvet and P. H. Hermans, *J. Polymer Sci.* **6**, 33 (1951).
29. E. Calvet, *J. Chem. Analytique* **176** (1950).
30. E. Calvet, *Compt. rend.* **189**, 530 (1929).
31. E. Calvet, *Compt. rend.* **192**, 1569 (1931).
32. E. Calvet, *Compt. rend.* **194**, 610 (1932).
33. E. Calvet, Thesis, University of Paris, Paris, 1932.
34. E. Calvet, H. Thibon, A. Maillard, and P. Boivinet, *Bull. soc. chim. France, Series* 5, **17**, 1308 (1950).
35. E. Calvet, H. Thibon, and A. Maillard, *Compt. rend.* **228**, 928 (1949).
36. E. Calvet, H. Thibon, A. Maillard, and P. Boivinet, *Bull. soc. chim. France, Series* 5 **18**, 402 (1951).
37. E. Calvet and J. Dhers-Pession, *Mém. services chim. état (Paris)* **35**, 45 (1950).
38. E. Calvet, *Compt. rend.* **226**, 1275 (1948).
39. E. Calvet and J. Chedin, *Mém. services chim. état (Paris)* **34**, 179 (1948).
40. E. Calvet and H. Prat, *Compt. rend. soc. biol. Marseille* (June 1944).
41. E. Calvet and H. Prat, *Compt. rend.* **220**, 117 (1945).
42. E. Calvet and H. Prat, *Compt. rend.* **220**, 470 (1945).
43. E. Calvet, J. Fricker, and H. Prat, *Compt. rend.* **220**, 797 (1945).
44. E. Calvet, J. Fricker, and H. Prat, *Canada Rev. Biology* (January 1946).

# CHAPTER 13

# Physicochemical Standards for Thermochemistry

GUY WADDINGTON

**1. Introduction.** The primary aim of thermochemical investigations is to determine the change in internal energy when specific reactants in known thermodynamic states are converted into specific products also in known thermodynamic states. The experimental devices employed to achieve this general purpose will perforce differ according to the chemical nature and physical state of the reactants and products. Moreover, different investigators may devise quite dissimilar methods for obtaining the same thermochemical quantity. However, one requirement which all methods have in common is that it is necessary to have a means of evaluating the number of units of energy involved in the specific thermochemical process which takes place in the calorimetric equipment. This fact necessitates the calibration of the instrument in use so that the energy effect accompanying an observed thermodynamic change may be expressed in terms of an accepted energy unit.

The most direct method of calibration is to determine the temperature increment produced in the apparatus by a measured quantity of electrical energy under conditions as nearly as possible identical with those of the thermochemical experiments. In some types of thermochemical investigations [e.g., Kistiakowski and co-workers' (1) studies of heats of hydrogenation of unsaturated hydrocarbons by a flow method] electrical calibration of the apparatus is the most convenient method. In combustion calorimetry of the highest accuracy electrical calibration is the basic method on which the accuracy of less direct methods must rest. Because of the specialized skills, expensive equipment, and reliable standards of resistance and electromotive

287

force required, electrical calibration of combustion bomb calorimeters is carried out in a few laboratories only. Other laboratories must determine the energy equivalent of the calorimetric system by use of a standard reference substance certified by a standardizing laboratory as to the amount of heat it will produce when a specified mass of the substance is burned in a bomb under prescribed conditions. The use of a standard reference substance for calibration of a bomb calorimeter is in effect a device for transferring the unit of energy from the standardizing laboratory to the investigator's laboratory. The prime requirement of the reference substance is that it must transfer accurately the unit of energy from the standardizing laboratory to the laboratory of the investigator.

**2. Benzoic acid as a primary standard for bomb combustions.** Early investigators in the field of bomb calorimetry used several different substances for reference purposes. These included naphthalene, sucrose, and benzoic acid (2). Accumulated experience revealed the shortcomings of the former two and the advantages of the latter. Benzoic acid has long been recognized internationally as the primary standard reference substance for bomb calorimetry and was formally recommended in 1934 for that purpose by the former Commission on Thermochemistry of the International Union of Chemistry (3). It is available as a certified Standard Sample from the National Bureau of Standards, Washington, D. C. The certificate issued with the sample gives the heat of combustion of benzoic acid for the standard bomb process, the conditions under which the experiment should be performed, and the corrections that must be applied to the results when experimental conditions deviate from those prescribed.

The requirements that benzoic acid or any other substance to be employed as a primary reference substance in bomb calorimetry must satisfy have been enumerated by Beckers (4). The choice of secondary reference standards for use in the study of compounds containing elements other than carbon, hydrogen and oxygen may impose additional criteria, but those cited by Beckers and others are common to most situations and will, therefore, be discussed in some detail for the case of benzoic acid. The minimum requirements for a substance to be used as a primary reference standard are: (a) it should be obtainable in a pure state; (b) it should be stable; (c) it should not be hygroscopic; (d) it should not be too volatile; (e) it should be easily compressible into pellets; (f) it should ignite readily and burn completely in the bomb.

The reliability of the entire body of modern thermochemical data depends in large measure on the reliability of certified standard samples of benzoic acid. It is, therefore, essential that it should meet the property requirements of a standard reference substance. The results of tests of its suitability as a standard are discussed in the following paragraphs.

The certificates issued by the National Bureau of Standards with standard samples of benzoic acid give purity values based on titration of the sample. For example, standard samples 39f and 39g are reported to analyze 100.03 and 99.99 per cent, respectively. Jessup and Green (5) obtained a measure of the purity of sample 39d from the mass of carbon dioxide formed in the combustion of a known mass of sample. They reported a purity of $99.95_9$ per cent, but if their calculations are revised in terms of 1951 International Atomic Weights (6), the result is a purity of $99.99_5$ per cent. The purity of Sample 39f has been reported by Schwab and Wichers (7) to be 99.983 mole per cent from studies of the freezing range and $99.989_8$ from the results of heat capacity measurements made at temperatures just below the melting point. None of the methods mentioned for determining purity is free from minor objections, but the weight of accumulated evidence indicates that the amounts of impurities in standard samples of benzoic acid are small. It is obvious that significant amounts of impurities are undesirable, but small amounts may be tolerated provided each batch is perfectly homogeneous and successive batches have heats of combustion that approximate closely to one another. If these conditions are satisfied, the standard sample can fulfill its purpose of transferring the unit of energy from the national standardizing laboratory to the laboratory of the investigator. The purities of successive batches of NBS standard sample benzoic acid (39f, 39g, etc.), may vary slightly, but it has been established (8) that the heats of combustion under bomb conditions of the various samples and of specially purified material are essentially identical.

Observations on the stability of benzoic acid have been made by several investigators. Weaver (9) states that it decomposes above 150°C. Schwab and Wichers (7) obtained evidence of oxidation at 200°C and also rather conclusive evidence of a slow, reversible dissociation into benzoic anhydride and water at temperatures as low as 135°C. However, they conclude that benzoic acid is sufficiently stable to be able to withstand any thermal treatment normally encountered during its preparation and use as a standard sample.

The hygroscopicity of benzoic acid has been tested carefully by Schwab and Wichers (7). NBS standard sample 39f in its ordinary condition was found to contain 0.0015 to 0.0018 per cent moisture. After 6 weeks exposure to a relative humidity of 90 per cent at 23°, the moisture content had not increased. Jessup (10) calibrated a calorimeter with samples of 39e which had been (a) taken from a freshly opened bottle, (b) taken from a bottle open to the atmosphere for a year but protected from dust, and (c) maintained at a relative humidity of 79 per cent for a year. The results obtained with the three samples were essentially identical. The foregoing results indicate that benzoic acid as prepared and distributed for standard sample use meets the requirement of nonhygroscopicity.

The volatility of benzoic acid was tested (10) by exposing a 1.5-g briquet to an ambient temperature of 29 to 32° for 3 weeks. The rate of loss was 0.15 mg per day or 0.01 per cent. No significant error will result if the briquet is used promptly after it is weighed. However, in regard to volatility, the properties of benzoic acid are marginal, and the investigator should be careful to avoid conditions that might cause loss of material.

Benzoic acid may easily be made into small briquets by use of a "pellet" press. The press used must be scrupulously clean. The briquets are firm and coherent and remain so when stored for long periods. They may be handled safely and scraped with an appropriate sharp-edged implement to reduce them to the desired mass.

If the products resulting from the combustion of standard sample benzoic acid in the calibration experiment are not identical with those obtained by the standardizing laboratory, the certificate value of the heat of combustion of the standard sample will have no significance to the investigator. It is, therefore, of prime importance that benzoic acid should burn completely to form only carbon dioxide and water. Under optimum conditions benzoic acid burns completely in a conventional bomb. However, a small residue of carbonaceous material may be found after some combustions. Such experiments are usually rejected. Each investigator must determine the conditions that will yield a preponderance of "clean" combustions. The shape, mass, and position of the crucible in the bomb are variables which may affect the completeness of combustion reaction. Jessup and Green (5) report absence of unburned carbon for a complete series of combustions. The same observers also tested for carbon monoxide among the products of combustion with negative results. Huffman (11) observed unweighable amounts of carbon in a few combustions of a series and states that "the effect of incomplete combustion was within the experimental error of our measurements." Coops states that "soot" is occasionally produced in his calibration experiments. The evidence indicates that benzoic acid will burn completely to form carbon dioxide and water under proper conditions but that the investigator must be alert to the possibility of incomplete combustion.

**3. Secondary standards for bomb combustions.** Benzoic acid has come to be accepted as the one required standard for all investigators in the field of bomb calorimetry. It is the primary standard in the sense that it is the recommended means for transferring the unit of energy to the laboratory of the investigator who is not able to employ electrical calibration methods. It is to be used for determining the energy equivalent of the calorimeter whether the compounds to be studied subsequently contain C, H, and O; C, H, O, and N; C, H, O, and S or other elements or combinations of elements. Early investigators (12,13) considered the desirability of having available a secondary standard to supplement the primary standard. In 1936 the then Commission on Thermochemistry (14) adopted in principle succinic acid as a secondary standard. Apparently it has suitable properties (13) but as yet has not found widespread acceptance nor is it available as a combustion standard from a recognized standardizing laboratory. Huffman (11) determined the heat of combustion of succinic acid and obtained values in good agreement with those of Roth and Beckers (15), Keffler (13), and Beckers (12).

The Commission (14) also recommended that efforts be made to establish separate secondary standards for use in bomb combustions of compounds containing nitrogen, sulfur, chlorine, bromine, or iodine. The function of the proposed secondary standards for bomb combustions differs somewhat from that of the primary standard, benzoic acid. In studies of compounds that contain one of the above-mentioned elements the products of combustion and conditions of the experiment may differ considerably from those common in studies of compounds containing carbon, hydrogen, and oxygen. The chemistry of the combustion process may be uncertain and the nature and magnitude of the corrections necessary to obtain the standard heat of combustion may not be known accurately. When these uncertainties exist, the availability of an appropriate secondary standard or "test substance" will permit intercomparison of the results of different investigators and essentially serves to control the chemical part of the investigation. As the various difficulties are resolved, the accuracy of reported values of the standard heat of combustion of the test substance will improve. Initially the substance will serve as a guide to investigators exploring a somewhat new field; finally, when adequately tested, it can become the criterion for judging the correctness of procedures and the accuracy of results.

The Commission (14) has suggested the investigation of the following test substances for controlling the chemical part of thermochemical investigations utilizing bomb combustions: for sulfur compounds, *sym*-diphenylthiourea or thioglycolic acid; for fluorine compounds, *m*-trifluorotoluic acid; for chlorine compounds, trichlorophenol; for bromine compounds, *o*-bromobenzoic acid; and for iodine compounds, *m*-iodobenzoic acid. Other substances have been suggested as test substances for sulfur and chlorine compound combustion studies and will be discussed later. Huffman (11) has recommended hippuric acid as a "secondary standard" or test substance for nitrogen compound investigations.

**4. Test substances for sulfur compounds.** Sunner and Lundin (16) have analyzed in considerable detail the requirements for a test substance for sulfur compounds. They point out that in addition to the requirements for a good combustion standard given by Huffman (11) that a sulfur compound used as a test substance should yield a final state similar to average final states encountered in actual investigations. This requirement means that a quantity of the substance that will evolve the required amount of energy when burned in the bomb must also yield a sulfuric acid solution in the approximate range 1 to $2N$. This range is based on ($a$) the use of 10 ml of water in the bomb (see Chap. 7), and ($b$) the necessity of maintaining the amount of sulfur below a level at which incomplete oxidation to the $+6$ state might occur. Sunner and Lundin show that of the two substances recommended for study by the Commission (14) *sym*-diphenylthiourea has too low and thioglycolic acid too high a sulfur content to make them suitable as standards.

Sunner and Lundin (16) have investigated carefully the possible use of thianthrene, $C_{12}H_8S_2$, as a test substance for use in sulfur compound combustion studies. According to these investigators it "pellets" readily, ignites easily, and burns completely. It is nonhygroscopic, nonvolatile, and stable within the requirements of a combustion standard. Samples that have an estimated purity of 99.8 mole per cent have been prepared. Concerning the special requirements for sulfur compound standards mentioned earlier, thianthrene has a heat of combustion of approximately 8 kcal/g for the reaction

$$C_{12}H_8S_2(s) + 17O_2(g) + 228H_2O(liq.) = 12CO_2(g) + (2H_2SO_4 \cdot 115H_2O)(liq.).$$

Consequently, briquets of from 0.6 to 1.0 g mass, when burned in a conventional bomb, will produce an adequate temperature rise and a sulfuric acid concentration in the range desired. Hubbard et al. (17) determined the standard heat of the foregoing reaction in two different investigations, and a value has been reported by Sunner and Lundin (16). The agreement of the three results is not quite as close as desirable for a reference substance. However, the disagreement illustrates one of the main functions of a test substance. The investigators in question employed somewhat different calibration procedures (with benzoic acid), and also their treatments of the Washburn corrections were not identical. The differences in results may be traceable in whole or in part to these differences in procedure and treatment of data. The use of a test substance by the two groups of investigators calls attention to the need for a systematic effort to find the cause of the discrepancies.

**5. Test substances for halogen compounds.** No intensive studies have been made of the test substances proposed by the Commission on Thermochemistry (14) for use in studies of the bomb combustion of halogen-containing substances. In fact, it is only recently that methods for the study of chlorine, bromine, and iodine compounds have reached a state of development such that a test substance or secondary standard would be useful. L. Smith (18) has proposed p-chlorobenzoic acid as a reference substance, and preliminary tests of its properties are promising.

**6. Test substances for nitrogen compounds.** Huffman (11) has stated the need for a secondary standard for nitrogen-compound combustion studies and has proposed the use of hippuric acid for this purpose. Stohmann and Langbein (19) also used this substance as a reference substance. Huffman made a series of tests, similar to those of Jessup (10) on benzoic acid, as to its suitability for use as a test substance. Samples of hippuric acid obtained from different commercial sources may be purified readily by crystallization from water so that essentially identical heats of combustion are obtained for the different samples. The nonhygroscopicity, nonvolatility, and stability are excellent. It can be pressed into briquets that are somewhat more fragile than those made from benzoic acid. It is readily inflammable and usually burns completely. As with benzoic acid, small residues of carbonaceous material (0.01 to 0.02 mg) are sometimes found in the bomb after a combustion, but Huffman states that the quantities of unburned carbon are usually negligible. Cole and Gilbert (20) have used hippuric acid as a test substance, and obtained results the same as Huffman (11).

There should be no confusion concerning the functions of the primary standard benzoic acid and of a test substance for a particular problem. The former is to be used to determine the energy equivalent of the calorimeter. The latter is a check on the chemical aspects of the combustion problem. It is hoped that the search for suitable test substances will parallel the development of methods for studying new types of chemical substances. Even if the status of the test substance does not progress beyond informal recognition by workers in the field of thermochemistry, it will serve a useful function.

**7. Standard reaction for combustions in a flame at constant pressure.** In 1934, the former Commission on Thermochemistry (3) established the reaction of the combustion of hydrogen and oxygen to form water as the standard reaction for combustions in a flame at constant pressure, and selected as the reference value for the heat of this reaction that obtained from the work of Rossini (21). Details regarding reactions in a flame at constant pressure are given in Chapter 4.

### References

1. G. B. Kistiakowski, H. Romeyn, Jr., J. R. Ruhoff, H. A. Smith, and W. E. Vaughan, *J. Am. Chem. Soc.* **57,** 65 (1935).
2. H. C. Dickinson, *Bull. Natl. Bur. Standards* **11,** 189 (1915).
3. Premier Rapport de la Commission Permanente de Thermochimie, Union International de Chimie, Paris, 1934.
4. M. Beckers, *Bull. soc. chim. Belges* **40,** 518 (1931).
5. R. S. Jessup and C. B. Green, *J. Research Natl. Bur. Standards* **13,** 469 (1934).
6. E. Wichers, *J. Am. Chem. Soc.* **74,** 2447 (1952).
7. F. W. Schwab and E. Wichers, *J. Research Natl. Bur. Standards* **25,** 747 (1940).
8. J. Coops, unpublished.

9. E. R. Weaver, *J. Am. Chem. Soc.* **35**, 1309 (1913).
10. R. S. Jessup, *J. Research Natl. Bur. Standards* **29**, 247 (1942).
11. H. M. Huffman, *J. Am. Chem. Soc.* **60**, 1171 (1938).
12. M. Beckers, *Bull. soc. chim. Belges* **40**, 871 (1931).
13. L. J. P. Keffler, *J. Phys. Chem.* **38**, 717 (1934).
14. Revue Analytique and Critique de Thermochimie Organique, Appendices au 1$^{er}$ Rapport de la Commission Permanente de Thermochimie, Paris, 1936.
15. W. A. Roth and G. Beckers, *Z. physik. chem.* **A179**, 450 (1937).
16. S. Sunner and B. Lundin, *Acta Chem. Scand.* **7**, 1112 (1953).
17. W. N. Hubbard, C. Katz, and G. Waddington, *J. Phys. Chem.* **58**, 142 (1954); also unpublished data, U. S. Bureau of Mines, Bartlesville, Oklahoma.
18. Lennart Smith, personal communication.
19. Stohmann and Langbein, *J. prakt. Chem.* [2] **49**, 99 (1894).
20. L. G. Cole and E. C. Gilbert, *J. Am. Chem. Soc.* **73**, 5425 (1951).
21. F. D. Rossini, *J. Research Natl. Bur. Standards* **6**, 1 (1931); **7**, 329 (1931).

# CHAPTER 14

# Assignment of Uncertainties to Thermochemical Data*

FREDERICK D. ROSSINI

**1. Introduction.** In order that the results of thermochemical measurements made in different laboratories may be compared and appraised, it is desirable that experimenters use a uniform procedure for expressing the consistency of their data, or be explicit regarding such consistency, particularly with regard to the estimation of the uncertainty or confidence interval to be attached to the published value of a thermochemical constant. Anyone to whom the experimental details and the original numerical data are available can form his own opinions by whatever method he likes; however, since full details are often too extensive for publication, understanding among workers in different laboratories and in different countries will be promoted if all the investigators will be careful to give the information that is essential for evaluating the consistencies of their final values.

**2. Precision and accuracy.** Precision and accuracy are terms invented for convenience in discussing errors of observation, uncertainties, and related matters. The precision of a set of observations is measured by the consistency or internal agreement as the series is extended under controlled conditions. Precision measures the ability of an investigator to reproduce his observations. If they fluctuate widely, his precision is low; but if they fluctuate within a narrower range, his precision is higher.

In contrast to precision and internal agreement, accuracy is related to the discrepancy between the mean of a set of observations and the true but "unknown" value of whatever quantity is being meas-

* The material in this chapter is taken from Rossini and Deming (1).

ured.   A piece of experimentation may be at once extremely precise yet hopelessly inaccurate because of constant or systematic errors, unpredictable or even unsuspected.   There are three ways of going about the problem of discovering the existence of constant or systematic errors: first, by investigating the physical principles involved in the action of the apparatus; second, by ascertaining whether there exists any unnatural trend of the final values with any one of the variables involved in the measurements; and third, by comparing the results obtained in different laboratories.   Incompatible discrepancies between the results obtained by two different laboratories may convince one that constant errors are present in the work of one or both of them, but the actual recognition of the errors must be made by an investigation of the principles of the measurements.   It is of course possible, by accident, for the means of two sets of experiments to be in good agreement even though one or both sets are afflicted with systematic errors.   Moreover, if the number of experiments is small, the two sets of data may be in disagreement and yet free from constant errors;   poor agreement merely suggests, but does not prove, the presence of constant errors.

In speaking of incompatible discrepancies between two sets of observations supposed to measure the same quantity, one must have in mind some measure of internal consistency for the two sets of observations and some way of comparing these internal consistencies with the difference between the means from the two sets.   The important consideration is not how large the discrepancy is, but rather how the discrepancy compares in magnitude with the internal consistencies of the two sets of data.   Statisticians have set up mathematical models for calculating odds against discrepancies between two means exceeding different multiples of a certain function of the measure of uncertainty of the two sets of observations, and these odds will be correct if the experiments fit the assumptions on which the calculations are based.   The existence of this concordance between experiments and assumptions is difficult to ascertain in actual physical and chemical experimentation, because any one series of observations is rarely extended long enough to be compared with the mathematical model.

**3. The single sample or set of observations.**   In the theory of errors, a set of $n$ equally reliable observations is considered as a sample of $n$ drawn at random from an indefinitely large supply (parent population) of observations that theoretically might be made if time and opportunity would permit. In the state of statistical control or randomness, the observations behave as if they are numbers being drawn from a hat, after thorough mixing and blindfolding. This limiting state is a goal toward which the efforts of experimentation are always directed, but the requirement for its full attainment, as judged by Shewhart's "Criterion I" (2), is much more exacting than that in the experimenter's judgment the observations have all been taken under "essentially the same conditions."

If there were no constant errors, and if randomness were attained, the mean of the parent population of observations would be the true value of the quantity being measured. The effect of a constant error is to displace the mean of the parent population above or below the true value; the correction, if ever isolated and evaluated, can be added to or subtracted from the mean of the parent population to obtain the true value.

The object of making observations is to estimate the limits within which various percentages of the next hundred or thousand observations will lie: that is, statistically, to estimate the position (value) of the mean of the parent population. Because the number taken must necessarily remain finite, the exact value of the mean of the parent population can only be approached, even in controlled experiments, where randomness exists, and one becomes increasingly interested in the probabilities associated with certain properties of the observations that are actually made. That is to say, if $\bar{x}$ is the mean of $n$ observations and $\mu$ is the (unknown) mean of the parent population, one might be interested in knowing the proportion of means in sets of $n$ observations each that will differ from $\mu$ by a stated amount, or the proportion in which an interval such as $\bar{x} \pm a$ will cover $\mu$.

In the present discussion the observations will be considered randomly drawn from a parent population that is normal (Gaussian) or nearly so. There are four reasons for this choice: first, mathematically, the normal error curve is the easiest to deal with; second, it is usually an excellent approximation when control exists, third, several investigations on non-normal populations have shown that even considerable departures from normality do not produce appreciable alterations in many important deductions based on the normal curve; and, fourth, it has been established that the distribution curve formed by the means of samples drawn from a non-normal parent population is usually much more nearly normal than the population itself. While there exist several types of measurement that by nature do not have normal parent populations, deductions based on the normal law will rarely fail to be valid, provided control exists.

It is to be understood that the extreme tails or ends of the normal error curve do not represent probabilities for large errors. By the nature of the apparatus, extremely large errors may be absolutely impossible, yet the approximating normal curve attributes to these large errors a finite chance of occurrence. The normal curve is an approximation not expected to hold for large errors; it is the main portion of the curve that contributes most to the calculations: if the tails of the curve were cut off, the mathematical difficulties would be exceedingly complex, but with results, in moderate and large samples, practically not different from those obtained by the customary and simpler theory which includes the tails.

If $\mu$ denotes the mean of the parent population, then the true error of an observation $x_i$ drawn therefrom will be

$$\epsilon_i = x_i - \mu. \tag{1}$$

Since $\mu$ is unknown, the error $\epsilon_i$ is also unknown. So, instead of dealing with the true but unknown errors $\epsilon_i$, we shall find it advisable to work with the known residuals or apparent errors $v_i$, which are measured from the known mean $\bar{x}$ of the sample rather than from the unknown mean $\mu$ of the parent population. The definition of the residual corresponding to the observation $x_i$ is mathematically

$$v_i = x_i - \bar{x}, \tag{2}$$

where $\bar{x}$ is the mean of the sample, defined mathematically as

$$\bar{x} = (1/n)(x_1 + x_2 + \ldots + x_n), \tag{3}$$

$x_1, x_2, \ldots, x_n$ constituting the sample of $n$ observations.

The only difficulty in replacing $\mu$ by $\bar{x}$ and thus passing from the unknown errors ($\epsilon$) to the known residuals ($v$) is that $\bar{x}$ itself fluctuates from one sample to another, and in any particular sample (set of observations) the discrepancy $u$ between $\bar{x}$ and $\mu$ is in practice not known. This unknown error in $\bar{x}$ we shall denote by $u$, writing

$$u = \bar{x} - \mu. \tag{4}$$

Most of the deductions made from experimental data, by probability theory or any other method, are mainly concerned with the magnitude of $u$, the unknown error in the sample mean $\bar{x}$.

For laying odds concerning the error $u$ in the mean $\bar{x}$, the most important piece of information provided by the sample is the standard deviation for single observations of the set, denoted by $s$ and defined by

$$s^2 = (1/n)\Sigma(x_i - \bar{x})^2. \tag{5}$$

The standard deviation received its name from Karl Pearson. It is not standard in the sense of being fixed, since it fluctuates from one set of observations to another. It does, however, provide a standard measure for expressing the consistency of a set of observations, for comparing their consistency with that of another set, and for judging statistically from the results obtained at two laboratories whether constant errors are present in one or another of them.

In the usual form of probability theory, which applies when control has been attained, it is assumed that as the number of observations is increased indefinitely, the mean $\bar{x}$ approaches statistically the limit $\mu$, and also that the standard deviation, $s$, approaches a limit $\sigma$, called the standard deviation of the parent population. In symbols,

$$\lim_{n \to \infty} \bar{x} = \mu \quad \text{and} \quad \lim_{n \to \infty} s = \sigma. \tag{6}$$

Under these conditions, the experiments are "under control." When the assumption of such limits does not lead to useful results, the probability theory in the usual form is not applicable.

The standard deviation, $s$, as defined in Equation 5, or any multiple thereof, possesses two important properties that make it the most desirable function to use as a measure of consistency. The first of these arises from the theorem known as Tchebycheff's inequality (3,4), which has been stated in a variety of forms, one corollary being that of the $n$ observations, $x_1, x_2, \ldots, x_n$, not more than $1/\lambda^2$ of them can be outside the interval $\bar{x} \pm \lambda s$, when $\lambda > 1$. The second is Gauss's discovery that when the observations have a normal distribution, the standard deviation, $s$, is more efficient for estimating $\sigma$ than any other function. For example, the standard deviation is 14 per cent more efficient than the average residual taken without regard to sign, and 9 per cent more efficient than the mean cube of the residuals (5). That is to say, the standard deviation of 100 observations provides as statistically reliable an estimate of $\sigma$ as the average residual, taken without regard to sign, from 114 observations; etc.

When an observer performs a number of sets of measurements of the same quantity with the same apparatus, he will find that the standard deviation fluctuates from one set of measurements to another, as has been stated. These fluctuations will occur even under the best controlled conditions. The larger the number $n$ of observations in a given set, the smaller are the fluctuations in $s$. When $n$ is large, considerable confidence may be placed in the precision of a set of experiments estimated from their standard deviation. The number of observations $n$ enables one to judge the reliability of the estimates of the precision of the observations from their standard deviations. The number $n$ tells how many figures are significant in recording $s$, a good rule being to remember that the standard deviation of $s$ itself is about $\sigma/\sqrt{2(n-1)}$. For example, if $n = 9$, $1/\sqrt{2(n-1)} = \frac{1}{4}$, and therefore one need record not more than two figures in $s$ and, at that, the second figure is barely significant. More than two figures in $s$ will hardly ever be required, though one extra figure will avoid errors of rounding off.

Various tests have been proposed by statisticians for determining the probability that a sample of $n$ observations will reproduce the properties of the parent population within stated limits, that is to say, how well the mean $\bar{x}$ and the standard deviation, $s$, of a finite number of observations $n$ will represent the mean $\mu$ and the standard deviation $\sigma$ that would be obtained by continuing the measurements indefinitely. Also, calculations have been made for evaluating the odds on the occurrence of given differences between the means of two sets of observations.

The normal curve showing the distribution of the mean values of samples or sets of $n$ observations has for its standard deviation $\sigma/\sqrt{n}$, which is smaller than $\sigma$ because of the denominator $\sqrt{n}$. This quantity $\sigma/\sqrt{n}$ can be used to compute the probability that expresses the chance $P_\tau$ of the occurrence of an error $u$ in $\bar{x}$ greater than some stated amount, say $E$. The graph in Figure 1, from reference (1), shows $P_\tau$ as a function of $\tau$, where

$$\tau = E/(\sigma/\sqrt{n}). \tag{7}$$

This quantity $\tau$ is the "standardized error," or the stated error $E$ expressed in units of the standard deviation of the error $u$ in $\bar{x}$. In the long run of repeated sampling under controlled conditions the standard deviation of the error $u$ is $\sigma/\sqrt{n}$, as has already been mentioned, and $P_\tau$ is the fractional number of times that the error $u$ in $\bar{x}$ will in the long run exceed the stated error $E$.   The calculation of $\tau$ and the corresponding $P_\tau$ is called the normal test for the significance of $\bar{x}$.

Reliable estimates of $\sigma$ for the normal test can sometimes be made antecedently from a long series of previous observations, or from several short series (6), and it is to be noted that in the absence of a

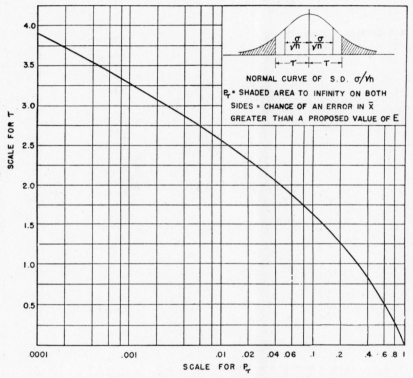

Figure 1. Areas under the normal curve.   $P_r$ is the area in both tails beyond the abscissas $\pm r$.   The whole area under the curve is unity, i.e. $P_r = 1$ when $r = 0$.   From reference (1).

reliable estimate of $\sigma$, one cannot compute $\tau$ and hence cannot look up $P_\tau$ in the tables.   The best one can do in such circumstances is to use the Student "$t$" test (6,7), which involves the fluctuating standard deviation, $s$, of the single sample, in place of the steady (but now supposedly unknown) $\sigma$.   The "$t$" test is made by estimating $\sigma$ from the one sample according to the formula

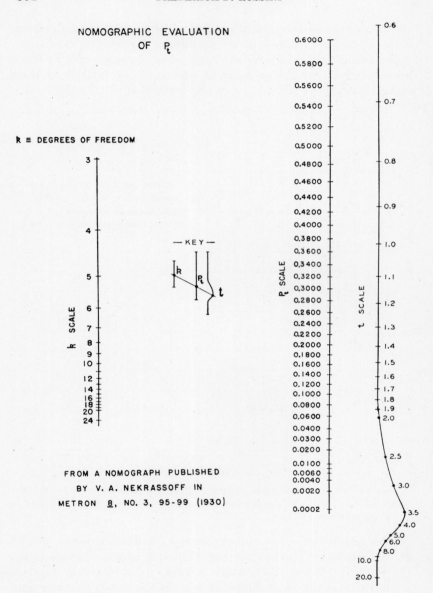

Figure 2. Nomographic evaluation of $P_t$. (Courtesy Bell Telephone Laboratories, Inc.)

$$s' = s \sqrt{n/(n-1)} = \sqrt{\frac{\Sigma(x_i - \bar{x})^2}{n-1}}, \tag{8}$$

and then measuring $E$ in terms of $s'/\sqrt{n}$, calling the result $t$. Now if $s'$ is an estimate of $\sigma$, then $s'/\sqrt{n}$ is an estimate of $\sigma/\sqrt{n}$, wherefore, if we write

$$t = E/(s'/\sqrt{n}) = E \div \sqrt{\frac{\Sigma(x_i - \bar{x})^2}{n(n-1)}}, \tag{9}$$

we may look upon $t$ as an estimate of $\tau$, the only distinction being that $\tau$ in Equation 7 is the stated error $E$ measured in units of $\sigma/\sqrt{n}$, whereas $t$ in Equation 9 is measured in units of an *estimate* of $\sigma/\sqrt{n}$. In words, $t$ is the stated error $E$ measured in units of the estimated standard deviation of the error $u$ in $\bar{x}$. Otherwise written, we may say that

$$t = (E/s)\sqrt{k}, \tag{9a}$$

wherein $k = n - 1$, and $s$ is computed according to Equation 5. In place of the probabilities $P_\tau$ in terms of $\tau$ in Figure 1, we now have the probabilities $P_t$ in terms of $t$ and $k$ in Nekrassoff's nomograph shown as Figure 2, from reference (1), $P_\tau$ is to be used when $\sigma$ is known; $P_t$ when $\sigma$ is not known.

It is to be kept in mind that $P_\tau$, when we are able to calculate it, may be found different from $P_t$; in fact, the two will agree only when the observed $s$ happens to be an "average" $s$. If $s$ is unusually high or low, as it will be once in a while, then $P_t$ will be correspondingly high or low compared with $P_\tau$. It is to be remembered also that neither the normal test nor the "$t$" test is valid except in statistical control, and by the time this state is attained the experimenter usually knows his $\sigma$ and has no need of the "$t$" test (6). In statistical control, as $n$ increases indefinitely, $s'$ approaches $\sigma$, $t$ approaches $\tau$, and $P_t$ approaches $P_\tau$.

**4. A pair of samples or sets of observations.** The following information will be available from the recorded data of the two sets of observations:

|  | 1st set | 2nd set |
|---|---|---|
| Mean | $\bar{x}_1$ | $\bar{x}_2$ |
| Standard deviation | $s_1$ | $s_2$ |
| Number of observations | $n_1$ | $n_2$ |

In examining the concordance of two sets of measurements supposedly made on the same magnitude, the important fact to keep in mind is that if both sets are under control, then, in repeated sampling, the difference $\bar{x}_1 - \bar{x}_2$ between the two means will be distributed normally about 0 with standard deviation $(\sigma_1{}^2/n_1 + \sigma_2{}^2/n_2)^{1/2}$, $\sigma_1$ and $\sigma_2$ being the precisions of single observations in the two samples. To discover the probability of a difference as great as or greater than that actually observed, we need only calculate

$$\tau = |\bar{x}_1 - \bar{x}_2|/(\sigma_1{}^2/n_1 + \sigma_2{}^2/n_2)^{1/2}, \tag{10}$$

and then look up $P_\tau$ in Figure 1 or in any table of the normal integral.

In the case of the single sample we ran into the difficulty that $\sigma$ is sometimes unknown, and we were forced to the "$t$" test. So it is with a pair of samples also; when $\sigma_1$ and $\sigma_2$ are both unknown, we cannot compute $\tau$ in Equation 10 and hence cannot look up $P_\tau$. But if, as frequently happens, it can be asserted that $\sigma_1$ and $\sigma_2$ have a common value, say $\sigma$, then we may apply the "$t$" test by calculating

$$t = |\bar{x}_1 - \bar{x}_2|/s' \left(\frac{1}{n_1} + \frac{1}{n_2}\right)^{1/2}, \tag{11}$$

with

$$(s')^2 = \frac{n_1 s_1{}^2 + n_2 s_2{}^2}{n_1 + n_2 - 2}, \tag{12}$$

and then looking up $P_t$ on Nekrassoff's nomograph (Figure 2) with $k = n_1 + n_2 - 2$. It is to be noted that $s'$ is an estimate of $\sigma$ obtained by pooling both samples, and that $t$ as defined in Equation 11 is the difference $|\bar{x}_1 - \bar{x}_2|$ divided by $s' (1/n_1 + 1/n_2)^{1/2}$, which is the estimated standard deviation of the sampling fluctuation of $\bar{x}_1 - \bar{x}_2$. We may therefore look upon $t$ in Equation 11 as an estimate of the $\tau$ in Equation 10, the relation between them being similar to that between the $t$ and $\tau$ of Equations 9 and 7.

In the state of statistical control, $P_t$ represents the relative frequency of occurrence, in the long run, of values of $t$ as large as or larger than that calculated in Equation 11, the presumption being that both sets of observations were made on the same thing, i.e., that both sets were afflicted with the same constant errors. A large value of $t$, giving a low value of $P_t$, is an indication that the two means $\bar{x}_1$ and $\bar{x}_2$ are unduly discordant compared with their internal consistencies as measured by $s_1$ and $s_2$. Since unequal constant errors in the two experiments would separate $\bar{x}_1$ and $\bar{x}_2$, on the average, leaving $s_1$ and $s_2$ and $s'$ unaffected, we may regard a low value of $P_t$ as statistical "evidence" of unequal constant errors. A low value of $P_t$, e.g., 0.01, is of course no proof of the existence of constant errors, but rather an indication that an investigation into the possibility should be made. On the other hand, a high value of $P_t$ is no assurance that constant errors are absent or operating equally. One can only assert that an unequal distribution of constant errors causes low values of $P_t$ to occur more frequently than would happen by chance under ideal conditions.

When, because of unavoidable circumstances, the numerical data of a given investigation cannot be published in complete detail, the procedure of estimating and reporting the measure of the precision should preserve as much as possible of the information contained in the full series of observations. In those cases where complete publication is not possible, condensation of the numerical data becomes necessary, and the investigator should report at least the three following pieces of information: (i) the number of observations, $n$; (ii) the mean $\bar{x}$ of the observed values, calculated to as many figures as are judged significant in consideration of the standard deviation; (iii) the standard deviation, $s$, given to as many figures as are judged significant in consideration of the number of observations.

The number of significant figures to which the mean value $\bar{x}$ is reported should be dictated by the internal consistency of the observations, that is, by the magnitude of the standard deviation, and not by what one may consider to be the accuracy of the experiments. If one or more decimals are dropped from a mean, it may be impossible to correct it to a more accurate value later on when one or more constant errors may be traced and evaluated. Furthermore, a comparison of the discrepancy between two means with the internal consistencies of the two sets of observations is hardly possible unless each mean is carried out to as many significant figures as are warranted by the standard deviations.

**5. Functional concordance.** Hitherto the $n$ measurements were all supposed to have been made on a single magnitude. Quite commonly, however, one has to deal with a more complicated case of curve fitting; some measurements may be here, and others there, as happens for example when a vapor pressure is observed as a function of the temperature. As the temperature changes, so does the vapor pressure, and one may wish to observe the vapor pressure at several different temperatures, and afterward fit a curve to the observed points. Sometimes only one measurement is taken on $y$ for a given $x$, or on $x$ for a given $y$, but it is highly desirable that repeated observations be made whenever possible, in order to see how well the curve fits [see, for example, pp. 20–25 of Deming's *Least Squares* (8)]. Sometimes only $y$ is subject to error; but more generally $x$ and $y$ may both be in error, in which case the problem of adjustment is still easily taken care of [cf. Deming (8), pp. 82 and 83 ff]. In any event, when the curve has been fitted, an estimate of the precisions of the observations on $y$ and $x$ can be made.

**6. Propagation and combination of errors.** If the quantity $F$ is a function of $x$, $y$, and $z$, and these are in error by the amounts $\Delta x$, $\Delta y$, and $\Delta z$, respectively, then $F$ will be in error by an amount $\Delta F$ whose value is given approximately by the linear terms of a Taylor's series:

$$\Delta F = F_x \Delta x + F_y \Delta y + F_z \Delta z + \ldots \tag{13}$$

Here the higher powers and products of $\Delta x$, $\Delta y$, and $\Delta z$ have been neglected, since it is assumed that the errors are small. ($F_x$, $F_y$, and $F_z$, stand for $dF/dx$, $dF/dy$, and $dF/dz$, respectively, and each derivative is to be evaluated at or near the correct values of $x$, $y$, and $z$.) Equation 13 is the equation of propagation of error.

In practice, one does not know the individual errors in $x$, $y$, and $z$, but may have some knowledge regarding their standard deviations from long series of measurements. These standard deviations, denoted by $\sigma_x$, $\sigma_y$, and $\sigma_z$, are respectively the square roots of the averages of $(\Delta x)^2$, $(\Delta y)^2$, and $(\Delta z)^2$ in very long series of observations.

Upon squaring both sides of Equation 13 we have

$$(\Delta F)^2 = (F_x \Delta x)^2 + (F_y \Delta y)^2 + (F_z \Delta z)^2 + 2F_x F_y \Delta x \Delta y$$
$$+ 2F_x F_z \Delta x \Delta z + 2F_y F_z \Delta y \Delta z. \tag{14}$$

Assuming that $F_x$, $F_y$, and $F_z$ remain substantially constant while $\Delta x$, $\Delta y$, and $\Delta z$ vary over their allowable ranges, and that the averages of the cross products $\Delta x \Delta y$, $\Delta x \Delta z$, and $\Delta y \Delta z$ are zero, as will be true if $\Delta x$, $\Delta y$, and $\Delta z$ are uncorrelated, one may average each term of Equation 14 and obtain

$$\sigma_F{}^2 = F_x{}^2 \sigma_x{}^2 + F_y{}^2 \sigma_y{}^2 + F_z{}^2 \sigma_z{}^2. \tag{15}$$

This is the equation of the propagation of the standard deviation, when the errors are independent. Two examples of its application to various simple functions follow.

(i) If

$$F = ax + by + cz, \tag{16}$$

where the errors in $x$, $y$, and $z$ are independent of one another, then the standard deviation of $F$, resulting from the errors in $x$, $y$, and $z$, is given by the relation

$$\sigma_F = \{(a\sigma_x)^2 + (b\sigma_y)^2 + (c\sigma_z)^2\}^{1/2}. \tag{17}$$

Here $\sigma_x$, $\sigma_y$, and $\sigma_z$ are the standard deviations of the errors in $x$, $y$, and $z$. It is to be noted that this formula remains unaltered if $a$, $b$, or $c$ changes sign.

(ii) If

$$F = x^\alpha y^\beta x^\gamma, \tag{18}$$

where the errors in $x$, $y$, and $z$ are independent of one another, then the resulting standard deviation of $F$ is

$$\sigma_F = F\{(\alpha\sigma_x/x)^2 + (\beta\sigma_y/y)^2 + (\gamma\sigma_z/z)^2\}^{1/2}. \tag{19}$$

This formula remains unaltered if $\alpha$, $\beta$, or $\gamma$ changes sign.

Separately obtained mean values, if within reasonable accord with one another, may be combined by weighting them inversely as the squares of their standard deviations. (Just whether two sets of observations are in accord with one another is a matter that cannot be decided objectively, but the normal test or the "$t$" test will at times be of assistance.) If, for example, three sets of measurements of a certain quantity yield the three means $\bar{x}_1$, $\bar{x}_2$, and $\bar{x}_3$, the resulting weighted mean will be

$$\bar{x} = \frac{n_1\bar{x}_1/\sigma_1{}^2 + n_2\bar{x}_2/\sigma_2{}^2 + n_3\bar{x}_3/\sigma_3{}^2}{n_1/\sigma_1{}^2 + n_2/\sigma_2{}^2 + n_3/\sigma_3{}^2}, \tag{20}$$

wherein $n_1$, $n_2$, and $n_3$ are the numbers of measurements in the three sets, and $\sigma_1$, $\sigma_2$, and $\sigma_3$ express the standard deviations of single observations.

The standard deviation to be assigned to the resulting weighted mean $\bar{x}$ will be

$$\bar{\sigma}_x = 1/(n_1/\sigma_1{}^2 + n_2/\sigma_2{}^2 + n_3/\sigma_3{}^2)^{1/2}. \tag{21}$$

The bar over the $\sigma$ is a reminder that the character refers to a mean.

If in the same symbolism $\bar{\sigma}_1$, $\bar{\sigma}_2$, and $\bar{\sigma}_3$ refer to the standard deviations of the three separate means $\bar{x}_1$, $\bar{x}_2$, and $\bar{x}_3$, Equations 20 and 21 take the forms

$$\bar{x} = \frac{\bar{x}_1/\bar{\sigma}_1{}^2 + \bar{x}_2/\bar{\sigma}_2{}^2 + \bar{x}_3/\bar{\sigma}_3{}^2}{1/\bar{\sigma}_1{}^2 + 1/\bar{\sigma}_2{}^2 + 1/\bar{\sigma}_3{}^2}, \tag{22}$$

$$\bar{\sigma}_{\bar{x}} = 1/(1/\bar{\sigma}_1{}^2 + 1/\bar{\sigma}_2{}^2 + 1/\bar{\sigma}_3{}^2)^{1/2}. \tag{23}$$

These formulas are easily extended to any number of sets of observations.

**7. Application to measurements in general.** The calculations outlined on the preceding pages may be applied to any experiment that is in statistical control; i.e., when the data are known to be random (2). Possible examples that can be developed in general physical and chemical measurements are the determinations of heats of chemical reactions, heat capacities, heats of fusion and vaporization, freezing and boiling points, volumes, molecular weights, densities, refractive indices, solubilities, and various chemical analyses.

Physical and chemical measurements may be divided roughly into two classes, absolute measurements and comparative measurements. The latter class may be further subdivided into measurements by successive comparison or measurements by simultaneous comparison.

In physicochemical measurements, the investigator must carefully distinguish between the precision and the accuracy of his results, and, furthermore, he must establish beyond reasonable doubt that the purity of the chemical substances upon which the measurements are being made is sufficient for the purposes of the investigation.

There are relatively few investigations that in themselves completely determine the final value of a desired property. Usually the final value is a function of a number of quantities, only one of which will be evaluated in the investigation, the others being "accepted" from other sources. For example, the final value $Q$ may be a function of the quantities $A$, $B$, and $C$, of which $C$ is the only one that is evaluated in the investigation: thus, it might be that

$$Q = ABC. \tag{24}$$

The precision of the measurements on $C$ is a measure of the precision of $C$ but not of $Q$. The precision of $C(= Q/AB)$ may be considered the "immediate" precision of the measurements, and this is to be contrasted with the "over-all" precision of $Q$, which must include the precisions of $A$ and $B$ as well as of $C$. The standard deviation to be assigned to $A$ and $B$ should be estimated, in a manner similar to that used in estimating the standard deviation of $C$, from measurements made in the laboratories where $A$ and $B$ were determined. When no systematic errors exist in $A$ or $B$ or $C$, then the "over-all" standard deviation, estimated by the propagation of the standard deviations of the various component parts, gives an idea of the accuracy of the experiment. It is only through the concordance of different methods of measurement that a measurable characteristic is ever said to have an existence that is operationally verifiable; but no matter how close this concordance appears to be, there is always the possibility that future experimental or theoretical work may reveal the presence of constant errors, whereupon our ideas concerning the accuracy of a measured quantity will need to be revised [cf. Shewhart (2), Chapter 4].

Absolute or primary measurements are those in which the resulting magnitude is measured in terms of fundamental or absolute standards. Examples of this class include the determination of the density of water in terms of the fundamental units of mass and volume; the heat of formation of water in terms of the fundamental unit of energy; and the absolute viscosity of water in terms of fundamental units. For such measurements the finally determined value of $Q$ will be the resultant of sets of measurements on one or more magnitudes. The standard deviation of the magnitude resulting from each of the component sets of observations may be estimated according to the procedure already discussed, these separate standard deviations then being combined by the procedure given for the propagation of errors. Strictly, the formulas developed are valid only for the true values of the standard deviations involved, but they will be sufficiently close for the purpose when used with estimated standard deviations.

Comparative or secondary measurements are those in which the resulting magnitude is determined by comparison with a selected standard or reference substance, in terms of a "best" value more or less arbitrarily assigned or accepted for the standard. For such measurements, it is to be emphasized that the evaluation of the "over-all" standard deviation of the resulting value entails a consideration not only of the errors in the immediate experiment, but also of the uncertainty in the value selected for the standard substance in terms of the fundamental units. This latter uncertainty must be inferred from absolute or primary measurements made in a laboratory adequately equipped to determine the value for the standard substance in terms of the fundamental units.

Secondary measurements involving successive comparison with the standard or reference substance include, for example, the determination of the viscosity of a liquid with a viscosimeter standardized with water (using an "accepted" value for the latter) and the determination of the heat of combustion of an organic substance with a bomb-calorimetric apparatus standardized with benzoic acid. In such measurements, the final value $Q$ is the resultant of two sets of measurements with the same apparatus under as nearly the same conditions as possible. In one set the reference substance is measured, and in the other the experimental substance. This type of measurement determines the ratio of the property for the one to that for the other, as for example, $Q_w/Q_r$. If the estimated standard deviations are respectively $\sigma_w$ and $\sigma_r$, then for $Q_w/Q_r$, which measures $Q_w$ in terms of the units and value accepted for the standard, the resulting standard deviation is that obtained by combining $\sigma_w$ and $\sigma_r$ in the manner already indicated. It should be noted that this result takes no account of the uncertainty in the value selected for the standard substance.

Secondary measurements involving simultaneous comparisons of the given substance with the standard or reference, include, for example, the determination of relative heat capacities with "twin" calorimeters, of relative $P$-$V$-$T$ data with "twin" bombs, and of relative densities with "twin" pycnometers. In such measurements, the final value $Q$ is usually the result of measurements with a "twin" apparatus containing both the given substance and the reference or standard. This type of measurement substantially determines the difference between the value of the property for the experimental substance and that for the reference substance, as for example, $Q_w - Q_r$. In practice the reference substance is selected to make the observed difference $Q_w - Q_r$ small in comparison with $Q_r$. The resulting standard deviation for the value of $Q_w$, expressed in terms of the units and value adopted for the reference substance, will be simply the standard deviation for the value $Q_w - Q_r$, evaluated from the data according to the procedure already given. This standard deviation likewise takes no account of the uncertainty in the value selected for the reference substance.

**8. Specific recommendations for thermochemistry.** In thermochemical investigations, systematic errors may arise from a number of sources, including the evaluation of the energy equivalent of the calorimeter, the determination of the amount of reaction, etc. Such systematic errors, which affect the accuracy but usually not the precision of the results, may preclude agreement among different laboratories as to the results of measuring what is supposedly the same thing, even though the consistency of the measurements in each of the laboratories by itself is entirely satisfactory.

The standard deviations associated with the "accepted" constants and other constant factors entering into the reduction of the data should be incorporated, so far as they are significant, into the final "over-all" standard deviation assigned to the quantity being evaluated. In the report of an investigation, such constants and their assigned standard deviations should be identified and the reasons for their selection given.

The standard deviation that is to be associated with the mean $\bar{x}$ of a set of $n$ observations in a state of statistical control is $1/\sqrt{n}$ times the standard deviation (for single observations) of the parent population from which the observations are drawn. An estimate $\bar{s}'$ of the standard deviation of $\bar{x}$ can therefore be obtained by multiplying $s'$ in Equation 8 by $1/\sqrt{n}$, whence

$$\bar{s}' = s'/\sqrt{n} = \sqrt{\Sigma v_i^2/n(n-1)}, \qquad (25)$$

where $\Sigma v_i^2$ is the sum of the squares of the deviations, each deviation being measured from $\bar{x}$, that is, $v_i = x_i - \bar{x}$, as in Equation 2. (It will be recalled that $s'$ is the estimated standard deviation for single observations of a given set, and that $\bar{s}'$ is the estimated standard deviation of the mean $\bar{x}$.)

It is again emphasized that the procedure described here for treating the observations of experimental thermochemistry statistically is applicable only if the observations are in a state of statistical control.

Following the general classification already given, calorimetric investigations of the heats of chemical reactions may be divided into those involving absolute measurements and comparative measurements.

In thermochemical investigations involving absolute measurements, the heat evolved by a measured amount of chemical reaction is compared with the heat evolved by a measured amount of electrical energy, using the calorimeter system as the absorber and comparator of the two kinds of energies. In the ideal case, both a fixed calorimeter system and a fixed temperature rise would be used, so that a direct equality would be obtained between a measured amount of electrical energy and a measured amount of chemical reaction. [See Chapter 18 of reference (9) and Chapter 1 of this book.]

For the given calorimeter system, the energy equivalent, $\mathcal{E}$, is determined as the amount of electrical energy $q_e$ added to the fixed calorimeter system divided by the temperature rise $\Delta t_e$. The relation used in computing the energy equivalent of the calorimeter system is

$$\mathcal{E}/f = q_e/\Delta t_e, \tag{26}$$

where $f$ is a constant whose value is the resultant of the various calibration factors associated with the instruments used in measuring the electrical energy, such as the standard resistances, standard cell, resistance coils of the potentiometer, timing apparatus, etc. The product $fq_e$ gives the electrical energy in terms of fundamental units. In the experiments with electrical energy, the quantities actually observed are $q_e$ and $\Delta t_E$, and for each experiment there is determined a value of the ratio $q_e/\Delta t_E$. From a series of $n$ such determinations of $q_e/\Delta t_E$, there is obtained an average value of $q_e/\Delta t_E$, this average being the experimental determination of $\mathcal{E}/f$ according to Equation 26. By applying Equation 25 to the measurements of $q_e/\Delta t_E$ one may calculate

$$\bar{s}'_{\mathcal{E}/f} = \sqrt{\Sigma v_i^2/n(n-1)} \tag{27}$$

as an estimate of the standard deviation to be assigned to the determination of $\mathcal{E}/f$.

In a series of calorimetric reaction experiments, there is measured the amount of chemical reaction that produces, in the calorimeter, a temperature rise substantially equal to the selected "standard" temperature rise. The relation used in reducing the data of these experiments is

$$Bg = \Delta t_r/M_r, \tag{28}$$

where $\Delta t_r$ is the observed temperature rise, $M_r$ is the observed mass of the substance (either reactant or product) that is used to determine the amount of reaction, $B$ is the temperature rise per unit mass of the selected substance that determines the amount of reaction, and $g$ is a factor whose value is the resultant of the various factors required to convert the observed mass of the selected substance to the number of moles of the desired pure reaction, which conversion involves the molecular weight of the selected substance, a correction for any impurity in the reaction, etc.    In the experiments with chemical energy, the quantities actually observed are $\Delta t_r$ and $M_r$, and for each experiment there is determined a value of the ratio $\Delta t_r/M_r$.    From a series of $n$ such determinations of $\Delta t_r/M_r$, there is obtained an average value of $\Delta t_r/M_r$, this average being the experimental determination of $Bg$ according to Equation 28.    By applying Equation 25 to the measurements of $\Delta t_r/M_r$ one calculates

$$\bar{s}'_{Bg} = \sqrt{\Sigma v_i^2/n(n-1)} \tag{29}$$

as an estimate of the standard deviation to be assigned to the determination of $Bg$.

The experimental value of the heat $Q$ of one mole of the reaction being studied is obtained from the relation

$$Q = \mathcal{E}B, \tag{30}$$

which can be written

$$Q = (q_e/\Delta t_e)(\Delta t_r/M_r)f/g. \tag{31}$$

The ratios $q_e/\Delta t_e$ and $\Delta t_r/M_r$ are evaluated in the electrical energy and the chemical reaction experiments, respectively, and the ratio $f/g$ includes all the constant factors involved in the reduction of the data. In the experiments, $\Delta t_e$ and $\Delta t_r$ are made as nearly alike as possible, and since these temperature rises occur in Equation 31 only as the ratio $\Delta t_r/\Delta t_e$, the thermometer need not be calibrated in an absolute sense.    In fact, the substitutional nature of the experiments can be further emphasized by reporting the values of $\Delta t_e$ and $\Delta t_r$ in the units in which they are actually measured (microvolts if the thermometric device is a thermoelement and ohms if it is a resistance thermometer) without conversion to degrees on the temperature scale.

By an appropriate analysis of the information supplied by the standardizing and other laboratories, the investigator may be able to estimate the magnitude of the standard deviations associated with the constant factors $f$ and $g$ used in reducing the data.    If these estimates are denoted by $\bar{s}'_f$ and $\bar{s}'_g$, then, by comparing Equations 18 and 31 and applying Equation 19, the final "over-all" standard deviation to be assigned to the experimental value of $Q$ is found to be

$$\bar{s}_Q' = Q\sqrt{[\bar{s}'_{\mathcal{E}/f}/(\mathcal{E}/f)]^2 + [\bar{s}'_{Bg}/Bg]^2 + [\bar{s}'_f/f]^2 + [\bar{s}'_g/g]^2}. \quad (32)$$

The value of $\bar{s}'_Q$ given by Equation 32 is seen to be derived from a combination of four terms, the first from the experiments with electrical energy, the second from the experiments with chemical energy, and the third and fourth from the constant factors used in reducing the data. In the actual practice of thermochemical investigations, the uncertainties in the calibration factors to be applied to the nominal values of the standard resistances, standard cells, etc., are nearly always negligible, or can be made so by appropriate calibration at the national standardizing laboratory. Likewise, the correction for an impurity in the reaction, if any is present, can usually be made with negligible uncertainty by application of the appropriate analytical technique in the chemical analysis of the reaction. It appears, therefore, that by adequate calibration and chemical techniques, the uncertainties in the factors $f$ and $g$ in Equation 31 can usually be made negligible in comparison with those of $\mathcal{E}/f$ and $Bg$. Under such circumstances the last two terms under the radical in Equation 32 may be neglected, and the final "over-all" standard deviation to be assigned to the experimental value of $Q$ becomes simply

$$\bar{s}'_Q = Q\sqrt{[\bar{s}'_{\mathcal{E}/f}/(\mathcal{E}/f)]^2 + [\bar{s}'_{Bg}/Bg]^2}. \quad (33)$$

In thermochemical investigations involving comparative measurements, the heat evolved by a measured amount of the given chemical reaction is compared with the heat evolved by a measured amount of a selected "standard" or reference reaction, using a fixed calorimeter system with a substantially constant temperature rise. The heat evolved per unit amount of the selected reference reaction, which is chemically similar to the one being investigated, has been determined, in terms of fundamental units for the reaction occurring under certain standard conditions, in an appropriate standardizing laboratory. These comparative thermochemical measurements are the same as the absolute ones except that the energy equivalent of the calorimeter is determined not with electrical energy but with the heat evolved by a measured amount of the standard or reference reaction taken under "standard" conditions.

The relation used in computing the energy equivalent of the calorimeter from the data of the experiments with the reference reaction is

$$\mathcal{E}/D = M_s/\Delta t_s, \tag{34}$$

where $M_s$ is the observed mass of that reactant or product of the standardizing reaction which is used to determine the amount of reaction, $\Delta t_s$ is the observed temperature rise, $\mathcal{E}$ is the energy equivalent of the calorimeter in terms of the value and units assigned to the standardizing reaction, and $D$ is the value assigned to the standardizing reaction for the heat evolved per unit mass of the reactant or product that determines the amount of reaction when the reaction occurs under the conditions maintained in the experiments in the standardizing laboratory. In the experiments with the reference reaction, the quantities actually observed are $M_s$ and $\Delta t_s$, and for each experiment there is determined a value of the ratio $M_s/\Delta t_s$. From a series of $n$ such determinations of $M_s/\Delta t_s$, there is obtained an average value of $M_s/\Delta t_s$, this average being the experimental determination of $\mathcal{E}/D$ according to Equation 34. By applying Equation 25 to the measurements of $M_s/\Delta t_s$, one may calculate

$$\bar{s}'_{\mathcal{E}/D} = \sqrt{\Sigma v_i^2/n(n-1)} \tag{35}$$

as an estimate of the standard deviation to be assigned to the determination of $\mathcal{E}/D$.

In a series of calorimetric reaction experiments, the reaction whose heat is to be determined is carried out under conditions substantially identical to those maintained in the experiments with the standardizing reaction. The relation used in reducing the data of these experiments is

$$Bg = \Delta t_r/M_r, \tag{36}$$

where $\Delta t_r$ is the observed temperature rise, $M_r$ is the observed mass of the reactant or product of the given reaction that is used to determine the amount of reaction, $B$ is the temperature rise per unit mass of the selected substance that determines the amount of reaction, and $g$ has the same significance as in Equation 28. In these experiments, the quantities actually observed are $\Delta t_r$ and $M_r$, and for each experiment there is determined a value of the ratio $\Delta t_r/M_r$. From a series of $n$ such determinations of $\Delta t_r/M_r$, there is obtained an average value of $\Delta t_r/M_r$, this average being the experimental determination of $Bg$ according to Equation 36. By applying Equation 25 to the measurements of $\Delta t_r/M_r$ one may calculate

$$\bar{s}'_{Bg} = \sqrt{\Sigma v_i^2/n(n-1)} \tag{37}$$

as an estimate of the standard deviation to be assigned to the determination of $Bg$.

The experimental value of the heat $Q$ of one mole of the reaction under investigation is obtained from the relation

$$Q = \mathcal{E}B, \tag{38}$$

which can be written

$$Q = (M_s/\Delta t_s)(\Delta t_r/M_r)D/g. \tag{39}$$

The ratios $M_s/\Delta t_s$ and $\Delta t_r/M_r$ are measured in the two series of calorimetric reaction experiments, the first with the standardizing reaction and the second with the reaction whose heat is to be determined. The ratio $D/g$ contains all the constant factors involved in the reduction of the data, including the value assigned for the heat of a unit amount of the standardizing reaction. As in the absolute or primary measurements, the temperature changes are made substantially the same in all experiments. The statement concerning the calibration of the thermometer following Equation 31 is also applicable here.

The value assigned to $D$, the heat of a unit amount of the standardizing reaction, has been previously determined in a standardizing laboratory and carries with it a standard deviation $\bar{s}'_D$ estimated according to the procedure outlined under absolute or primary measurements. Then the final "over-all" standard deviation to be assigned to the experimental value of Q that is obtained from these comparative or secondary measurements is

$$\bar{s}'_Q = Q\sqrt{[\bar{s}'_{\mathcal{E}/D}/(\mathcal{E}/D)]^2 + [\bar{s}'_{Bg}/Bg]^2 + [\bar{s}'_D/D]^2 + [\bar{s}'_g/g]^2}, \tag{40}$$

where $g$ and $\bar{s}_g$ have the same significance as in Equations 28 and 32.

If, as in the previous case, the uncertainty in the factor $g$ is negligible in comparison with the others, then this equation may be simplified to

$$\bar{s}'_Q = Q\sqrt{[\bar{s}'_{\mathcal{E}/D}/(\mathcal{E}/D)]^2 + [\bar{s}'_{Bg}/Bg]^2 + [\bar{s}'_D/D]^2}, \tag{41}$$

where the first two terms under the radical arise from the two kinds of experiments performed by the investigator, and the third arises from the experiments made in the standardizing laboratory.

**9. Discussion.** In connection with the foregoing procedure for evaluating the final "over-all" standard deviations to be assigned to thermochemical values obtained either from absolute or comparative measurements, the following points are to be noted:

(a) If more than one set of measurements of a given kind is made, the means and their respective standard deviations may be combined according to the procedure given by Equations 15 ff;

(b)   The number of experiments in any one set should be made sufficiently large to insure that the estimated standard deviations obtained for the magnitudes $\mathcal{E}/f$, $Bg$, or $\mathcal{E}/D$ (see above) reasonably represent the behavior of the apparatus;

(c)   Acceptable experiments include all except those in which a mistake or gross error has obviously been made, or in which an extraordinarily large deviation can be accounted for by purely physical means.

It is important to note also that the following assumptions have been made in estimating the standard deviations according to the procedure outlined here:

(a)   The experiments are performed under conditions corresponding to a state of statistical control;

(b)   The customary theory of probability, when applied to data in statistical control, gives in the long run the relative frequency with which intervals $\bar{x} \pm \lambda s$ (based on the observed mean value $\bar{x}$ and the consistency of the data, past or present) actually overlap the mean of a large number of observations;

(c)   The limiting mean $\mu$ is called the value of the quantity whose measurement is the purpose of the measurements.

**10. The uncertainty interval.** Investigators in modern thermochemistry have by experience found it convenient to assign to each determined thermochemical constant a range representing the uncertainty interval (2,3) within which future determinations of the same thermochemical constant may with reasonable certainty be expected to lie. By convention, the uncertainty interval is taken as twice the final over-all standard deviation,

$$\text{Uncertainty interval} = 2\bar{s}'_Q, \tag{42}$$

where $\bar{s}'_Q$ is given by Equation 32 for the absolute or primary measurements, and by Equation 40 for the comparative or secondary measurements.

When two investigations yield, for a given thermochemical constant, values which differ by more than the sum of the two assigned uncertainty intervals, it is probable, but not at all certain, that a systematic error or combination of errors exists in one or both of the investigations. Conversely, when the two values are in accord within their assigned uncertainty intervals, it is probable, but not at all certain, that systematic errors are absent. When two such values differ by more than the sum of the assigned uncertainty intervals, it is desirable to re-examine the data of the experiments and ascertain whether all the necessary constant factors have been included and properly evaluated, and whether the standard deviations assigned to these constant factors have been properly estimated. Need of revision may be discovered either in the numerical values of the constant factors, or in the standard deviations assigned to them, or in both.

## References

1. F. D. Rossini and W. E. Deming, *J. Wash. Acad. Sci.* 29, 416 (1939).
2. W. A. Shewhart, "Statistical methods from the viewpoint of quality control," Graduate School, U. S. Department of Agriculture, Washington, D. C., 1939.
3. W. A. Shewhart, *The Economic Control of Quality*, D. Van Nostrand Co., New York, 1931.
4. D. E. Smith, *Source Book in Mathematics*, McGraw-Hill Book Co., New York, 1929.
5. E. T. Whittaker and G. Robinson, *Calculus of Observations*, Blackie and Son, London, 1924.
6. W. E. Deming and R. T. Birge, *Revs. Mod. Phys.* 6, 119 (1934).
7. R. A. Fisher, *Statistical Methods for Research Workers*, Oliver and Boyd, Edinburgh, 1932.
8. W. E. Deming, "Least squares," Graduate School, U. S. Department of Agriculture, Washington, D. C., 1938.
9. F. D. Rossini, *Chemical Thermodynamics*, John Wiley and Sons, New York, 1950.

# Author Index

# Subject Index